TALES
OF
HASHISH

TALES
❧ OF ❧
HASHISH

EDITED AND ANNOTATED BY

ANDREW C. KIMMENS

WILLIAM MORROW AND COMPANY, INC.
New York   1977

Printed in the United States of America.

1   2   3   4   5   6   7   8   9   10

Library of Congress Cataloging in Publication Data

Main entry under title:

Tales of hashish.

    1. Hashish—Addresses, essays, lectures
I.   Kimmens, Andrew C.
HV5822.H3T34   301.2′2   77-1934
ISBN 0-688-03194-3
ISBN 0-688-08194-0 pbk.

BOOK DESIGN   CARL WEISS

❧ CONTENTS ❧

7   INTRODUCTION

15   **THE OLD MAN OF THE MOUNTAIN AND THE ASSASSINS**

17   ARNOLD OF LÜBECK (1210?)

18   MARCO POLO (1298)

21   ANTOINE SYLVESTRE DE SACY (1809)

26   "HOW HASHISH WAS DISCOVERED" (THIRTEENTH CENTURY)

29   **THREE TALES FROM THE *THOUSAND AND ONE NIGHTS***

30   "THE TALE OF THE HASHISH EATER"

32   "THE TALE OF THE TWO HASHISH EATERS"

36   "THE TALE OF THE SECOND CAPTAIN OF POLICE"

40   ***LE CLUB DES HACHICHINS—* THE HASHISH-EATERS CLUB**

42   THÉOPHILE GAUTIER, "REMEMBERING BAUDELAIRE" (1868)

52   CHARLES BAUDELAIRE, "THE HASHISH POEM" (1860)

86   GAUTIER, "THE HASHISH-EATERS CLUB" (1846)

104   GÉRARD DE NERVAL, "HASHISH" (1850)

113   **FRANÇOIS LALLEMAND, *HASHISH* (1843)**

125   **ALEXANDRE DUMAS PÈRE, "SINBAD THE SAILOR"** (1844)

141   **BAYARD TAYLOR, "A SLIGHT EXPERIENCE OF HASHEESH" (1855)**

156   **"THE HASHEESH EATER" (1856)**

172   **FITZ HUGH LUDLOW, *THE HASHEESH EATER* (1857)**

217   **LOUISA MAY ALCOTT, "PERILOUS PLAY" (1869)**

233   **"A HASHISH-HOUSE IN NEW YORK" (1888)**

✸ 247 **JULES GIRAUD, "HOW I CAME TO HASHISH" (1913)**

263   **HENRY DE MONFREID, *THE HASHISH CROSSING* (1933)**

269   **TRAVELERS' TALES**

270   HERODOTUS (FIFTH CENTURY B.C.)

271   GARCIA DA ORTA (1563)

272   JAN HUYGHEN VAN LINSCHOTEN (1598)

274   LAURENT D'ARVIEUX (1711)

277   JEAN CHARDIN (1686)

279   GERHARD ROHLFS (1874)

281   HENRI A. JUNOD (1927)

285   **INDEX**

INTRODUCTION

CANNABIS SATIVA and the various euphoric drugs that come from it have been illegal in America, on both the state and federal levels, since the unopposed passage by Congress of the Marihuana Tax Act of 1937. In the West generally, illegality has been enforced even longer. The drug had been known to Westerners and was quite accessible for about a century; society's prohibition was not imposed until people had had about a hundred years of free experimentation, fairly easily arrived at and openly enjoyed.

Active interest in the drug resulted from a general growth of awareness about the Orient. The early nineteenth century saw the beginning of much European travel to lands that were about to be absorbed into empire, particularly India and the Middle East. The one characteristic that all these places had in common for Westerners, their most highly desired export, was exoticism. Anything from the Orient that was novel or different—food, clothing, furniture, architecture, or experiences—was quickly taken up and popularized. The idea was not simply to copy the East, but to transplant the best of it into another culture, adding touches of Oriental refinement to the solid Occidental stock.

This accounts in part for the attraction of hashish. People in the nineteenth century did not feel, at least not as widely as they do today, a need to obliterate an unwelcome reality—total oblivion, in any case, was readily available to the poor in alcohol for pennies. Nor were the preparations of cannabis the only drugs available: Opium from the Ottoman Empire had been widely available in Europe for centuries, typically in the liquid form of laudanum, and opium sometimes accompanied or occasioned Oriental fantasies, as in the classic case of Coleridge's poem *Kubla Khan*. Cannabis had long been grown in Europe as a textile crop, but as an intoxicant it was a fresh, new idea: It was not considered likely to become the resort of nervous elderly ladies (as was laudanum) or the laboring poor (in the case of alcohol), and so it grew fashionable, and was limited to a self-selecting group of initiates.

More than for most of the other Oriental imports, the printed word had much to do with spreading the popularity of cannabis. As far as the reading public was concerned, it was discovered and appropriated, as a subject and as a drug, by poets and writers. The works of these hashish eaters, their contributions to public consciousness, are the subject of this book. The tales brought together here belong to a class of writing now almost impossible to find, even in our society, where millions of people find cannabis essential and satisfying: that is, first-person narratives of drug-induced hallucinatory experiences. In our own time the illegality has radically limited creative possibility, entailed an intense, debilitating self-consciousness, and reduced expressive freedom.

The fact that the initial Western awareness of the drug came from the Orient rather than from Africa or South America, where it has also long been indigenously used, suggests much about its course here. Hashish—the refinement of the cannabis plant, the working of its gummy pollen with water, heat, and pressure to obtain a hard, resinous concentrate—was the normal form it took. When first brought to Europe it was usually eaten, rarely smoked. This form of consumption occurred partly because of travelers' misconceptions: In Arab Africa, especially Egypt, confections were made from hashish, adding spices, honey, and ground nuts (cantharides were often included for aphrodisiac purposes). The Arabic names for these preparations caught on to a limited extent in the West—*dawamesc* and *majoun*, *hendi* and *rumi*—yet somehow neophytes thought that all parts of the plant ought to be eaten. So we have the unconscious humor in Lallemand (p. 117), for example, where the dispensing doctor shows everyone at the dinner party his "hashish," a packet of twigs, seeds, and leaves, which his young initiates promptly proceed to swallow as is. The powerful experiences enjoyed or endured by the characters in these tales attest to the fact that eating hashish, for one who had never tried anything of the sort, was often an overwhelming and disorienting ordeal.

The words used in the West to describe the various cannabis preparations come generally from either the Indian languages or Arabic, and are often a source of some confusion. From India we have *bhang* (common unprocessed hemp, chewed, smoked, mixed into sweets or drinks; sometimes this word was used to mean hashish in the West), *ganja* (processed dried hemp, generally stronger than *bhang*), and *charas* (hashish); from Arabic come *hashish*, *kif* (see p. 97n), and the four words for sweetmeats mentioned above, which are no longer used outside the Middle East.

The experiences recounted in this book are roughly evenly divided between French and American. This does not suggest that other Westerners did not know about cannabis, but only confirms that for some reason they did not write about it. The English, in particular, were aware that hemp preparations of all sorts had been widely used in their Indian possessions for millennia. It would be incredible to suppose that they did not bring them home and try them,* yet we have no *English Hashish Eater* to accompany De

---

* Indeed, Sir Richard Burton writes, "I heard of a 'hashish-orgie' in London which ended in half the experimentalists being on their sofas for a week" (*The Book of the Thousand Nights and a Night*, vol. iii, London, Burton Club ed., n.d., p. 91). This anecdote attests to the use of hashish at least among the London fashionable set, rather a striking similarity to its social nexus in France.

Quincey's *Opium Eater,* and the absence of any such account is rather perplexing. Nor can we pretend there was any greater freedom for drug experimentation in nineteenth-century France and America than elsewhere for, in the first place, that sort of freedom, in a political sense, was nowhere seriously lacking: there was, despite what we are often led to believe, far greater freedom of manners in nineteenth-century Europe and America than there is today. Secondly, the anguish almost generally felt by the American hashish eaters testifies eloquently to the presence in this country of pervasive moral coercion—a perennial American problem—which yet did not prevent these people from taking cannabis frequently and writing about it (though they often did so anonymously). The answer to the anomaly might be simply that France and America provided literary climates suitable for this kind of expression. And once in vogue, descriptions of hashish dreams became in both countries almost a minor genre, one that persisted in France well into the present century. Naturally, significant differences can be discerned between the French and American descriptions. For example, cannabis in France was an antibourgeois social force from the beginning, and thus a subject of contention; the sense of its threat to middle-class society's institutions only emerged in America around the time it was declared illegal. This difference in perception, of course, is reflected in the tone of the stories.

In what way does the use of hashish in nineteenth-century America connect with marijuana use in our own day? The answer focuses on social interaction taking place in the first few years of the twentieth century, when the "hemp retreats" throughout the country, mentioned in the *Harper's* article (p. 233), might well have counted as members people who liked to smoke the potent dried cannabis just beginning to come into the United States from Mexico and Central America. There is no firm evidence of such interaction, but certainly the decline in the use of hashish in this country in the twentieth century has coincided with a growth in use of marijuana. This change in habits of cannabis consumption has no parallel in Europe.

All translations, except where noted differently, are my own, from the best sources available.

I want to thank the staff members of all sections of the Bibliothèque Nationale, the British Library, and the New York Public Library for their admirable patience in dealing with innumerable queries and special requests.

New York City
September 1976

THE HASCHISH

Of all that Orient lands can vaunt
    Of marvels with our own competing,
The strangest is the Haschish plant,
    And what will follow on its eating.

What pictures to the taster rise,
    Of Dervish or of Almeh dances!
Of Eblis, or of Paradise,
    Set all aglow with Houri glances!

The poppy visions of Cathay,
    The heavy beer-trance of the Suabian;
The wizard lights and demon play
    Of nights Walpurgis and Arabian!

The Mollah and the Christian dog
    Change place in mad metempsychosis;
The Muezzin climbs the synagogue,
    The Rabbi shakes his beard at Moses!

The Arab by his desert well
    Sits choosing from some Caliph's daugh-
        ters,
And hears his single camel's bell
    Sound welcome to his regal quarters.

The Koran's reader makes complaint
    Of Shitan dancing on and off it;
The robber offers alms, the saint
    Drinks Tokay and blasphemes the Pro-
        phet. . . .

—JOHN GREENLEAF WHITTIER, from
Anti-slavery Poems, Boston, 1854. The
poem goes on to compare hashish to
cotton, which makes Westerners, particularly Southern Americans, just as.
crazy.

THE OLD MAN
OF THE MOUNTAIN
AND THE ASSASSINS

*For centuries there has been intense interest in the Assassins, from the time of their flourishing in the twelfth century to today. Because they were a secret society within the Ismailis, an Islamic sect whose own tenets were secret, much speculation has always surrounded them. The name Assassin was brought to Europe by the returning crusaders, but at first it only meant one who was loyal: Troubadours compared their faithfulness to their lady as an Assassin's to his master, or a priest's to God. By Dante's time the story of the Assassins' deeds had got around, and the word had come to mean murderer; in Inferno, Canto 19, line 50, he described a murderer confessing to a priest as "lo perfido assassin." The name was then in use in many languages of Europe: The first attested English use is only in 1531, but around 1235 the English historian Roger of Wendover spoke of "the Saracen horde, whom the Christians call Assassins" (*hostam Saraceni quam Christiani Assisinos appellant.)*

The sect was founded in Persia in the late eleventh century by Hasan-i Sabbah (or Hasan ibn al-Sabbah), a great Islamic revolutionary. His aim was to extend Ismaili philosophy throughout

* Roger of Wendover, *Flores Historiarum*, II, ii, 246.

Islam, and to support the Ismaili Fatimite caliphate in Egypt, which came to a bloody end almost as soon as Hasan started his movement. In order to gain a seat of power, essential for any politicoreligious Islamic sect, Hasan seized the castle of Alamut, in an impregnable valley of northern Persia near the Caspian Sea. Other castles, more land, and more power came to Hasan, who soon expanded his activities into Syria, where his primary enemies, the Seljuks, were beginning to be powerful. As the rivalry soon became based on territorial ambitions as much as religious differences, all those who were not of the Ismaili persuasion and who held land and power were in danger of being killed. The first Christian lord to die was Marquis Conrad of Montferrat, king of the Latin Kingdom of Jerusalem, who was murdered in his castle at Tyre in 1192, perhaps with the connivance of King Richard of England.

Hasan and his successors relied on terror and obedience to accomplish their ends. The devotees were true fanatics, who would often study their victims' habits over a long time before they struck. They were usually successful, but if captured, no torture could make them divulge their origins or plans.

The Old Man of the Mountain was the leader of the sect; however, like the term Assassin itself, this title was never used concerning the original Persian organization, but only of its Syrian branch. It would have been natural for the Syrian Assassins to speak of their leader as sheik, *a common Arabic term of respect meaning "elder." This honorific became applied specifically to the Assassins' leader by Western commentators, and so passed into Western Oriental lore.*

The first of the important stories concerning the Assassins is by the early thirteenth-century German historian, Arnold, Abbot of Lübeck, who recounts the report of an agent sent to Syria in 1175 by Emperor Frederick Barbarossa.* Arnold did not know about

---

* Arnold of Lübeck, *Chronica Slavorum,* G. H. Pertz ed. *Scriptores rerum Germanicarum* (Hanover, 1868), vii, 8, pp. 274–275; iv, 16, pp. 145, 146.

hashish, and in the first sentence mistranslates the word Heyssessini, *yet he understood that there was a narcotic responsible for the Assassins' behavior.*

Arnold of Lübeck,
THE OLD MAN OF THE MOUNTAIN (1210?)

IN THE MOUNTAINS around Damascus, Antioch, and Aleppo there lives a race of Saracens [Moslems], who are called in their own language *Heyssessini,* and in Roman *segnors de montana.* These people live lawlessly, eating pig meat contrary to the Saracens' law, and freely using all available women, including their mothers and sisters. They live in the mountains, and their fortresses are impregnable. Their country is not fertile, so they live on their animals. They have also among them a lord, who thoroughly terrifies all the neighboring and distant Saracen princes, as well as the neighboring Christian lords, for he habitually kills them in an astonishing way. It is done in this way: the prince has in his mountain fastnesses many very beautiful palaces, surrounded by very high walls, so that no one may enter save by a small guarded door. Here he raises many of the sons of his peasants from their earliest childhood. They are taught many languages, such as Latin, Greek, Roman, Saracen, and many others. These youths are taught by their teachers to obey their lord's every word and command, and if they do so their lord, who has power over their living gods, will give to them the joys of paradise. They are told that this salvation is impossible for them if they fail in any way to do his bidding. They see no one other than their teachers and masters from earliest childhood until the time when their lord summons them to kill someone. Once they are in his presence, he asks them if they are willing to obey him, that he may give them paradise. Then, according to their instruction, with no objection or second thought, they throw themselves at his feet and fervently reply that they will obey him in everything that he may command. Then the lord gives them a

golden dagger and sends them to kill whatever lord he has selected. . . .

I shall tell you things about this Old Man that might appear
foolish, yet they have been sworn to me by reliable witnesses. This
Old Man has so bemused his countrymen by his sorcery that they
revere no god but him. Also, he strangely bewitches them by hopes
and promises of eternal pleasures, so that they would really rather
die than live. Some of them, on a high wall, will jump off at a
signal from him, dying horribly of a smashed skull. Those who are
most blessed, he says, shed others' blood and then are put to death
in expiation of these deeds. So when any choose to die in this way,
cunningly murdering someone and then being executed, he will
give them knives that are, so to speak, consecrated for this very
purpose, then he intoxicates them with a potion, so that they are
plunged into ecstasy and oblivion, and he shows them by means
of his magic some fantastic dreams, full of pleasures and delights—
or of foolishness, rather—and he promises them these things eter-
nally as their reward for such works.

Arnold's mention of intoxication by potion (poculo eos . . .
inebriat) *is the first mention of drugs in connection with the
Assassins. About seventy-five years later, Marco Polo was passing
through Persia on his way to Cathay and was told a surprisingly
similar story, which he included in his account of his journey.**

Marco Polo,
THE OLD MAN OF THE MOUNTAIN (1298)

MULECT IS A COUNTRY where the Old Man of the Mountain
used formerly to live. *Mulect* means in French, God-lander.† Now

---

* Marco Polo, *Il Milione,* ed. Dante Olivieri, Scrittori d'Italia (Bari, 1912), pp.
36–38.
† The word is actually a corruption of Arabic *mulhid,* deviator, a word applied
to any member of a deviant religious sect, particularly to the Ismailis.

I will tell you his whole story just as I, Marco Polo, heard it told by several men of this country.

The Old Man was called in their language, Aloadin. He caused to be enclosed in a valley between two mountains, the grandest and most beautiful garden that anyone ever saw, full of all the fruits of the earth. There were found the most beautiful houses and palaces that anyone ever saw, all gilded and decorated with beautiful frescos. There were also canals filled with wine, milk, honey, and water. And it was full of ladies and maidens, the most beautiful in the world, who knew how to play every instrument, to sing marvelously, and to dance so well that it was a delight to see them. And he made all believe, the Old Man, that this garden was Paradise. He had made it according to the description that Mohammed gave of Paradise: beautiful gardens, full of canals of wine, milk, honey, and water, and full of beautiful women for everyone's delectation.

No one entered this garden save those whom he wished to make his Hasisins. There was a castle at the entrance to the garden, so strong that no one could ever capture it, and no one could enter the garden save through that castle. The Old Man kept in his royal court the young people of his country, from twelve to twenty years, who wanted to become his men at arms, and he spoke to them just as Mohammed described Paradise, in the manner I have told you; and they believed everything just as the Saracens do. And what shall I tell you? He had them installed in his garden, in groups of ten, six, and four, in the following manner: He had them drink a brew that put them to sleep immediately, then he had them carried into the garden. And when they awoke, they found themselves there.

When they find themselves there, they are in such a beautiful place that they think they really are in Paradise. The ladies and maidens do their bidding all day long, so that, having all that they want, these men would never willingly leave the garden. The Old Man holds a noble, grand court, and makes the simple people who surround him believe that he is a great prophet. And when he wants to send one of his Hasisins somewhere, he gives some of his brew to one or another of them who are in his garden, and has them carried into his palace. And when the man awakes, he finds himself out of his paradise, in the castle, which makes him very astonished and ill at ease. The Old Man then summons the man before him, as before one who really believes he is a prophet. And the Old Man asks him where he has come from. And he says that he comes from Paradise, made just as Mohammed described it in his law. And all who hear him, who have not seen that garden, have a great desire to go there, and would die to go there.

And when the Old Man wants to kill a great lord, he says to them, "Go and kill this person, and when you return, I will have you carried by my angels into Paradise. And if you die on this mission, I will command my angels to take you up into Paradise."

This is what he made them believe. Thus they did his commands, not fearing any danger, in the hope of returning to Paradise. And in this way the Old Man had them kill all he commanded them to kill. And on account of the great fear that the other lords had of him, they paid him tribute for his peace and friendship.

Now that I have told you the story of the Old Man of the Mountain and his Hasisins, I will tell you how he was destroyed and by whom. In the year of Christ's incarnation 1242, Alau, lord of the Levantine Tartars, learned of the great wickedness of the Old Man and resolved to destroy him.* Therefore he sent one of his barons to the castle with a great army. They besieged the castle for three years without being able to take it, so strong it was, and they would never have taken it if those defending the castle had had enough to eat. But after three years food was scarce. They were captured, and the Old Man was killed along with his men. And

---

* Hülegü, grandson of Genghis Khan, was then conquering Persia, and realized the threat that the Ismailis presented. He imprisoned the last of the Persian leaders, Rukn al-Din, lord of Alamut, and put him to death in 1256. The end of Ismaili power in Syria followed soon after.

from that time until today there has been no Old Man nor any Hasisins, and with him ended the evils that the Old Man of the Mountain had done.

The land of the Assassins was not actually seen by Marco Polo, but only described by him, and he was accustomed to include such secondhand descriptions in his travelogue. His book, of course, became extremely popular throughout Europe, and though his accounts of many things were disbelieved, nearly all of them, even those most disputed, passed into the folk memory.

The Assassins thus were not forgotten. Travel and interest in the Orient greatly increased during the Renaissance. The meaning of their name was speculated upon throughout the eighteenth century, but no one guessed the correct etymology until Antoine Sylvestre de Sacy, the foremost Arabist of his day, turned his attention to the problem in the early nineteenth century. On July 7, 1809, at a public meeting of the Institut de France, he read a paper "On the Dynasty of the Assassins and the Origin of their Name." The most interesting part of his study concerned the etymology and his defense of his interpretation.*

Antoine Sylvestre de Sacy,
ON THE ASSASSINS' DYNASTY (1809)

Let us now pass to the name Assassin. This word . . . has been written in a variety of ways; but to confine myself to those possessing the best authority I shall state that it has been pronounced *Assassini, Assissini,* and *Heississini.* . . . All [who previously attempted to solve this problem have] been mistaken, because they had probably never encountered the word in any Arabic author. The Assassins are almost always called by Oriental historians Is-

---

* Antoine Sylvestre de Sacy, *"Mémoire sur la dynastie des Assassins, et sur l'origine de leur nom," Mémoires de l'Institut Royal,* iv (118), 81–85.

mailis, Mulahid (that is, impious ones), or Batenites, meaning "partisans of the allegorical sense." Only one literary person . . . had a glimpse of the true etymology, but he had erected it on bad foundations, as he had not the slightest suspicion of the motive that led to the Ismailis being designated by this term.

Certainly one of the most illustrious of the victims of the Ismailis' fury is Saladin.* True, this great prince escaped their attacks, but twice he was on the point of losing his life by these evil men's daggers, for which he afterward reaped a striking revenge. In considering the story of these repeated attempts in certain Arab authors, contemporaries of Saladin and eyewitnesses to what they relate, I am convinced that the Ismailis, or at least the men they employed to execute their terrible projects, were called *Hashishin* in the plural, and *Hashishi* in the singular. This name, slightly altered by the Latin writers, has been expressed as exactly as possible by several Greek historians, and by the Jew, Benjamin of Tudela.

As to the origin of the name in question, although I have not gleaned it from any of the Oriental historians I have consulted, I have no doubt that that denomination was given to the Ismailis, on account of their using an intoxicating liquid or preparation still known in the East by the name of hashish. Hemp leaves, and some other parts of the same plant, form the basis of this preparation, which is employed in different ways: in liquid, in the form of pastilles, mixed with sweet substances, or even in smoking. The intoxication produced by the hashish causes an ecstasy similar to that which the Orientals get by using opium. From the testimony of a great number of travelers we may affirm that those who fall into this state of delirium imagine they enjoy every object of their desires, and taste happiness cheaply. Too frequent enjoyment weakens the constitution, producing first wasting, then death. Some

* The Assassins twice tried to kill Saladin, one of the greatest Islamic generals, proponent of Islamic unity and orthodoxy, in 1174 and 1176. He then besieged Masyaf, one of the Assassins' Syrian strongholds, but shortly thereafter withdrew and was never again threatened by the Assassins.

people, in this state of temporary insanity, forgetting their condition, commit the most brutal actions and disturb the public peace. It has not been forgotten that when the French army was in Egypt, Napoleon, the general-in-chief, was forced to prohibit, with severe penalties, the sale and use of these pernicious substances, habitual use of which has produced a great demand among the Egyptians, especially the lower orders. Those who indulge in this custom are to this very day called *Hashishin,* and this explains why the historians of the crusades called the Ismailis sometimes *Assissini,* sometimes *Assassini.*

Let me answer an objection to the origin of the name Assassins, when applied to the Ismailis. If the use of intoxicating substances prepared from hemp leaves can disturb the reason, if it throws a man into a kind of delirium and makes him mistake dreams for realities, how could it be possible for people who needed all their coolness and mental calmness in order to do the murders they were charged with, and who were known to travel to countries very remote from their own, to wait many days for an opportunity to strike, to mix among the soldiers of the prince whom they were about to kill, following their chief's orders, to fight under his colors, and cunningly to seize the moment offered by fortune to their purpose? Certainly this is not the conduct of delirious people or of madmen, carried away by a fury they can no longer control, as travelers describe those who run amuck, so much dreaded among the Malayans and Indians. One word will suffice to answer this objection, and Marco Polo's account will supply it. This traveler, whose veracity is now generally acknowledged, informs us that the Old Man of the Mountain educated young men, selected from the most robust inhabitants of the places he ruled, so as to make them the executioners of his barbarous decrees. The whole object of their education was to convince them that, by blindly obeying their chief's orders they could assure themselves, after death, the enjoyment of every pleasure that can flatter the senses. . . .

Although there might be some exaggeration in the Venetian

traveler's account, and although, rather than believe in the existence of the enchanted gardens (which is, however, attested by many other writers), we should reduce all the wonders of that magnificent place to a phantom produced by the exalted imagination of young men intoxicated with hashish, who, from their infancy, had been nursed with the idea of this happiness, it would be no less true that we find here the use of a liquor to deaden the senses, and we cannot forget that its use or abuse is spread throughout a great part of Asia and Africa. At the time of Ismaili power these intoxicating preparations were not yet known in Moslem countries. It was only later that knowledge of them was brought from the most eastern regions, perhaps from India, into the Persian provinces. From there it was communicated to the Moslems of Asia Minor, Mesopotamia, Syria, and Egypt. No doubt the Ismailis, whose doctrines had several points of resemblance with those of the Indians, had acquired this knowledge earlier and preserved it as a precious secret, one of the main sources of their power. . . .

I shall conclude this memoir by observing that it is not impossible that hemp, or some part of that plant, mixed with other substances unknown to us, may have been sometimes used to produce a state of frenzy and violent madness. We know that opium, whose intoxicating effects are generally analogous to those of hemp, is nevertheless the means used by the Malays to make themselves furious when, being no longer masters of themselves, they murder everyone they meet and blindly throw themselves onto swords and lances. The means used to thus alter the effects of opium are, if travelers are to be believed, mixing it with lemon juice and allowing the mixture to sit for a few days.

Frenzy and violent madness from cannabis? Though no one knows what preparations the Assassins were using, this claim seems absurd, yet many believed it. The key point nearly everyone missed *about the Assassins is that they did not use hashish in order to carry out their murders; it was used on them without their knowledge in order to encourage fanatic obedience. Yet from this account, and from a similar one, even more celebrated, by Joseph von Hammer-Purgstall,* the cannabis takers of the nineteenth century —Dumas, Gautier, Baudelaire, and others who retold the story— learned their lore about the Old Man of the Mountain and his men. More modern research has shown that they were probably wrong, at least in part. The etymology of the name Assassin is unquestionably what Sylvestre de Sacy suggested, yet no surviving Arabic documents, written either by the Ismailis or their enemies, mention the use of hashish. The word* hashīsh *in Arabic originally meant herbage, dry fodder, and later acquired the particular meaning of the cannabis preparation, which was perhaps made at first from the dried plants, ground up whole. "The use and effects of hashish were known at the time, and were no secret; . . . even the name* hashīshī *[hashish eater, Assassin] is local to Syria, and is probably a term of popular abuse. In all probability it was the name that gave rise to the story, rather than the reverse. Of various explanations that have been offered, the likeliest is that it was an expression of contempt for the wild beliefs and extravagant behavior of the sectaries—a derisive comment on their conduct rather than a description of their practices. For Western observers in particular, such stories [of hashish taking and enchanted gardens] may also have served to provide a rational explanation for behavior that was otherwise totally inexplicable." †*

The gardens must also probably be discarded from our stock of

---

* Joseph von Hammer-Purgstall, *Geschichte der Assassinen aus morgenländischen Quellen* (History of the Assassins from Levantine Sources) Stuttgart, 1818. It was translated into French in 1833 and in 1835 into English. The book was written chiefly as a warning to nineteenth-century Europeans against secret societies and assassination in general, but the historical points made by Hammer-Purgstall, who was a competent Arabist, closely followed those of his colleague Sylvestre de Sacy.

† Bernard Lewis, *The Assassins: A Radical Sect in Islam*, London, 1963, p. 12.

Oriental images. In the late 1950s a British expedition was mounted to explore the still-inaccessible castles of the Persian Assassins. Some of these had not been visited by Westerners since the 1830s. Most had been uninhabited for the better part of a millennium, ever since Hülegü sacked them, but they were in remarkably good condition. They were still perched atop their mountains, dominating all the valleys around them. But no trace of gardens could be found, no place for them either within or without the walls; indeed, construction of such a fantasy would have been all but impossible for even the best Islamic architects of the time. The Syrian Assassins' castles have mostly vanished. They might have contained enchanted gardens, but they were in country just as remote, and in any case they would have taken their architectural designs and practices from their Persian colleagues.*

As to Sylvestre de Sacy's contention that hashish was unknown in Islam before the twelfth- and thirteenth-century Ismaili ascendancy, this is hard to disprove. There is a story preserved by Maqrizi (1364–1442) from the lost "Treatise on Hemp" by Hassan Mohammed ibn-Chirazi. The story comes from the middle of the thirteenth century, though it may be earlier, and describes the discovery by an ascetic sheik of hemp's intoxicating properties, his recommendation to his followers to keep it secret, and their eventual release of the secret to the world. This story takes place in Khorasan in northeastern Iran, not far from the original Persian home of the Assassins.

Hassan Mohammed ibn-Chirazi,
HOW HASHISH WAS DISCOVERED †
(THIRTEENTH CENTURY)

IN THE YEAR 658 [A.D. 1260], being at Tuster, I asked Sheik Jafar Chirazi, monk of the order of Haidar, on what occasion they had discovered the properties of the herb of the devotees, and how,

---

* See P. R. E. Willey, The Castles of the Assassins, London, 1963.
† Cited in G. Wiet, La grandeur d'Islam, Paris, 1961, pp. 245–246.

after being adopted by the devotees in particular, it had afterward come into general usage. Here is what he told me.

Haidar, chief of all the sheiks, practiced many exercises of devotion and mortification: he took but little nourishment, carried to a surprising extent the detachment from all worldly things, and was of an extraordinary piety. He was born at Nichapur, a city of Khorasan, and he made his home on a neighboring mountain. There he established a convent, and a great number of devotees came together around him. He lived alone in a corner of this convent, and spent more than ten years in this manner, never going out, and never seeing anyone at all except me, when I was acting as his servant. One day when it was very hot, at the hour of the very greatest heat, the sheik walked out alone into the countryside, and when he later returned to the convent, we saw on his face an expression of joy and gaiety very different from what we were accustomed to see there: he allowed his fellow devotees to come and visit him and began to converse with them. When we saw the sheik so humanized and conversing familiarly with us, after being for so long in an absolute retreat without any communication with men, we asked him the cause of this surprising effect.

"While I was in my retreat," he replied, "it occurred to my spirit to go out alone into the countryside. When I had done so I noticed that all the plants were in a perfect calm, not experiencing the least agitation, because of the extreme heat untempered by the slightest breath of wind. But passing by a certain plant covered with foliage I observed that, in that air, it was moving softly from side to side with a soft light movement, like a man dizzied by the fumes of wine. I began to gather the leaves of this plant and to eat them, and they have produced in me the gaiety that you witness. Come with me, then, that I may teach you to know it."

So we followed him into the countryside, and he showed us that plant. We told him, on seeing it, that it was the plant they call hemp. On his orders, we took the leaves of this plant and ate them, and once back in the convent experienced in ourselves the same

gay, joyous disposition that he had found impossible to hide from
us. When the sheik saw us in that state, he charged us to keep
secret the discovery that we had just made of the plant's virtues
and made us promise on oath never to reveal it to ordinary men
and never to hide it from religious men.

"God Almighty," he told us, "has granted you, as a special favor,
an awareness of the virtues of this leaf, so that your use of it will
dissipate the cares that obscure your souls and free your spirits
from everything that might hamper them. Keep carefully, then,
the deposit he has confided in you, and be faithful in hiding the
precious secret he has committed to you."

Sheik Haidar thus made known to us this secret during his life,
and ordered me to sow the plant around his tomb after his death,
so I cultivated it in the convent. The sheik lived for ten more
years after this event; during all the time I remained in his service
not a day went by that he did not use this leaf, and he recommended to us to eat little food and to take the herb instead. Sheik
Haidar died in the convent in the mountain in the year 618 [A.D.
1221]. They erected over his tomb a great chapel, and the inhabitants of Khorasan, full of veneration for his memory, came
there on pilgrimage, bringing many presents to fulfill their vows
and developing a great respect for his disciples. Before his death
he had recommended to his companions to tell their secret to the
most distinguished people of the province, and by instructing them
in the virtues of the plant they adopted its use. Thus hashish
spread rapidly in Khorasan and in the various departments of Fars
province, but they knew nothing about its use in Iraq until the
year 628 [A.D. 1231], in the reign of Calif Mustansir. At that time,
two princes whose states were among the maritime countries situ-
ated on the Persian Gulf, the Sovereign of Ormuz and the Prince
of Bahrein, having come into Iraq, men of their retinue brought
with them some hashish and taught the Iraqis to eat it. The drug
spread in Iraq, and the people of Syria, Egypt, and the lands of
Rum, having heard tell of it, took up the use of it.

THREE TALES FROM THE THOUSAND AND ONE NIGHTS

The collection of stories that we know as the Arabian Nights is around a thousand years old and gained immediate popularity in all Arabic-speaking countries. In the West its renown surpasses that of every Arabic literary work, including the Koran. From the time of the first Western edition (1704–1717) of Antoine Galland, people of all classes in Europe and America have come to see such characters as Ali Baba, Aladdin, and Scheherezade as virtually part of their own folklore.

Among the many strata of tales, Indian, Persian, Egyptian, and Arabian, the three tales that follow can be identified as of Baghdad origin, from the eighth century, the place and time of the first flourishing of Islamic civilization, during the caliphate of Haroun al-Rashid and his successors. These are brief, realistic tales of common people, with few elements of magic: none of the genies, flying carpets, and enchanted caves that fill dozens of the other tales. Into this atmosphere hashish enters quite naturally—it is nothing rare or unusual, just a drug that makes people do strange and funny things. All three of these tales concern both sexual activity and hashish taking, two subjects never far apart in the Arab mind.

This translation is from the French one (1899–1904) of J. C. V. Mardrus. He is often criticized for having left out some stories and *included spurious ones, but his sense of their style is superb, and they read far better than the purported best translation from the Arabic, the German one (1921–1928) by Enno Littmann.*

"The Tale of the Hashish Eater"

KNOW THAT the most delicious thing that my ear has ever heard, O my young lord, is this story that came to me of a hashish eater among hashish eaters.

There was a man who loved above everything the flesh of virgins, and occupied himself exclusively in the satisfaction of this appetite. Now such flesh, especially when it is choice, is very expensive, and as no fortune can last when the tastes of its owner are so costly, the man in question, who never gave himself any repose on this subject—for in anything it is only excess that is reprehensible—ended by being completely ruined.

One day, as he wandered in ragged clothing and naked feet in the market, begging his bread, a nail entered the bottom of his foot and made it bleed exceedingly. Then he sat down on the ground and tried to stanch the blood, and finally bound his foot with a piece of cloth. But, as the blood continued to flow, he said to himself, "Let us go to the hammam, the public baths, to wash our foot and plunge it in water; it will do it good." And he went to the hammam, and went to the public hall where the poor people went, which even so was exquisitely clean and gleaming bright. And he crouched over the central basin and began to wash his foot.

Beside him there sat a man who had finished his bath and was munching something. Seeing the movement of his jaws, the wounded man grew very eager to eat some of this thing also, so he said, "What are you chewing, neighbor?" The other man answered in a low voice so that no one else might hear, "Be quiet! It's hashish. I will give you a little if you want." "I would like some very much," answered the man. So the eater took a piece from his mouth and handed it over, saying, "May it lighten all your cares." Our man took the piece, chewed it up, and swallowed it; then, not being used to hashish, when the circulation

of the drug later affected his brain, he burst into extraordinary
hilarity and filled the hall with shouts of laughter. A moment later
he collapsed backward onto the marble floor and fell prey to hallucinations.

He dreamt that he lay naked under the hands of a terrifying
masseur and two vigorous slaves, who had taken total possession
of his body. He was a toy in their hands; they turned and manipu-
lated him every which way, and he felt their strong fingers digging
expertly into his flesh. He groaned under the heavy weight of their
knees on his belly as they massaged him skillfully, and then rejoiced as they rinsed him from copper basins and rubbed him with
vegetable fiber. At last the master masseur wished to wash certain
delicate parts of his person but, since this tickled him greatly, he
said, "I will do that myself." When the bath was over, the masseur
covered his body with three towels as white as jasmine, and said,
"The time has come, my lord, for you to enter to your bride, who
awaits you."

"What bride is that, masseur? I am a bachelor," cried the man.
"Have you by any chance been eating hashish, to have made so
great a mistake?"

"Do not jest so, my lord," said the masseur, "but follow, for
your bride awaits you with eagerness."

He threw a great veil of black silk about the man's shoulders and
led the way, while the two slaves held him up by the shoulders,
tickling his bottom from time to time, so that he laughed immoderately.

Then they brought him to a half-lit hall, very warm and smelling
of incense, where he found a basket filled with fruits, pastries, and
sherbets, and also vases filled with flowers. His three attendants
invited him to sit upon an ebony stool, then they asked his leave
to retire, and disappeared.

Soon a young boy came and stood before him, awaiting his
orders, and said to him, "O king of time, I am your slave." The
man roared with laughter and, quite ignoring the boy's beauty,
exclaimed, "By Allah, I think that everyone here must have eaten

hashish. They are calling me a king now." Then he said to the little boy, "You come here, and cut up half of a red, juicy watermelon—that's the fruit I like best. There is nothing like a watermelon to refresh my spirit. . . ." When the boy brought him the thing he had demanded, cut into admirable slices, he said, "Now go away, for you are not what I need. Run and fetch me my heart's desire, for there is nothing like fine virgin flesh to have with watermelon."

The boy departed, and soon returned with a little girl, who advanced toward him, moving her hips that were scarcely developed, for she was still a child. The man snorted with joy on seeing her. He took her in his arms and, holding her between his thighs, kissed her heatedly. He made her slip beneath him and, taking out the child of his father, placed it in her hand. Then suddenly, feeling intensely cold, he awoke from his dream.

He found himself surrounded by all the bathers in the hammam, laughing at him with all their hearts, with their mouths open like ovens. They were pointing out to each other his naked tool, which stood up in the air as far as was humanly possible, as great as that of an ass or an elephant. Some of them poured pitchers of cold water on it and they were all making those jests that are customary when comparing such matters in the hammam.

Completely confused, the man replaced the towel over his thighs and complained bitterly to those who were laughing at him, "Why did you take away the little girl, good people, just as I was about to put things in their right places?"

All the spectators shrieked with joy and clapped their hands at this remark, crying, "Are you not ashamed, hashish eater, still to have such desires, when you have already, under the effect of the herb you have swallowed, so thoroughly coupled with the air?"

(Night 141–142)

"The Tale of the Two Hashish Eaters"

THERE WAS ONCE, my lord, crown of my head, a man in a certain city who was a fisherman by trade and a hashish eater by occupation. Whenever he earned a daily wage, he would spend a bit on food and the rest on a sufficient quantity of that hilarious herb whose extract is hashish. He took the hashish three times a day: once in the morning on an empty stomach, once at noontime, and once at sunset. Thus he never missed being extravagantly happy. Yet he worked quite hard at fishing, though sometimes in a very unusual way. One evening, for example, when he had taken a larger dose of hashish than usual, he lit a tallow candle and sat in front of it, closely questioning himself, then answering himself with a ready wit. After several hours of this game, he was aware of the cool silence of the night around him and the clear light of a full moon over his head, and exclaimed affably to himself, "My dear friend, the silent streets and the coolness of the moonlight invite us to take a walk. Let us go forth, then, while all the world is asleep, and no one about to diminish our solitary exaltation." Speaking like this to himself, the fisherman left his house and began walking toward the river. But as he went, he saw the light of the full moon lying across the road, and took it to be the water of the river.

"My dear old friend the fisherman," he said, "here you are on the riverbank, and there is no other fisherman in sight but you. Go and fetch your line and catch the best of the fish while your rivals are in bed." Thus he thought, in his madness, and thus he did. Returning with his line, he went to sit on the curb and began to fish in the moonlight, casting his line into the reflecting patch in the middle of the road.

Soon an enormous dog, tempted by the smell of the bait, greedily gobbled up the hook and then, feeling the barb in his muzzle, made frantic attempts to get loose. The fisherman, believing he had a monstrous fish, pulled as hard as he could; and the dog, suffering great pain, pulled on his side, all the while yelping in terror. The fisherman struggled for some time against this fish, but finally he was pulled down and rolled on the ground. Even then he refused to let go of his line but held on grimly. Fearing he would drown in the river, he uttered terrified cries.

"Help, help me, good Moslems!" he shouted. "Help me land this mighty fish, for he is dragging me into the depths. Help, help me, good friends, for I am drowning!" The guards of the quarter heard the alarm and dashed forward, but immediately began to laugh at the fisherman's antics. However, when he then yelled, "Allah curse you, sons of dogs! Is it a time for laughter when I am drowning?" they became angry with him and, after giving him a sound beating, dragged him off into the presence of the kadi, the royal judge.

Now it was Allah's will that this kadi should also be accustomed to use hashish. He saw quickly that his prisoner was under its jocund influence, so he rebuked the guards harshly and dismissed them. Then he handed over the fisherman to his slaves, that they might put him to bed for some tranquil sleep. And he told himself that the man would be his companion for some pleasure that he had promised himself the following day.

After a refreshing night and an entire day given over to eating excellent food, the fisherman was summoned by the kadi in the evening and was received in all cordiality, like a brother. His host supped with him, and then the two sat opposite each other, the lighted candles between them, and each ate enough hashish to overturn a hundred-year-old elephant. When the drug heightened their natural dispositions, they undressed completely and began to dance about, singing and committing a thousand extravagances.

Now it happened at this time that the sultan and his vizier were walking through the city disguised as merchants, and heard a strange noise coming from the kadi's house. They entered through the unlocked door and found two naked men, who stopped dancing as they entered and bade them welcome without the slightest embarrassment. The sultan sat down to watch his venerable kadi dance some more, but when he saw that the other man had a dark and lively tool, so long that the eye would never reach the end of it, he whispered to his vizier, "By Allah, our kadi is not so well endowed as his guest!"

"What are you whispering about?" cried the fisherman. "I am

the sultan of this city and I order you to watch my dance with respect, or I will have your head cut off. I am the sultan, this is my vizier. I hold the whole world like a fish in the palm of my right hand."

The sultan and his vizier realized that they were in the presence of two hashish eaters of the most extraordinary sort, and the vizier, to amuse the sultan, said to the fisherman, "How long have you been sultan, dear master, and can you tell me what happened to our former master, your predecessor?"

"I deposed the fellow," answered the fisherman. "I said, 'Go away!' and he did."

"Did he not protest?" asked the vizier.

"Not at all. He was very happy to pass on to me the burdens of his kingship. He abdicated with such good grace that I keep him by me as a servant. Whenever he regrets his resignation, I tell him stories. Now I want to piss."

So saying, he lifted up his interminable tool and walked over to the sultan. He seemed to be about to urinate on him. "I also want to piss!" exclaimed the kadi, and he took up the same threatening position in front of the vizier. The two victims shouted with laughter and fled from the house, crying over their shoulders, "May Allah's curse be upon all hashish eaters like you!"

The next morning, to make the jest complete, the sultan called the kadi and his guest before him. "O representative of our law," he said, "I have summoned you because I wish to learn the most convenient manner of pissing. Should one squat and carefully lift the robe, as our religion prescribes? Should one stand up, as is the infidels' unclean habit? Or should one undress completely and piss against one's friends, as is the custom of two hashish eaters of my acquaintance?"

Knowing that the sultan was accustomed to walk about the city in disguise, the kadi realized in a flash the identity of his visitors of the previous night, and fell to his knees, crying, "My lord, my lord, it was the hashish that led me into this grossness and indelicacy."

But the fisherman, who because of his constant daily ingestion of the drug was always more or less under its influence, said to the sultan, "And what of it? You are in your palace this morning, we were in ours last night."

"O sweetest noise in all our kingdom!" answered the sultan, delighted at the fisherman's manner. "Since we are both sultans of this city, I think you had better henceforth stay with me in my palace. If you are a storyteller, I hope that you will at once sweeten our ears with a good one."

"With all my heart, and as homage to you, but not before you have pardoned my vizier kneeling there before you," replied the fisherman. So the sultan bade the kadi rise, forgave him his extravagances of the previous evening, and sent him back to his post. Then he dismissed everyone except the fisherman, who immediately began to tell him a story.

(*Night* 797–798)

"The Tale of the Second Captain of Police"

BEFORE ACCEPTING me as a husband, lord sultan, my cousin (may Allah save her in His mercy!) said to me, "Let us marry, certainly, son of my uncle, if it is God's will, but I can accept you only if you agree to the three conditions, no more no less, which I will now state."

"I see no objection to that," I replied, "but what are the conditions?"

Then she said, "You must never take hashish, you must never eat watermelon, and you must never sit on a chair."

"Your conditions are very demanding, daughter of my uncle," I replied. "But although I do not understand them I will accept them."

"That is just as well," she said, "for they are hard and fast. Take them or leave them."

"I accept them," I said, "with all my heart."

Then our marriage was celebrated, and everything happened correctly. For many years we lived together in tranquil unity. But one day it happened that my mind began to be tortured to know the reason for my wife's three conditions and I said to myself, "What possible object can she have in forbidding three things which are quite ordinary and harmless? There is a mystery at the bottom of this matter that I would give my eyes to penetrate." As my desire to do the forbidden things was as great as my curiosity about them, I entered the shop of one of my friends, and, as a beginning, sat down on a chair stuffed with straw. Then I called for a fine, cool watermelon and ate it up greedily. Finally, I swallowed a grain of hashish with the last of the fruit, and sent my soul away in search of happy dreams. Because of the hashish my soul knew perfect happiness, because of the watermelon my belly found felicity, and my poor bottom, after so many hard years, discovered ecstasy in the stuffed chair. But, O sultan, as soon as I returned home, there was hell to pay.

As soon as she saw me, my wife jumped up and drew her veil across her face, as if I were a perfect stranger. She looked daggers at me and cried, "O dog, and son of a dog, is this the way you keep your promises? Come with me at once to the kadi, for I insist on a divorce!" As my brain was still exalted by the hashish, my belly still pleasantly heavy with the watermelon, and my buttocks delightfully rested by the stuffed chair, I boldly denied my three sins, but at my first "No" the woman shrieked, "Hold your tongue, you pimp! Do you expect me not to believe the evidence of my own senses? You stink of hashish, your clothes are covered with watermelon droppings, and you have pressed your dark, dirty behind so hard upon a chair that the straws have left visible lines on your clothes. Henceforth we are finished!"

She gathered her veils about her and dragged me off to the kadi's court. Once we were in his presence, she cried out, "O lord kadi, your servant was legally married to this abject person here, and before the ceremony he swore he would observe certain conditions. For a while he kept his oath, but now he has broken it, and I demand a divorce, together with the return of my dowry and clothes." The kadi asked about the three conditions, and my wife enumerated them. "This gallows-child has sat on a chair,"

she said, "he has eaten a watermelon, and he has taken hashish."
Then she presented her proof, and it was so overwhelming I had
no heart to deny anything.

But the kadi was a kind old soul and pitied me. Therefore, before he delivered his decision, he said to my wife, "O daughter of
excellent parents, you are within your rights, but it would well
become you to be merciful." Then, as the woman declared in a
torrent of words that she would not listen to that argument, the
kadi, and all those with him, tried to persuade her to postpone any
action until she had reflected. They spoke so feelingly that at last
my wife, though she was quite prepared to argue all day long,
consented to a reconciliation with me, but only on condition that
the kadi would find out the answer to a question she wanted to
put to him. "Well, I am agreeable," answered the kadi. "Ask your
question, my good woman."

Then my wife said, "First I am a bone, then I am a muscle,
and finally I am flesh. What am I?"

The kadi stroked his beard and reflected a long time, then he
looked at his questioner and said, "I am so tired now by this long
court session that I cannot answer even the simplest question, but
this evening I will consult my books of jurisprudence, and if you
will return tomorrow morning you will have the answer."

Soon he adjourned the court and returned to his house, where
he became so immersed in the problem that he forgot the meal
that his daughter, a girl of fourteen, had prepared for him. "First
I am a bone," he mumbled to himself, "then I am a muscle, and
finally I am flesh. What am I? Yes, by Allah, what am I? Yes, yes,
what is he? Yes, yes, yes, what is it, in the name of Allah?" He
searched through his law books, his grammars, and his library of
medical works, but could find no hint of an answer, no shadow
of a hint of an answer. At last he cried, "I give up! There seems
to have been no book written on this subject!"

His daughter, who had observed his concern and heard these
words, questioned him: "What is the matter, dear father? Why
do you groan and pull at your hair?"

"Because I can see no solution to a great problem, my child," answered the kadi.

"Tell me about it," urged the girl, "for nothing is impossible to the wisdom of Allah." So the kadi told her about the case and repeated my wife's question. "Do you think that's difficult, Father?" she laughed. "It's as easy as running water. The answer is this: with respect to vigor and consistency a man's tool is a bone when he is between the ages of fifteen and thirty-five, a muscle when he is between thirty-five and sixty, and when he has passed sixty, it is nothing but a useless bit of hanging flesh."

The kadi rejoiced and said, "Glory be to Allah, who gives intelligence to the meanest of his people! You have not only preserved my reputation, O blessed daughter, but you have prevented the breaking up of a loving family." He rose impatiently at dawn and ran to the courthouse, where he had to wait a long time for my wife to appear, dragging me with her.

"O lord kadi," said my wife, "do you recall my question, and have you found the answer?"

"Glory be to Allah, who gave me light!" exclaimed the kadi. "O daughter of excellent parents, your question was too easy. Everybody knows that a man's tool from fifteen to thirty-five is like a bone, from thirty-five to sixty like a muscle, and after sixty only an inconsequential piece of flesh."

My wife, who saw in this answer the subtlety of the kadi's daughter, easily guessed what had happened, and craftily answered, "As Allah lives, many who have grown old in your profession could not have answered so well! I congratulate you most heartily on your daughter, my lord! She is only fourteen, but her head is twice as old. I think we can safely say that her future is assured."

She signaled to me to follow her, and walked out of the court, leaving the kadi in great confusion, from which he did not recover until the end of his days.

(Night 939–940)

LE CLUB DES HACHICHINS— THE HASHISH-EATERS CLUB

It was not so much a literary cénacle, this Assassins Club (the members intended the double meaning) as an excuse for a few young bohemians from the Parisian artistic set to get together from time to time in an elegant setting and take hashish. The drug was a romantic rage in Europe, and two factors brought it to France first. There was the Egyptian Expedition, mounted by Napoleon in 1798–1799 to demonstrate France's military power and imperial ambitions. The expedition successfully established a strong French presence in Egypt and in Syria, which then included Palestine and Lebanon as well. There was great public pride in Napoleon's success, and consequently an intense interest developed in the Levant. Trade and travel boomed. There was also the story, retold by Sylvestre de Sacy (p. 23) and often repeated, that when they were in Egypt the French soldiers, lonely for home, began to take hashish in great numbers, and continued doing so even after Napoleon himself forbade it. No personal memoir exists, however, from any of the men concerned.

Shortly thereafter came the revival of interest in the story of the Assassins, the complicated details of which were apparently resolved by two of the West's greatest Arabists. Once the explanation was known to be their use of a drug—and simple at that, made from a single plant—those who desired to try it for themselves could have easily found a way. Opium, another product of the Levant, had been in fairly common use in Europe for several hundred years. Though addiction was not well understood, it was observed that many people, from every stratum of society, could not get along without their daily doses. In any case, certain pharmacists began to stock hashish in the 1840s, usually in an oil-based extract, as demand for it increased. Travelers could always be imposed on to bring back some of the real thing from Beirut, Cairo, or Damascus. There was, of course, no prohibition on importation anywhere in the West.

The Hashish-eaters Club is mainly memorable because of three writers who were members. Théophile Gautier, probably, despite his story of initiation, a founding member, his friend Gérard de Nerval, and later Charles Baudelaire. At the time of their membership they were virtually unknown, but they later became very famous indeed. They shared passions for sensation, intoxication, life in all its forms, even orientalism, and these were passions burning brightest when they were young. They also shared, more or less, political and social ideals, and divided their disdain about evenly between the aristocracy and the bourgeoisie, whose stars have always seemed in the ascendant in France, particularly to young artists who have not yet tasted success.

There may well have been other cannabis clubs in Europe before the 1840s; there were quite probably individuals here and there who took the drug before then. If so, they left no record of their activities, and so we have not heard of them. The club on the Île Saint-Louis was fortunate in having two great recording secretaries with imaginations more than sufficient for the job of describing the vagaries of hashish intoxication, and doing so in a permanently memorable way. They brought to pass by these stories a considerable Western awareness of cannabis as an intoxicant. We begin with Gautier's (1811–1872) recollection of the club, which

*he wrote in the late 1860s when he was an old and respected
literary figure, the sole survivor of the group.*

Théophile Gautier,
"REMEMBERING BAUDELAIRE" * (1868)

THE FIRST TIME I met Baudelaire was about the middle of 1849
at the Hôtel † Pimodan, where I had fantastic rooms that communicated with those of Fernand Boissard by a staircase hidden in
the thick walls. Baudelaire was still an unpublished talent, preparing himself in shadows for the light, with that tenacious will
that doubled his inspiration; but his name had already begun to
be known among poets and artists with a kind of quivering antici-
pation, and the young generation that came after the great generation of 1830 seemed to expect a lot from him. In the heart of
that mysterious confraternity where future reputations are formed,
he was considered the greatest. I had often heard people speak of
him, but knew none of his works.

We were in the grand salon of the purest Louis XIV style, with
its paneling set off by tarnished gold leaf of a wonderful color.
Below the overhanging cornice some pupil of Lesueur or Poussin,
who had worked on the Hôtel Lambert, had painted a scene of
nymphs pursued by satyrs through the reeds, following the mythological taste of that time. On the huge mantelpiece of Pyrenean
marble, flecked in white and red, stood a clock in the form of a
golden, harnessed elephant that carried on its back an armed turret
on which was carved an enamel face with blue numerals. The armchairs and couches were old and upholstered with faded tapestries
of hunting scenes by Oudry or Desportes. In this room the meet-

* Théophile Gautier, "Charles Baudelaire," preface to the first posthumous edition of Baudelaire's *Œuvres complètes*, vol. i (Paris, 1868), pp. 1–2, 7–11, 67–
69, 71–74.
† There may have been a few travelers staying at a nineteenth-century Parisian
hôtel, but not necessarily. The word here means a large, usually luxurious house,
broken up into furnished apartments.

ings of the Hashish-eaters Club were held, of which I was a member, and which I have described elsewhere [see p. 86], with all its ecstasies, dreams, and hallucinations, followed by such profound prostration.

As I have said, the master of these rooms was Fernand Boissard, whose short, curly blond hair, rosy cheeks, gray eyes sparkling with light and wit, red lips, and teeth of pearl seemed to bear witness to a Rubens-like exuberance and health and to promise a life longer than the ordinary. But alas, who can foresee another's destiny? Boissard, who lacked none of the conditions for happiness, who had never even known the joyous misery of a well-connected youth, died quite a few years ago after having suffered a long time with the same illness that killed Baudelaire. Boissard was a young man of the very greatest gifts, with the most open intelligence; he knew painting, poetry, and music equally well, but in his constitution, perhaps, the dilettante was harmful to the artist: he spent too much time in admiration, exhausted himself in enthusiasm. No doubt if necessity had constrained him with an iron hand, he would have been an excellent painter. The success at the Salon of his *Episode on the Retreat from Russia* is the sure proof of this. But without abandoning painting, he allowed himself to be distracted by other arts: he played the violin, organized quartets, played at sight the music of Bach, Beethoven, Meyerbeer, and Mendelssohn, learned languages, wrote criticism, and composed charming sonnets. He was a great sensualist in all matters of art, and no one ever enjoyed masterpieces with more refinement, passion, and sensitivity. Because he admired the beautiful so much he forgot to express it, and believed he was reproducing what he felt so deeply. His conversation was delightful, full of gaiety and surprise; he had the rare quality of originality of word and phrase, and every kind of agreeably bizarre expression—Italian *concetti* and Spanish *agudezas*—would pass before your eyes when he spoke, like the fantastic figures of Callot, making their gracious and comical contortions. Like Baudelaire a lover of rarefied sensations, no matter how dangerous, he wanted to know well those artificial states of paradise whose lying ecstasies cost one so dear later on, and overindulgence in hashish probably spoiled his robust, flourishing health. This remembrance of a friend of my youth with whom I shared the same roof, of a romantic from the old days whom glory never visited because he loved the glory of others too much to worry about his own, is not misplaced here in this introduction to the complete works of a dead man who was the friend of us both.

Also present there the day of this visit was Jean Feuchères, a sculptor of the caliber of Jean Goujon, Germain Pilon, and Benvenuto Cellini, whose tasteful, inventive, and graceful work has now almost completely disappeared, hoarded by trading and commercial interests, and put out (it well deserved it) as the work of the most renowned sculptors so as to sell more dearly to rich collectors, who are really not cheated at all. Feuchères, besides his talent for statuary, had an incredible facility for mimicry that no actor ever equaled. He died the first; of the four artists assembled that night in the salon of the Hôtel Pimodan, I am the only one left. Those delightful hours of leisure are all gone, when decamerons of poets, artists, and beautiful women came together to talk of literature, art, and love, as in the time of Boccaccio. Time, death, and the imperious necessities of life scattered this group of free spirits, but the memory of that time remains dear to everyone fortunate enough to be admitted there, and I write these lines with an instinctively deep emotion. . . .

Now I come to a singular work of Baudelaire, half translated, half original, entitled *Les paradis artificiels,* at which I want to pause, because among the public, always happy to give credence to rumors unfavorable to writers, this work has done much to spread the story that the author of *Les fleurs du mal* was accustomed to look to drugs for inspiration. His death, which came as a result of a paralysis that rendered him powerless to communicate, though his mind remained active and vital, only confirms this popular belief. The paralysis, it is said, came doubtless because of his excessive consumption of hashish or opium, to which he was drawn first because of his peculiarity, then because of his fatal attraction to these deadly drugs. His illness had no other cause than the fatigues, wearinesses, chagrins, and burdens that fill the literary life of everyone whose talent does not lend itself to regular work of an easy output—newspaper work, for example—and whose original works appall the timid directors of reviews. Baudelaire was as sober as any worker, and while admitting that the need to make an artificial paradise by means of any stimulant—opium, hashish, wine, alcohol, or tobacco—seems to go to the bottom of man's nature since one finds it again and again in every time and place, in states of barbarity and civilization, and even in the state of nature, he saw in this a proof of original perversity, an impious attempt to escape from necessary suffering, an essentially satanic inclination to usurp, in the present, that happiness reserved for later as recompense for forbearance, goodwill, and virtue, for the persistent striving after the good and the beautiful. He held that the devil said to hashish eaters and opium drinkers, as he said long ago to our first parents, "If you eat of this fruit, you will become as gods," and he kept his word to them no more than to Adam and Eve, for the next day the god, enfeebled and enervated, has sunk lower than a beast, is isolated in an immense void, and has no other recourse to escape from himself than to return once again to his poison in gradually increasing doses. It is possible, even probable, that Baudelaire tried hashish once or twice as a physiological experiment, but he made no continual use of it. That happiness purchased at the pharmacy, which one carries about in the vest pocket, repelled him besides, and he compared its ecstasy to that of a maniac for whom painted canvasses and stage sets replaced real furnishings and gardens perfumed with real flowers. He came only rarely as an observer to the meetings at the Hôtel Pimodan. After about a dozen trials I myself renounced this enervating drug forever, not that it ever made me physically sick, but the true writer needs nothing but his natural dreams, and he does not want his mind to submit to the influence of any other agent. . . .

The monograph on hashish is medically very well done, and science might well draw from it precise data, for Baudelaire prided himself on his scrupulous exactness, and he would have never, for anything in the world, inserted the least poetic adornment to favor himself. He makes perfectly specific the proper character of hashish hallucinations, which create nothing but only develop the particular disposition of the individual, exaggerating it to the ultimate power. The individual sees only himself enlarged, sensitized, incredibly excited, away from time and space, whose very concept disappears, in surroundings at first real, which then become distorted, accentuated, exaggerated, so that every detail, in its extreme intensity, takes on a supernatural importance. This is easily understood by the hashish eater as he divines mysterious relationships between ordinarily disparate images. If you hear a piece of music that seems performed by a celestial orchestra with seraphic choirs, next to which the symphonies of Haydn, Mozart, and Beethoven are only irritating discord, know that someone's hand has lightly touched the keyboard of a piano with some vague prelude, or that a faraway organ is murmuring through the noise of the street a piece of an opera that you know. If your eyes are dazzled by streaming, scintillating, radiant fireworks of light, then assuredly a few candles must be burning in the chandeliers. When the wall stops being opaque and plunges into a vaporous, profound, bluish perspective, like a window open on the infinite, it is only a mirror glinting at the dreamer, a mirror whose diffuse shadows become mixed with a fantastic transparency. The nymphs and goddesses, the gracious, burlesque, or terrifying apparitions come only from paintings, tapestries, or statues displaying their mythological nudity in the corners of the room, or from the grotesque porcelain figurines on the shelves.

It is just the same with your olfactory ecstasies, where you become transported into perfumed paradises where marvelous flowers, lifting high their vessels like censers, offer you their aromatic fragrances, their innumerable, subtly penetrating odors, which make you think of other lives, of balmy far-off beaches, of primitive loves in the Tahiti of your dreams. There is no need to look far to find somewhere in the room a pot of heliotrope or tuberose, a pouch of Spanish leather, or a cashmere shawl impregnated with patchouli and thrown carelessly over a chair.

You understand, then, that if you want to enjoy fully the magic of hashish, you must prepare for it in advance, and somehow furnish the motifs for its extravagant variations and its unruly fantasies. It is important to be in a good dispositon—bodily and mentally—to have that day neither worry, work, nor appointment, and to be in rooms such as Baudelaire loved, and such as Poe described, furnished in poetic comfort, bizarre luxury, and mysterious elegance; a hidden retreat, secret from everyone, that seems to await a beloved spirit, the ideal feminine type, that Chateaubriand in his noble language called the sylphide. In such conditions it is probable, indeed almost certain, that naturally agreeable sensations will change into bliss, rapture, ecstasy, indescribable delight, neatly superior to the coarser joys promised the believers by Mohammed in his paradise that rather too much resembles a harem. Green, red, and white houris, emerging from the hollow pearl where they live, giving themselves to the faithful with their virginity endlessly renewed, seem like ugly whores compared to the nymphs, angels, sylphides, perfumed vapors, ideal transparencies, forms breathing rose and blue light clearly standing out against disks of sunlight, coming from the heart of the infinite on starry beams, like a sparkling liquor's silver globules in its crystal goblet. These the hashish eater sees pass before his eyes in innumerable legions in the dream he has while wide awake.

Without these precautions the ecstasy can very easily turn into a nightmare. Delight changes to suffering, joy into terror; a terrifying anguish seizes you by the throat, puts its knee on your stomach, and crushes you under its fantastically huge weight, as if the

Sphinx or the king of Siam's elephant were playing at flattening you. Other times, a glacial cold invades you, plunges you in icy marble up to your hips, like the king half changed into a statue in the *Thousand and One Nights,* whose wicked wife came every morning to beat him about the head, which had remained soft.

Baudelaire recounts two or three hallucinations of men of different characters, and another experienced by a woman in that hall of mirrors covered with a golden trellis festooned with flowers, a room not difficult to recognize as the bedroom at the Hôtel Pimodan, and he adds to each vision an analytical moral commentary, where he shows his invincible repugnance to all happiness gained by factitious means. He demolishes the notion that ideas of genius are extracted from hashish intoxication. In the first place, these ideas are not as beautiful as one might imagine; their charm comes mainly from the extreme nervous excitement in which the subject finds himself. Finally, the hashish that gives these ideas takes away at the same time the power to use them, for it annihilates the will and plunges its victims into a listless tedium, where the mind becomes incapable of any effort, any work, and from which it cannot free itself by taking a fresh dose.

This commentary, rather self-conscious and carefully moralistic, shows plainly that Gautier's appreciation of hashish had completely changed since the faraway heady days of the 1840s. The highly respectable poet belittles his own youthful curiosity about something that had remained of general interest to many artists. The reason for this change had little to do with public disapproval—for the most part there was little more of that in the 1860s than there had been twenty-five years earlier. It was simply the case of a poet grown serious and moralistic with age. Gautier had quite accepted the conditions for living set by his friend Baudelaire, whose elegy he was writing.

Charles Baudelaire was always, from his earliest youth, the most serious of men, with a tragic sense of life that permeated all he wrote, poetry and prose. He was extraordinarily interested in altered states of consciousness, believing that man "always aspires to rekindle his hopes and raise himself into the infinite." The use of all drugs, including alcohol—excitants they were then called— was man's most important means of "fleeing, if only for a few hours, his vile abode" in reality.

In 1851 Baudelaire published an essay, "On Wine and Hashish, Compared as Means of Individual Multiplication." * By the time he wrote it he had already come to several adverse conclusions about cannabis, based on personal experiments that might have begun as much as twelve years earlier, when he was a student in the law faculty at the Sorbonne. He had always loved wine, and greatly revered its place in French civilization, but hashish was something else: both led to "man's excessive poetic development," but "wine exalts the will, hashish annihilates it. . . . Wine makes people happy and sociable. Hashish isolates them. . . . Finally, wine is for working people, who need to drink it. Hashish belongs to the class of solitary pleasures; it is made for wretched idlers." His experiences with the Hashish-eaters Club were still fresh in his memory. He had a strong belief that among those who worked —and he always idealized labor as a saving virtue—poets and writers were preeminent.

He developed these thoughts more fully. In 1858 he wrote "On the Artificial Ideal—Hashish," † which two years later he retitled "The Hashish Poem" (Le poème du haschisch—it was a prose poem). He published it as half of a book about drugs and their human value called Les paradis artificiels.‡ *The other half was a*

---

partial translation of Thomas De Quincey's Confessions of an English Opium Eater.

He begins with a short essay, the first section, called "The Taste for the Infinite." Heightened states of consciousness are exceptionally valued in human life, he says. "I like to consider this abnormal mental condition as a real grace, a magic mirror in which man may see himself as beautiful—that is, as he ought to be and might be; a sort of angelic excitation, a call to order in a complimentary form." But man will always wish to return to this angelic state, and since he is a creature of horrible passions and vices—Baudelaire knew many of them well—he will not shrink from any means available to him. "This visible lord of a visible nature has thus been content to create his paradise out of a pharmacy . . . like a madman who has replaced solid furniture and real gardens with backdrops painted on canvas and mounted on frames."

It is a devastating indictment of intoxication, and shows pretty clearly Baudelaire's disdain for the greater part of humanity. "In this corruption of man's sense of the infinite lies, I believe, the reason for all sinful excesses, from the intoxication of the writer who must seek in opium relief from physical pain, and who, having thereby discovered a source of morbid pleasure, makes it bit by bit his only hope for health, the very sun of his spiritual life, down to the most disgusting drunkard of the slums who, his brain full of fire and glory, rolls ridiculously in the garbage of the gutter." Baudelaire condemns them all. His own years of dependence on opium—he began to take laudanum for a stomach condition and eventually reached 150 drops a day—and his experiments with hashish put him in an ideal position to judge man's constant demand for artificial spiritual elevation.

After another section, "What Is Hashish?", in which he briefly describes the history of the drug—primarily the story of the Assassins—and methods of preparing it, he turns to his central argument.

CHARLES BAUDELAIRE,
engraving by Edouard Manet / 1865

Charles Baudelaire,
"THE HASHISH POEM" * (1860)

THE THEATER OF THE SERAPHIM

WHAT DOES ONE experience? What does one see? Marvelous
things, of course? Extraordinary spectacles? Is it very beautiful?
Very dreadful? Very dangerous? These are the ordinary questions,
asked with a mixture of curiosity and dread, by the ignorant of
the adept. It is like a childish impatience to know, like that of
people who have never left their fireside, when they find themselves
face to face with a man who has returned from faraway and unknown lands. They imagine hashish intoxication as a prodigious
country, a vast theater of magic and conjuring, where everything
is miraculous and unforeseen. But that is a prejudice, a complete
misunderstanding. And, since for the generality of readers and
questioners the word *hashish* includes the idea of a strange and
bewildering world, the expectation of tremendous dreams (it would
be better to say hallucinations, which are moreover less frequent
than people think), I shall immediately note the important difference separating the effects of hashish from the phenomenon of
sleep. In sleep, the adventurous voyage of every night, there is
something positively miraculous, a miracle whose punctuality has
blunted its mystery. Man's dreams are of two classes. In the first
kind, full of his ordinary life, his preoccupations, desires, and vices
mix in a more or less bizarre way with objects glimpsed during the
day, which are carelessly attached to the vast canvas of his memory.
This is the natural dream; it is man himself. But the other kind
of dream! The absurd, unexpected dream, with neither rapport
nor connection with the character, life, or passions of the dreamer!
This dream, which I shall call hieroglyphic, apparently represents
the supernatural side of life, and it is precisely because it is absurd

* Charles Baudelaire, *"Le poème du haschisch," Les paradis artificiels* (Paris,
1860), sections 3–5.

that the ancients believed it divine. Because it is inexplicable by natural causes, they attributed to it a cause exterior to man; and even today, not counting the oneiromancers,* there is a philosophical school that sees in dreams of this kind sometimes a reproach, sometimes a counsel—in sum, a symbolic and moral tableau, engendered in the very spirit of the man who is sleeping. It is a dictionary that must be studied, a language to which wise men must obtain the key.

In hashish intoxication, there is nothing like this. We never leave the natural dream. The intoxication, in all its duration, will only be, it is true, a vast dream, thanks to the intensity of colors and the rapid succession of ideas; but it will always preserve the particular tonality of the individual. Man has wished to dream, the dream will rule the man, but the dream will surely be the son of its father. The lazy man has searched hard in order to introduce artificially the supernatural into his life and thought, but after all, despite the accidental energy of his sensations, it is only the same man enlarged, the same number raised to a very large power. He is mastered, but his misfortune is that this is only by himself, by the already dominant part of himself: *He wanted to be an angel, he has become a beast,*† momentarily very powerful, if one could call power an excessive sensibility, without a governor to moderate or utilize it.

Let the worldly and the ignorant know, those eager to experience exceptional delights, that they will find nothing miraculous in hashish, absolutely nothing but an excess of the natural. The brain and the organs on which hashish operates will show only their ordinary, individual phenomena, enlarged, it is true, in number and energy, but always faithful to their origin. Man will not escape the fate of his physical and moral temperament: the hashish will be, for his familiar impressions and thoughts, an enlarging mirror, but a clear one.

* Those who divine by dreams.
† One of the *Pensées* of Pascal.

Here is the drug under your very eyes: a bit of green preserves, as large as a nut, smelling peculiarly strong, so much that it raises a kind of repulsion and slight waves of nausea, as of course any fine and even agreeable odor would do, raised to its maximum strength and density. (Allow me to note in passing that this proposition might be reversed, and the most repugnant and revolting odor might perhaps become a pleasure, reduced to its minimum quantity and expansion.) So here is happiness!—filling up a small spoon—happiness with its intoxications, follies, and trifles! You may swallow it without fear, it won't kill you. Your physical organs will not be attacked. Perhaps later too frequent an appeal to its spell will diminish the strength of your will, you may be less human than you are today, but the punishment is so far away, the future disaster so hard to define! What do you risk? Perhaps a bit of nervous fatigue tomorrow. Don't you risk every day far greater punishments for far fewer rewards? So, it's done: you have even, to give it more strength and expansion, mixed your dose of the extract with a cup of black coffee; you have taken care to have an empty stomach, postponing until nine or ten o'clock any substantial meal, in order to give the poison complete freedom of action—the most you can take is a little light soup in an hour's time. You are now sufficiently nourished for a long and singular voyage. The whistle has blown, the sails are set, and you have the strange privilege over ordinary travelers of not knowing where you are going. You have willed it: long live fate!

I assume that you have chosen well the moment for this adventurous expedition. Every perfect debauch needs its perfect leisure. You know moreover that hashish exaggerates not only the individual, but also his circumstance and surroundings. You have no work to do that requires punctuality or exactness, no family or love problems. Take care: Any problem or worry, any memory of work claiming your will or attention at a particular time, will sound a knell across your intoxication and poison your pleasure. Any worry will become an anguish, any problem a torture. All these conditions being observed, if you are in favorable surround-ings, such as a picturesque countryside or a poetically furnished room, and if you can even expect a little music, then everything is for the best.

Generally there are three phases of hashish intoxication, rather easy to distinguish, and it is a curious thing to observe in novices the first symptoms of the first phase. You've vaguely heard about the marvelous effects of hashish; your imagination has a precon-ceived idea that it is some kind of ideal rapture; you long to know whether its reality will be up to your expectation. This is enough to throw you from the very beginning into an anxious state, rather favorable to the invading and conquering spirit of the poison. Most novices, when first trying it, complain about the slowness of its effects: they wait for them with a childish impatience, and the drug doesn't act quickly enough for their liking, so they indulge in blustering incredulity that is very entertaining to the initiates, who know how hashish works. The first effects, like the signs of a gathering storm, appear and multiply in the very midst of this in-credulity. There is at first a bit of hilarity, ridiculous and irresistible, which seizes you. This seizure of groundless gaiety, which you are almost ashamed of, happens again and again, cutting across intervals of stupor when you try in vain to recollect yourself. The simplest words, the most trivial ideas, take on a bizarre new aspect: you are even astonished at having found them so simple. Incon-gruous resemblances and comparisons, impossible to foresee, in-terminable word games, and comic sketches flow continually from your brain. The demon has invaded you: it is useless to balk at this hilarity, as painful as tickling. From time to time you laugh at yourself, at your silliness and folly, and your friends, if they are there, laugh both at your state and their own; but since they are without malice, you are without rancor.

This gaiety, by turns languid and poignant, the uneasiness in the joy, this insecurity and indecision in the malady, generally last only a rather short time. Soon the relationships between ideas become so vague, the thread linking your conceptions so tenuous, that only your companions can understand you. Furthermore, on this subject, there is no means of verification: they may well believe they understand you, and the illusion is reciprocal. This frolicking about, these outbursts of laughter, which are like explosions, appear to be real madness, or at least the foolishness of a maniac, to anyone not in the same state as you. Likewise prudence and good sense, regularity of thought in any prudent witness who is not intoxicated, amuses you as a special kind of dementia. Your roles are inverted: his self-control pushes you to the limits of irony. Isn't it a mysteriously comic situation when a man is pushed into incomprehensible gaiety because of someone who is not in the same situation as himself? The fool takes pity on the wise man, and from that time the idea of his superiority begins to dawn on the horizon of his intellect. Soon it will grow, swell, and burst like a meteor.

I was witness to a scene of this kind that had gone on for a long while, whose grotesque feature was only intelligible for those who knew, at least by observing others, the effects of the substance and the enormous difference in pitch it creates between two supposedly equal intelligences. A famous musician, who knew nothing of the effects of hashish, who perhaps had never even heard of it, arrives in the middle of a party where several people have taken some. They try to make him understand its marvelous effects. He smiles graciously and complacently at these prodigious accounts, as if he would gladly pretend for several minutes. His doubts are quickly guessed by those wits sharpened by poison, and their laughter wounds him. These outbursts of joy, these word games, these altered faces, irritate him and make him declare, earlier perhaps than he would have wished, "This is a bad imitation of an artist, and moreover it must be rather tiring for those who have undertaken it." This comedy lights up all these wits like a flash of lightning. Their joy is redoubled. "This imitation may seem good to you, but not to me," he says. "It only has to seem good to us," egotistically replies one of the patients. Not knowing whether he is dealing with real madmen or merely with people faking madness, the man thinks the wisest thing to do is to leave, but someone should lock the door and hide the key. Someone else, kneeling before him, asks him pardon in the name of society, and tells him insolently, but tearfully, that despite his spiritual inferiority, which might excite some pity, everyone is filled with a deep friendship for him. So he resigns himself to stay, and even agrees, at their insistence, to play a little music. But the sounds of the violin, spreading in the room like a new contagion, grip first one patient, then another. There are deep hoarse sighs, sudden sobs, rivers of silent tears. Horrified, the musician stops, and going up to one who in his bliss is making the most noise, asks him if he is suffering, and what can be done to comfort him. One of the onlookers, a practical man, suggests lemonade and fruit juices. But the patient, ecstasy in his eyes, looks at them both with an ineffable scorn. Imagine wanting to cure a man sick from too much life, sick from joy!

As one sees by this anecdote, kindness holds a rather important place in the sensations caused by hashish: a soft, lazy, mute kindness, deriving from the sharpening of the nerves. In support of this observation, a person told me of an adventure that had happened to him in this state of rapture, and since he had kept a very exact memory of his sensations, I can perfectly understand his grotesque and inexplicable embarrassment at the difference of pitch and level I am speaking of. I don't remember whether this man was having his first or second hashish experience. Had he taken too strong a dose, or had the hashish produced, with no other apparent assistance (this happens frequently) much stronger effects? He told me that across his supreme enjoyment at feeling full of life and genius, came a sudden meeting with an object of terror. At first overcome by the beauty of his sensations, he became quickly horrified. He asked himself what would become of his intelligence and his organs, if this state, which he took to be supernatural, continued to grow, if his nerves became more and more delicate. Because of the enlarging faculty that the wit of the patient possesses, this fear must be an incredible torture. "I was like a wild horse," he said, "running toward an abyss, wanting to stop, yet not being able to. In effect, it was a terrifying gallop, and my mind, the slave of circumstance, surroundings, accident, and everything implied in the word *chance*, had taken an absolutely ecstatic turn. It is too late, I repeated to myself endlessly in despair. When this feeling ceased, and it seemed to go on for an infinite time though it probably lasted only a few minutes, when I thought I could finally plunge into that bliss, so dear to Orientals, that comes after this furious phase, I was stricken by a new misfortune. A new worry, very trivial and childish, came over me. All of a sudden I remembered that I had been invited to a dinner with important men. I saw myself going through the middle of a careful and discreet crowd, where everyone is master of himself, obliged to conceal my state under the light of numerous lamps. I thought that I had succeeded at it, but then I nearly fainted when I thought of the effort of will I had to make. By some accident or other, the words of the Gospel came surging into my memory, 'Woe to him who brings scandal!' * and in wishing to forget them, in trying to forget them, I repeated them endlessly in my mind. My misfortune (and it was a real misfortune) then took on grandiose proportions. I resolved, despite my weakness, to exert myself to go and consult a pharmacist, for I didn't know any antidotes, and I wanted to go with a free spirit into the world, where my work called me. But on the steps of the shop a sudden thought struck me, which stopped me for several instants and made me reflect. I had just seen myself in the mirror of a shop front, and my face had astonished me. The pallor, the sunken lips, the swollen eyes! I shall worry this good man, I said to myself, and for what foolishness! Add to that the sense of ridicule that I wanted to avoid, and the fear of finding people in the shop. But my sudden feeling of goodwill toward this unknown pharmacist dominated all my other sen-

* Matt. 18:7.

timents. I imagined the man as sensitive as myself at that unhappy instant, and, as I thought that his ear and his soul, like mine, would vibrate at the slightest noise, I resolved to enter the shop on tiptoe. I told myself that I couldn't show too much discretion toward a man whose kindness I was going to beg. And then I told myself to lower my voice as I had the sound of my steps—do you know it, the hashish voice?—grave, profound, guttural, much resembling that of inveterate opium eaters. The result was the contrary of what I wanted. Instead of reassuring the pharmacist, I horrified him. He knew nothing of this 'illness,' he had never even heard of it. Yet he looked at me with a curiosity strongly mixed with suspicion. Did he take me for a fool, a criminal, a beggar? For none of them, no doubt, but all those absurd ideas crossed my mind. I had to explain to him at length (what a job!) what hemp preserves were and what use was made of them, repeating to him ceaselessly that there was no danger, that there was no reason for *him* to become alarmed, and that I was only asking for a means of softening the effects, or of contravening them, frequently mentioning the sincere chagrin I felt at causing him any bother. Finally— understand all the humiliation for me contained in these words— he simply asked me to leave. This was the repayment for my exaggerated charity and kindness. I went to my dinner: I scandalized no one. No one suspected the superhuman efforts I had to make in order to seem like everyone else. But I shall never forget the tortures of an ultrapoetic intoxication, inhibited by decorum and impeded by an appointment."

Though naturally inclined to sympathize with all pains born in the imagination, I cannot help laughing at this story. The man who told it to me has not reformed. He is still seeking in those cursed preserves the stimulus one must find in oneself, but as he is a prudent, ordered man, a man of the world, he has lessened his doses, which has allowed him to increase their frequency. Later he will collect the rotten fruits of his hygiene.

I now return to the regular development of the intoxication.

After this first phase of infantile gaiety, there is a kind of momentary quieting. But new events are soon announced by a cool sensation in the extremities (that can actually become an intense cold in some people) and a great weakness in all the limbs: your hands are powerless, and in your head and all your being you feel a troublesome stupor. Your eyes enlarge, as if they were drawn out in all directions by an implacable ecstasy. Your face becomes drowned in pallor. Your lips become thin and drawn into the mouth, with that quick breathing characteristic of a man enthralled by great plans, oppressed by vast thoughts, or gathering his breath before jumping. The throat closes up, so to speak. The palate is dry with a thirst it would be infinitely sweet to satisfy, if the delightful laziness were not more agreeable and opposed to the least bodily movement. Deep, hoarse sighs come from your chest, as if your old body could no longer support the wishes and activity of your new soul. From time to time a shock runs through you and causes a momentary shudder, like those starts which, after a day's work or during a troubled night, come just before real sleep.

Before going further, I would like to tell another story about this sensation of coolness, a story that shows just how much the effects, even the purely physical ones, can vary in different individuals. This time it is a literary man speaking, and I believe we can find in certain passages of his tale indications of a literary temperament.

"I had taken a moderate dose of the extract," he told me, "and everything was going well. The attack of unhealthy laughter had lasted only a short time, and I found myself in that languid and astonished condition that was almost happiness. I saw a tranquil and carefree evening ahead. Chance unfortunately constrained me to accompany someone to the theater. I did my duty bravely, resolved to hide my great desire for quiet and immobility. All the cabs in the neighborhood were taken, and I had to resign myself to a long walk, through the loud street noises, the stupid conversations of the pedestrians, through an ocean of triviality. A slight coolness had already appeared at the ends of my fingers, and soon it became a piercing cold, as if my hands were plunged in a bucket of icy water. But it was not painful: this acute sensation pierced me rather like a delight. Yet it seemed that the cold invaded me more and more throughout the interminable walk. Two or three times I asked the person I was going with if it was really very cold; he replied that on the contrary the temperature was more than warm. Finally at the theater, in the box we had reserved, with three or four hours of rest ahead of me, I thought I had arrived in the promised land. The feelings I had repressed on the way, with all the poor energy at my disposal, at last all came out, and I freely gave myself up to this mute frenzy. The cold increased constantly, and yet I was seeing people lightly dressed, even wearily wiping their brows. The amusing idea struck me that I was a privileged man, alone given the right to be cold at the theater in summer. The cold built up to an alarming point, but above all I was curious to know just how cold it could get. Finally it became so completely and totally cold that all my ideas froze, so to speak: I was a thinking piece of ice; I thought I was a statue carved from a single block of ice, and this mad hallucination stimulated in me such a pride and emotional well-being that I cannot describe them to you. What added to my abominable amusement was my certainty that all the spectators were ignorant of my condition and my superiority over them, and also the happiness of knowing that my friend had not for an instant suspected the bizarre feelings that possessed me. I had my reward for this pretense, and my exceptional pleasure was a real secret.

"Furthermore, I had scarcely entered the box when I was struck with an impression of darkness that seemed somehow connected with the idea of cold. It may well be that these two ideas lent strength to each other. You know that hashish always calls forth grand displays of light, glorious radiance, and showers of liquid gold; every light seems good with hashish, the light that shimmers all at once and that which is fixed at certain points, the candelabras in the drawing rooms, the candles of Mary's month, the rosy avalanches of sunset. It seemed that this miserable glimmer gave off a quite insufficient light to satisfy my insatiable thirst for clarity: I seemed to enter, as I said, a world of shadows, which actually deepened bit by bit, while I was dreaming of polar nights and eternal winter. As to the play (it was in the comic genre), it alone was luminous, though infinitely small and placed far away, as at the end of a huge stereoscope. I won't tell you that I heard the players—you know that that is impossible; from time to time my mind caught up a shred of phrase, and like an expert dancer used it as a trampoline to jump off into faraway reveries. You might think that a drama heard in this fashion might lack logic and sequence, but you are wrong: I discovered a very subtle meaning in the drama which was created by my inattention. Nothing offended me; I was a little like that poet, seeing *Esther* for the first time, who found it entirely natural that Aman should declare his love to the queen. That was, as you can guess, the moment when he throws himself at Esther's feet to ask pardon for his crimes. If every drama were heard according to this method, they would all reach a great beauty, even those of Racine.

"The players seemed extremely small, and surrounded by a precise and careful outline, like Meissen figurines. I not only saw distinctly the most minute details of their costumes, like the designs of the material, the sewing, the buttons, and so forth, but even the line separating the false hairline from the real, the colors and all the tricks of makeup. And these lilliputians were arrayed in a cold, magic clarity, like the one a very clear glass gives to an oil painting. When I was finally able to leave this cavern of frozen shadows, and when the interior fantasies had gone and I had returned to my old self, I felt a greater tiredness than any long, forced work had ever caused me."

Indeed at this period in the intoxication a new acuteness and a superior delicacy are perceived in all the senses. Smell, sight, hearing, and touch participate equally in this progression. The eyes glimpse the infinite, the ears perceive the faintest sounds from amid the most roaring tumult. Then the hallucinations begin. External objects slowly and successively take on peculiar forms, become deformed and transformed. Then ambiguities occur, doubts, and transpositions of ideas. Sounds put on colors, and colors contain music. One might say that this is only natural, and any poetic brain, in its normal, healthy condition, could easily conceive such analogies. But I have already warned the reader that there is nothing positively supernatural in hashish intoxication. The only thing that happens is that these analogies put on an unaccustomed liveliness; they penetrate, invade, and overcome the spirit in their despotic way. Musical notes become numbers, and if your mind is at all endowed with mathematical aptitude, the melody and harmony, all the while keeping its sensual character, transforms itself into a vast problem in arithmetic, in which numbers engender numbers whose changes and appearances you can follow with inexplicable ease, with an agility equal to the musician's.

It sometimes happens that personality disappears and objectivity, the property of pantheist poets, develops so abnormally in you that your contemplation of exterior objects makes you forget your own existence, and soon you confuse yourself with them. Your eye fixes on a harmonious tree bending in the wind: in a few seconds what would be in a poet's brain only a natural comparison becomes in yours a reality. First you give the tree your passions, your desire, or your melancholy; its shivering and vibration become your own, and soon you are the tree. Likewise, the bird that soars in the sky first represents the age-old desire to soar above human things, but you are already the bird itself. Suppose you are sitting down and smoking. Your attention may rest a bit too long on the bluish clouds coming from your pipe. The idea of a slow, continuous, eternal evaporation takes hold of your mind, and soon you are applying this idea to your own thoughts, your thinking matter. By a singular misunderstanding, a transposition, or an intellectual error, you feel yourself evaporating, and you attribute to your pipe (into which you are stuffed and packed like tobacco) the strange ability to *smoke you.*

Happily, this interminable fantasy has lasted only a minute, and a lucid interval, won with great effort, allows you to examine the clock. But another rush of ideas carries you away: it rolls you around for a minute in its living vortex, and this minute too will be an eternity. For the proportions of time and being are completely upset by the number and intensity of feelings and ideas. One might seem to live several human lives in the space of one hour. Are you not like some fantastic novel that is lived instead of written? There is no longer any equation between the origins of the pleasures and the pleasures themselves, and from this idea comes the blame due to this dangerous experiment in which freedom disappears.

When I speak of hallucinations, I do not mean the word in its strictest sense. There is an important difference between the pure hallucination, which doctors often have the opportunity to study, and the hallucination—or rather the error of the senses, in the mental state caused by hashish. In the first case, the hallucination is sudden, perfect, and inevitable; in addition, it finds neither pretext nor excuse in the world of external objects. The patient sees shapes or hears sounds where none exist. In the second case, the hallucination is progressive, nearly voluntary, and does not become perfect: it only ripens in the action of the imagination. Finally, there is always an excuse for it: a sound will speak, saying distinct things, but there was a sound to begin with. The intoxicated eye of the man on hashish sees strange shapes, but before becoming strange or monstrous these shapes were simple and natural. The energy, the lifelike quality of the hallucination in no way invalidates this original distinction. One kind has its origins in the surroundings and in present time, the other does not.

In order for you better to understand this turbulence of imagination, this dreamlike development and poetic outpouring to which a brain affected by hashish is condemned, I shall tell another story.

This time, it is no leisured youth speaking, nor yet a man of letters: It's a woman, a bit mature and curious, of an excitable spirit, who succumbed to the desire to know the poison, and here describes, to another woman, the essential points of her visions. I am transcribing literally:

"However strange and new these sensations might be that I got from my twelve hours of madness (twelve or twenty? I really can't tell), I'll never try it again. The mental excitement is too strong, the resultant fatigue too great; and to tell the truth, I find in this childishness something rather criminal. But I finally gave in to curiosity; and then it was to be a group madness, with old friends, where I saw no great danger in losing a bit of dignity. First of all I must tell you that this wretched hashish is a very tricky substance: Sometimes one feels the intoxication has disappeared, but it's only a false calm. There are moments of rest, but then it starts all over again. So, around ten in the evening, I found myself in one of those momentary states of repose: I thought I'd been delivered from this excess of liveliness that had occasioned me much amusement, true, but not without worry and a bit of fear. I ate my supper with pleasure, as if tired by a long journey. I hadn't eaten till then out of prudence. But before I'd even left the table, my frenzy seized me again, as a cat would a mouse, and the poison began once again to play with my poor brain. Though my own house is only a short distance from our friends', and though there was a carriage at my disposal, I felt so overcome by the desire to dream and to give myself up to this irresistible madness, that I joyfully accepted their offer to put me up until the next day. You know their château, how they have rearranged and refurbished in a modern style the part they live in, but that the part that is not lived in has been left as it was, in its old style and decoration. They decided to improvise for me a bedroom in the old part of the house, and so chose the smallest room, a kind of faded and decrepit boudoir, though quite charming. I must describe it to you carefully, so that you can understand the peculiar vision which affected me and which took up the whole night, so that I had no time to see the hours flying by.

"The room is very small and narrow. Above the molding the ceiling becomes vaulted; the walls are covered with long, narrow mirrors separated with panels painted with country scenes in the rather loose style of the rest of the decor. Exactly at the molding, on each of the four walls, various allegorical figures are represented, some in attitudes of repose, others running or jumping. Above them are several brilliant birds and flowers. Behind the figures a trellis is painted on the wall, which follows naturally the curve of the ceiling. The ceiling is gilt. All the spaces are also gilt, only interrupted by the geometric form of the painted trellis. You can see that this resembles a very large cage, a very beautiful cage for a very large bird. I should add that the night was fine, transparent, and the moon very bright, so bright that after I blew out the candle the whole room remained visible, not lit by the eye of my imagination, as you might think, but illuminated by this lovely night, whose beams picked out all these gildings, mirrors, and varied colors.

"At first I was very amazed to see great spaces spread out before me, beside me, everywhere: clear rivers and verdant scenes were reflected in tranquil waters. You can guess the effect of the panels interspersed with mirrors. Lifting my eyes, I saw a setting sun like fused metal cooling. That was the gold on the ceiling, but the trellis made me think that I was in a kind of cage or house open on all sides, and it was only the bars of my magnificent prison that separated me from all these marvels. At first I laughed at my illusion, but the more I looked at it, the more the magic increased and took on life, transparence, and an absolute reality. From that time the idea of being shut in controlled my mind, without entirely negating, I must say, the varied pleasures I drew from the spectacle around me. I thought of myself as closed away for a long time, perhaps for thousands of years, in this sumptuous cage, in an enchanted countryside, between wondrous horizons. I thought of Sleeping Beauty, of the punishment I had to suffer, and of my future deliverance. Above my head flew the brilliant tropical birds, and because my ear heard the neck bells of the horses on the highway in the distance, these two sensations combined into a unique idea: I thought the birds had a strange coppery song, and that they sang through metallic throats. They were obviously talking about me and enjoying my captivity. Leaping monkeys and grotesque satyrs made fun of me, a prisoner lying immobile. But all the mythological divinities looked at me with a charming smile, as if to encourage me to endure my fate patiently, and their every look was sidelong so as to seize my attention. I concluded that if some ancient faults, some sins I was ignorant of, had necessitated this temporal punishment, yet I could still count on a higher goodness which, even if wisely condemning me, still offered me pleasures more serious than those that filled our youth. You can see that moral considerations were not absent from my dream, but I observed that the pleasure of seeing these brilliant shapes and colors, of believing myself the center of a fantastic drama, frequently absorbed all my other thoughts. This state lasted a very long time. Did it last until morning? I don't know. All of a sudden I saw the morning sun in my room: I was greatly astonished, and despite great efforts of memory it was impossible to know whether I had slept or had patiently endured a delicious insomnia. A while ago it was night, and now it's daytime! The notion of time, or rather the measure of time, being abolished, the whole night was only measurable for me in the multitude of my thoughts. However long it seems to me from here, yet then it seemed to last only a few seconds, or perhaps it never happened at all.

"I haven't even spoken of my fatigue—it was immense. They say that poetic and creative effort resembles what I experienced, though I've always thought that those people whose job is to move us must be endowed with a calm disposition; but if poetic ecstasy resembles that which was contained in a little spoonful of preserves, I think that the public's pleasure must cost the poets dearly, and it's not without a sort of well-being, a prosaic satisfaction, that I finally find myself back to normal, in my intellectual normality, I mean in real life."

This is obviously a reasonable woman, but we shall only use her tale to draw several useful notes to complete our brief description of the main sensations that hashish causes.

She spoke of supper as a pleasure arriving at just the right time, at a time when a momentary calm, which seemed definitive, allowed her to return to real life. But there are, as I have said, intermittent false calms, and often the hashish causes a voracious hunger and almost always an excessive thirst. Often dinner or supper, instead of leading to a long rest, creates a redoubled action, the giddy crisis of which this lady has complained, and which was followed by a series of enchanted visions, lightly touched with fear, to which she with good humor resigned herself. This tyrannical hunger and thirst cannot be sated without a considerable effort. For one feels so above material things that one must develop one's courage to take up a bottle or a fork.

The final crisis caused by the digestion of food is actually very violent: it is impossible to struggle against it. It would be unendurable if it lasted too long and did not soon give way to another phase of the intoxication which in the case just cited became splendid visions, slightly terrifying and at the same time consoling. This state is what the Orientals call *kif*: no longer something roiling and turbulent, it's a calm and immobile blessedness, a glorious resignation. For a long time you haven't been your own master, but you don't bother about it anymore. Pain and the idea of time have disappeared, or if they dare to show themselves again, they are transfigured by the dominating sensation, and are thus, relative to their usual form, what poetic melancholy is to actual pain.

But above all, let us note that in this lady's story (this is why I have transcribed it) the hallucination is a bastard kind, and draws its being from an exterior spectacle: the mind is only a mirror in which the reflected surroundings are transformed in an exaggerated way. Finally, we witnessed what I would willingly call a moral hallucination: the subject thought she was submitting to a punishment, but the female temperament, unsuited to analysis, did not allow her to note the singularly optimistic nature of the hallucination. The Olympian divinities' benevolent regard was poeticized by what was essentially a hashish eater's gloss. I would not say that this lady skirted remorse, but her thoughts, briefly turned to melancholy and regret, became rapidly colored by hope. It is a change we shall again have occasion to observe.

She spoke of the next day's fatigue, and indeed it is great, but it doesn't show up immediately, and when you are obliged to recognize it, it is always with astonishment. For first of all, when you see a new day arising in your life, you experience an incredible well-being—you seem to enjoy a marvelous lightness of spirit. But you are scarcely out of bed when an old remnant of the intoxication catches up with you and slows you down, like the ball and chain of your recent servitude. Your weak legs rather timidly lead you about, and at every instant you are afraid of breaking yourself like some fragile object. A great languor (some people think it doesn't lack charm) seizes your mind and spreads over your faculties like fog over the countryside. And there you are for several more hours, incapable of work, action, or energy. This is the punishment for the unholy prodigality with which you have spent your nervous energy. You have flung your personality to the four winds, and now what trouble you will have in collecting it again and concentrating it!

THE MAN-GOD

It is time to put aside all this juggling and these great puppets, born of the fumes of childish brains. Haven't we something more important to talk about: the modification of human feelings, the morality of hashish?

Until now I've only written one brief monograph on intoxication, and limited myself to describing its main traits, especially the material ones. But what is most important for spiritual man, I think, is to know the action of the poison on his spirit, I mean the enlarging, deforming, and exaggerating of his normal feelings and moral perceptions, which then show, in such an exceptional atmosphere, a real refractive phenomenon.

The man who for a long time has surrendered to opium or hashish, weakened by his servitude, yet has been able to find the necessary energy to free himself, this man seems to me like a runaway prisoner. He seems to me more admirable than the prudent man who has never fallen, having always been careful to avoid temptation. The English frequently use, concerning opium eaters, words that only innocents, those ignorant of the horrors of this decay, could find excessive: enchained, fettered, enslaved! They are chains indeed, beside which all others, chains of duty, or of illicit love, are merely gauzy webs, spiders' cloth. What an appalling marriage of man with himself! "I became a slave to opium: it held me in its bonds, and all my works and plans took on the color of my dreams," said Ligeia's * husband; but in how many wonderful passages has Edgar Poe, incomparable poet, irrefutable philosopher, whom one must always quote concerning mysterious illnesses of the spirit, in how many places has he described the somber, endearing pleasures of opium? The lover of the radiant Berenice, the metaphysician Egoeus, speaks of a change in his powers that makes him give an abnormal, monstrous value to the simplest phenomena: "To reflect tirelessly for hours, my attention fixed on some puerile quotation in the margin or text of a book, to remain absorbed, the greater part of a summer day, in a strange shadow, lengthening obliquely along the rug or floor, to abandon myself for an entire night in studying the straight flame of a lamp, or the fire in the hearth, to dream away entire days in a flower's perfume, to repeat monotonously some vulgar word, until the sound, from being repeated, ceases to give the

---

* This and the following are characters from E. A. Poe's short stories, which Baudelaire had recently translated.

mind any idea at all—these were some of the commonest and least pernicious aberrations in my mental faculties, aberrations that were doubtless not unprecedented, but that certainly baffled any explanation and analysis." And the high-strung August Bedloe, who swallows his dose of opium every morning before his walk, states that the main benefit he draws from this daily poisoning is to find in everything, even the most trivial, a profound interest: "Yet the opium produced its usual effects, giving to all the external world an intense interest. The trembling of a leaf, the color of a blade of grass, the shape of a clover, the buzzing of a bee, the brightness of a dewdrop, the sigh of the wind, the faint forest smells, everything produced a world of inspirations, a magnificent and varied procession of chaotic and rhapsodic thoughts."

Thus the master of the horrible, the prince of mystery, expresses himself through the mouths of his characters. These two qualities of opium are perfectly applicable to hashish: With both drugs intelligence, formerly free, becomes enslaved. But the word *rhapsodic* which suggests so well a train of thoughts suggested and dominated by the external world and the force of circumstance, has a more real and terrible truth in the case of hashish. There reason is but a wreckage at the mercy of every current, and the train of thought is infinitely more accelerated and more rhapsodic. That is to say, in a sufficiently clear manner, that hashish is, in its immediate effect, much more vehement than opium, much more the enemy of an ordered life—in a word, much more disturbing. I do not know whether ten years of hashish intoxication would lead to disasters equal to those caused by ten years of opium addiction, I can only say that for the present hour and the day after hashish has the more fatal results: One drug is a peaceful seducer, the other a chaotic devil.

In this last part I want to define and analyze the moral ravages caused by these dangerous and delicious gymnastics, ravages so great, with dangers so profound, that those who return from the battle only slightly injured seem to me like courageous escapees from the cave of some multiform Proteus, as Orpheuses who have conquered Hell. Let those who wish take this sort of language as excessively metaphorical; I only know that I see stimulant drugs as the most terrible and sure means at the disposal of the Spirit of Darkness to recruit and subjugate deplorable humanity, even as one of his most perfect embodiments.

Here, to shorten my task and make my analysis clearer, rather than collecting scattered anecdotes I will include a group of observations in one imaginary character. So I need to imagine a soul of my choice. In De Quincey's *Confessions* he correctly states that opium, rather than putting someone to sleep, excites him, but only in his own way, and thus in considering opium's wonders it would be absurd to talk about a cattle buyer, because he would only dream of steers and pastures. So I am not going to describe the heavy visions of some breeder intoxicated by hashish—who would read them with pleasure, or at all? To idealize my subject, I must concentrate all the light into a single circle, and polarize it. And in this tragic circle will be, as I say, a soul of my choice, someone analogous to what the eighteenth century called "sensitive man," what the romantics called "misunderstood man," and what the families of the bourgeois masses usually refer to scornfully as "eccentric man."

A disposition half nervous, half morose is most favorable for developing the intoxication; let us add a cultivated mind, trained in the study of form and color; a tender heart, wearied by misfortune but still eager for restoration; we will even go so far as to allow a few old habits, if you wish, as well as that which must occur in an easily excitable nature—if not real remorse, at least regret for thoroughly wasted time. A taste for metaphysics, a knowledge of the different philosophical hypotheses about human destiny —these qualities are certainly not completely useless, no more than is love of virtue, of the stoic or mystical sort, which is set up in all our modern children's books as the highest summit a distinguished soul can climb. Add to that a great refinement of the senses, which I had omitted as a superfluous condition, and I think I've assembled the general and commoner elements of the modern sensitive man, of what one might call the banal shape of eccentricity. Now let us see what will happen to this construct pushed to exaggeration by hashish. Let us follow this progress of human imagination to its final, splendid resting place: the individual's belief in his own divinity.

If you are one of these souls, your innate love of form and color will quickly find an immense canvas in the early development of your intoxication. Colors will take on an unwonted energy, and will enter your brain with a victorious intensity. Whether it be fine, mediocre, or even bad, the paint on the ceiling will take on a frightening life of its own; the worst hotel grade of wallpaper will rise and fall like a splendid panorama. Nymphs with glowing skin look at you with huge eyes, more deep and liquid than air or water; characters out of antiquity, got up in clerical or military costumes, trade with you deepest confidences in a single glance. The sinuousness of lines is an absolutely clear language where you can read souls' disturbance and desire. Yet there also develops that strange, temporary state of mind when the mystery of life, surrounded by its multitudes of problems, is revealed in all its clarity, when the first thing you look at, however natural or trivial, becomes a talking symbol. Fourier and Swedenborg, one with his analogies, the other with his correspondences, become incarnated in the vegetable and animal things you see, and instead of teaching you by voice, they do so by shape and color. The meaning of the allegory seems to take on proportions unknown to you; we note in passing that allegory, that most spiritual of genres, which inept painters have taught us to despise, but which is really one of the earliest and most natural forms of poetry, takes up its rightful domination in the mind illuminated by hashish. The drug thus spreads out over all life like a magic glaze, coloring it with splendor and enlightening all its mysteries. Delicate country scenes, distant horizons, cityscapes whitened by the deadly livid color of a storm or lit by the concentrated brilliance of sunsets; the depth of space, an allegory for the depth of time; an actor's dance, gesture, or line, if you happen to be at the theater; the first sentence you read if your eyes fall upon a book—everything, finally, the universality of creation rises before you with a new glory you never before suspected. Even arid grammar itself turns into a sort of evocative charm: words put on flesh and blood—the substantive in all its substantial majesty; the adjective, the transparent gown that dresses and colors it; and the verb, angel of movement, giving motion to the sentence. Music, another language dear to the idle or to deep minds searching for repose from their various labors, speaks to you of yourself, recites to you the poem of your life: it becomes embodied in you, and you drown in it. It speaks of your passion, not in some vague, ill-defined manner as it does at parties or a night at the opera, but in a detailed and positive way, every movement finding its counterpart in your soul, every note becoming a word, and the entire poem entering your brain like a dictionary gifted with life.

You must not believe that all these phenomena occur in the mind willy-nilly, in the shrill voice of reality and the chaos of everyday life. The internal eye transforms everything, giving everything the beauty it lacks to be really worthy of pleasing. We must relate this basically voluptuous and sensual phase to the love of water, clear, running, or stagnant, that occurs in the cerebral intoxication of some artists. Mirrors give a pretext for a reverie that is like a spiritual thirst, like that physical thirst I described above; flowing water, playing water, harmonious waterfalls, the blue vastness of the sea, all rolling, singing, sleeping with an ineffable charm. Water becomes a real enchantress, and though I don't much believe that acts of madness are caused by hashish, I couldn't swear that contemplating a clear pool would be altogether safe for a mind in love with space and clarity, and that the old story of Ondine would not become a tragic reality.

I suppose I have sufficiently spoken of the monstrous increase of time and space, two concepts that are always connected, which the mind confronts without sadness or fear. The mind looks with a melancholy pleasure across the depth of years, and dives boldly into infinite perspectives. You have guessed, I suppose, that this abnormal and tyrannical increase applies equally to all feelings and to all ideas: So I have given a fairly good account of kindness, I think, and of beauty, and of love. An idea of beauty must naturally find a large place in a spiritual disposition such as I have supposed. Harmony, balance of line, rhythm in movement, appear to the dreamer as necessities, even as duties, not only toward all created things, but toward himself, as he finds himself, in this crisis, marvelously able to understand the immortal and universal rhythm. If our fanatic lacks personal beauty, never fear that he will suffer long from this realization, nor that he will consider himself like a discordant note in the world of harmony and beauty called up by his imagination. Hashish's sophisms are numerous and admirable, and they tend generally to the optimistic; one of the main ones, and the most efficacious, is that which changes desire into reality. Of course it's the same in many cases of real life, but how much more earnestness and subtlety there is here! How, moreover, could someone gifted at understanding harmony, a sort of priest of beauty, make such an exception, a blot on his own theory? Moral beauty and its power, grace and its attractions, eloquence and its prowess—all these are quickly seen as correctives to an embarrassing ugliness, then as consolers, and finally as perfect adulators of an imaginary scepter.

As to love, I have heard many people, stirred up with a student's curiosity, trying to get information from those who know it about the use of hashish. What would love's intoxication, so strong in its natural state, be like when enclosed in the other intoxication, like a sun inside a sun? This is the question that often arises in that crowd of wits which I call the gapers of the intellectual world. To answer a dirty hidden part of their question, which they don't dare to mention, I would refer the reader to Pliny, who has somewhere spoken of the properties of hemp in such a way as to dissipate many illusions on this subject. We also know that sluggishness is the usual result when people abuse their nerves with stimulating substances. But since it is not a question here of real power, but of emotion or sensitivity, I will only ask the reader to consider how the imagination of a nervous man can be pushed by hashish to an amazing degree, as little determinable as the extremest possible strength of wind in a hurricane, at the same time that his senses become rarefied to a point just as difficult to define. Thus one might well believe that the lightest and most innocent caress, a handshake, for example, could have its meaning increased a hundredfold by the state of the soul and the senses, and might lead them very rapidly to that swoon which vulgar mortals consider as the highest point of happiness. It is not to be doubted that hashish awakens sweet memories in lovelorn natures, to which pain and unhappiness even give a new luster. It is no less certain that a strong dose of sensuality combines well with these agitations of the mind: and it is useful to remark (let this witness to the immorality of hashish) that a sect of Ismailites—from which came the Assassins—were led in their adorations well beyond the impartial lingam to the absolute and exclusive cult of the feminine part of the symbol. It would only be natural, each man being the representation of history, to see an obscene heresy, a monstrous religion produced in a mind carelessly given over to the mercy of a hellish drug, and smiling at the diminution of its own powers.

Since we have seen in hashish intoxication a peculiar kindness shown even to strangers, a kind of philanthropy showing more pity than love (here is the first germ of the satanic spirit that will develop in such an extraordinary way), but which goes out of its way to avoid the slightest distress, we can see what would become of a localized sentimentality when it is applied to a beloved person who plays or has played an important part in the moral life of the patient. Veneration, adoration, prayer, dreams of happiness jump forth and dance about with the energy and brightness of fireworks, and like these they burst and vanish in the darkness. There is no sentimental combination to which the pliant love of a hashish slave will not yield. The desire to protect, an ardent and devout feeling of fatherhood might become mixed with a guilty sensuality, but hashish will always be able to excuse and absolve. It goes yet further. Imagine that some old faults have left bitter traces in the soul, a husband or lover thinking only with sadness (in his normal state) of his stormy past; but this bitterness then becomes sweet, the need for pardon makes the imagination more cunning and pliant, and remorse itself, in this diabolical drama that expresses itself only in a long monologue, might act as a stimulant to stir up the heart all over again. Remorse! Was I wrong to say that hashish appears to a truly philosophical mind as a perfect satanic instrument? Remorse, essential ingredient in pleasure, is soon drowned in the delicious contemplation of remorse, in a kind of voluptuous analysis, one so rapid that man, that natural devil—to speak as the Swedenborgians do—cannot see how much that analysis is involuntary, and how closely, from minute to minute, it approaches diabolical perfection. He admires his remorse and glorifies it, while he is in the process of losing his liberty.

So here is my imaginary man, the mind of my choice, arrived at that pitch of joy and serenity where he is constrained to admire himself. All contradictions are wiped out, every philosophical problem becomes clear, or at least appears to be. Everything is a cause for pleasure. The abundance of his actual life inspires in him a measureless pride. A voice speaks to him (it's his own, alas) which says, "Now you have the right to consider yourself superior to everyone; no one knows or could ever understand everything you think and feel; they would even be unable to understand the kindness they inspire in you. You are a king whom passersby do not recognize, who lives in the solitude of his conviction. But what does that matter to you? Don't you possess that sovereign scorn that makes the soul so good?"

Yet we may imagine that from time to time a biting memory crosses and corrupts this happiness. A suggestion coming from outside might revive a past that is unpleasant to contemplate. How many foolish, vile actions fill the past which are truly unworthy of this king and which defile all ideal dignity? You may be sure that the hashish eater will bravely confront these reproachful phantoms and even that he will be able to draw from these hideous memories new elements of pleasure and pride. This will be the line of his argument: Once the first feeling of pain has passed, he will analyze with curiosity this action or feeling whose memory has troubled his present glorification, the motives that made him act so, the circumstances that surrounded him, and if he doesn't find in these circumstances sufficient reasons to extenuate, if not to absolve his sin, don't think for a moment that he will feel vanquished. I can see his reasoning—it's like a watch movement under a transparent case: "This ridiculous, cowardly, or vile action, whose memory has just been stirred up, is in complete contradiction to my real, present nature, and the very energy with which I condemn it, the inquisitive care with which I analyze and judge it, prove my lofty and divine aptitude for virtue. How many men in this world are as quick to judge themselves, as severe in condemnation?" He not only condemns himself, he glorifies himself. The horrible memory is absorbed in this way into the contemplation of an ideal virtue, an ideal charity, an ideal genius: He frankly indulges in a triumphant spiritual orgy. We have seen how, counterfeiting sacrilegiously the sacrament of penance, he is at once penitent and confessor, giving himself an easy absolution, or worse yet, he draws from his condemnation a new field for his pride. Now, from contemplating his virtuous dreams and projects, he infers his practical aptitude for virtue; the loving energy with which he embraces this phantom of virtue appears to him sufficient proof of the vital energy necessary to accomplish his ideal. He completely mixes up dream and action, and his imagination becomes more and more heated before the enchanting vision of his own corrected and idealized nature, substituting this fascinating image of himself for his individual reality that is so poor in will-power, so rich in vanity, that he can finally decree his apotheosis in these neat and simple terms, which contain for him a whole world of abominable pleasures: "I am the most virtuous of men!"

Doesn't he remind you of Jean-Jacques,* who also, after having confessed to the universe, not without a certain delight, dared to utter the same shout of triumph (at least the difference is very small) with the same sincerity and conviction? The enthusiasm with which he admired virtue, the nervous compassion that filled his eyes with tears at the sight of a beautiful action or at the thought of all the beautiful actions he would be able to accom-plish, were sufficient to give him a superior idea of his moral worth. Jean-Jacques was intoxicated without hashish.

Shall I go further in the analysis of this triumphant mono-mania? Shall I explain how, under the poison, this character soon makes himself the center of the universe? How he becomes the living and outward expression of the proverb that passion refers everything to itself? He believes in his virtue and genius; can't he guess its end? All the objects that surround him are just so many suggestions awakening in him a world of thoughts, all of them more colorful, lively, and subtle than ever, and decked out with a magical gloss. "These magnificent cities," he says to himself, "where proud buildings are spread out as on stage sets; these beauti-ful ships, floating idly and nostalgically at anchor, which seem to translate our thought: When do we depart for happiness?; these museums which overflow with fine shapes and intoxicating colors; these libraries in which are kept Science's works and the Muse's dreams; these collected musical instruments which speak as with one voice; these enchanting women, made more charming by the science of adornment and the economics of a glance—all these things have been created *for me, for me, for me!* Humanity has

---

* Rousseau, eighteenth-century philosopher, whose self-indulgence Baudelaire despised.

worked, been martyred and sacrificed for me, all to give me a field for my implacable appetite for emotion, knowledge, and beauty!" I am jumping and abridging a little. Let no one be astonished when a final, supreme thought leaps from the dreamer's brain: "I have become God!" This wild, ardent cry comes from him with such energy and power that if the wishes and beliefs of an intoxicated man were the least bit effectual, this cry would knock over the angels spread out on the roads of heaven. "I am God!" But soon this hurricane of pride changes into a calm, quiet, mute beatitude, and the universe of beings shows itself colored and lit up by a sulfurous dawn. If by chance a vague memory creeps into the soul of this deplorable blessed man: Isn't there another God?, do you think he will stand erect before Him, question His will, and face Him without terror? Who was the French philosopher who, in order to scoff at modern German doctrines, said, "I am a god who has had a bad dinner"? * This irony would not be biting to a mind raised up by hashish; he would tranquilly reply, "I may have had a bad dinner, but I am a god."

MORAL

But the next day! The dreadful next day! All the organs slack, fatigued, the nerves strung out, the feeling that you want to cry, the impossibility of applying yourself to any consecutive work—all these signs tell you that you have been playing a forbidden game. Nature is hideous, stripped of her luminousness of the evening before, and seems like the sad leftovers of a feast. Your will is especially affected, and of all your faculties this is the most precious. It is said, and it's almost true, that this substance causes no physical harm, or at least no grave one. But can one really say that a man who is incapable of action, good only for dreaming, is really well, though his body seems in good condition? Now we are acquainted well enough with human nature to know that any man who can

* Voltaire, whose witty cynicism Baudelaire greatly admired.

instantly gain all the good things of heaven and earth with a spoonful of preserves will never try to win the smallest part of them by work. Can you imagine a country where all the citizens took hashish constantly? What citizens, soldiers, and legislators! Even in the Orient, where its use is so widespread, there are governments that have realized the need to forbid it. Man is forbidden, in effect, on pain of decay and intellectual death, to disturb the primordial conditions of his existence and to break the equilibrium between his faculties and the ways in which they work; in a word, to disturb his destiny in order to substitute for it a new kind of fate. Let us remember Melmoth,* that admirable emblem. His appalling suffering lies in the disproportion between his wondrous faculties, instantly acquired by a bargain with the devil, and his surroundings, where he must live as a creature of God. And none of those he wishes to win over will agree to buy from him, under the same conditions, his terrifying privilege. Every man that will not accept the conditions of life sells his soul. It is easy to grasp the connection between the satanic creations of poets and living creatures devoted to stimulants. Man wanted to be God, but soon, because of an incontrovertible moral law, he has fallen lower than his actual nature. He has sold his soul for a trifle.

Balzac doubtless thought that for man there is no greater shame or livelier suffering than the abdication of his will. I once saw him at a party where the question arose of the great effects of hashish. He listened and questioned attentively and humorously. Those people who knew him thought he must be interested. But the idea of thoughts he couldn't control shocked him deeply. Someone handed him some hashish; he examined it, sniffed it, and gave it back without tasting it. The struggle between his almost childish curiosity and a hatred of abdication passed across his expressive face in a striking way. His love of dignity got the better of him.

* Hero of *Melmoth, the Wanderer: A Tale,* a novel published in 1820, written by Charles Robert Maturin. It was the last of the classic English gothic romances.

It is hard indeed to imagine this theoretician of the will, this spiritual twin of Louis Lambert, agreeing to lose even the smallest part of that will.* Despite the admirable benefits of ether and chloroform, it seems to me that viewed from spiritualist philosophy the same moral blot applies to all those modern inventions which lessen human freedom and unavoidable pain. I wonder at the paradox once told me by an officer of a difficult operation performed on a French general at El Aghouat, from which the general died despite chloroform. The general was a very brave man—even something more than brave: one of those souls to which the word *chivalrous* applies. "It wasn't chloroform he needed," the officer said, "but the support of the whole army and regimental music. That way he might have been saved!" The surgeon did not share the same opinion, but the chaplain might have understood.

It is really superfluous, after all these considerations, to dwell on the immoral nature of hashish. If I compare it to suicide, to lingering death, to a weapon always bloody yet always sharp, no reasonable mind could criticize any of these comparisons. If I liken it to a magic or sorcery by which man tries to effect a forbidden domination by means that no one can prove either false or valid, no philosophical soul can criticize this comparison. If the church condemns magic and sorcery, it is because they militate against the

---

* Gautier has a comment on Balzac's refusal of hashish:
"I was at the Hôtel Pimodan that evening, and can verify the perfect exactness of this little anecdote. I would only add this particular detail: when handing back the spoonful of *dawamesc* that had been offered him, Balzac said that any such experiment was useless and that he was sure hashish would have no effect on his brain.

"That was certainly possible. That powerful brain, where will, strengthened by study, was enthroned, which was saturated by the subtle aroma of mocha, and which even three bottles of the headiest Vouvray could not faze in the slightest, would have been more than able to resist any passing intoxication by Indian hemp" ("Charles Baudelaire," pp. 70–71).

Yet four years before, Balzac, in a long letter to Mme. Hanska (17–28 December 1845) affirmed having tasted hashish, and even having felt a few effects, but said these were weakened by the strength of his brain.

intentions of God, because they undermine the work of time and
try to make superfluous the states of purity and morality, and because the church only considers legitimate those treasures won by
careful and diligent work. We call that player a cheat who has
found the means to win every time; what should we call the man
who would buy happiness and genius with a small sum of money?
It is in the very infallibility of the means that the immorality lies,
just as magic's supposed infallibility gives it its hellish stigma. Let
me only add that hashish, like all solitary pleasures, makes the
individual useless to other men and society useless to him, forcing
him to contemplate himself more and more, and pushing him day
by day toward that luminous pool where, like Narcissus, he loves
only his own image.

But what if man, even at the price of his dignity, honesty, and
free choice, could yet extract from hashish great spiritual benefits,
making of it a kind of thinking machine, a productive instrument?
I have often heard that question asked, so let me answer it. First
of all, as I have carefully explained, hashish reveals nothing to the
individual but himself. It is true that he is pushed to the third
power, to the extreme, and since it is also true that a memory of
his impressions survives the drugged orgy, some hope of the utility
of the experience may not appear entirely unreasonable at first.
But let me note that his thoughts, which he places so much re-
liance upon, are not really as beautiful as they appeared to be in
their momentary disguise, covered with magic rags. They have
more to do with earth than heaven, owing a lot of their beauty to
nervous agitation and to the eagerness with which the mind throws
itself upon them. Finally, this hope becomes a vicious circle; let us
grant for a moment that hashish gives, or at least increases, genius,
yet it cannot be forgotten that it is the nature of hashish to diminish the will; thus it gives with one hand what it takes away with
the other; it gives imagination without the ability to use it. Finally,
even supposing someone adroit and strong enough to withdraw
from this alternative, there is another danger, which is the same

with all habits: they all quickly become necessities. Whoever has recourse to a poison in order to think will soon not be able to think without it. Imagine the frightful fate of the man whose paralyzed imagination could not function without the help of hashish or opium.

In philosophic studies the human mind, imitating celestial harmony, follows a curve that brings it back to its point of departure. To conclude is to close the circle. At the beginning I spoke of the wondrous condition in which man's mind sometimes finds itself thrown as if by a special grace; I said that in hoping constantly to keep his hopes alive and to rise toward the infinite he demonstrates, in every place and time, a frantic taste for every substance, no matter how dangerous, that might, while exalting his personality raise before his eyes for even an instant the chance of paradise, the object of his every desire. This foolhardy man, pushing on without knowing it toward hell, thus witnesses its original grandeur. But man is not so abandoned, so destitute of honest ways to gain heaven, that he is obliged to call upon pharmacy or sorcery; he doesn't need to sell his soul to buy the intoxicated caresses of houris. What is that paradise that one can buy at the price of one's eternal salvation? I can imagine a man (whether a brahmin, a poet, or a Christian philosopher) placed on the steep Olympus of spirituality. Around him the muses of Raphael or Mantegna devise the noblest dances to console him for his long fasts and diligent prayers, looking at him with their sweet eyes and sparkling smiles; divine Apollo, master of all knowledge (the master of Francavilla, Dürer, and Goltzius, and of others, what does it matter—is there not an Apollo for every man who deserves him?) caresses the singing strings with his bow. Below this man, at the foot of the mountain, in the brambles and mud, the flock of humans, the band of helots mimic the smiles of pleasure and utter screams extracted from them by the poison's sting. The poet, saddened, says to himself, "These unfortunate people who have neither fasted nor prayed, and who refuse redemption by work, ask of black magic the means of raising them in one bound to supernatural existence. The magic fools them and holds up to them a false happiness and a false light, while we, poets and philosophers, have regenerated our souls by constant work and contemplation; by the rigorous exercise of will and permanent nobility of purpose we have created for our own use a garden of true beauty. Believing the promise that says that faith moves mountains, we have accomplished the only miracle for which God has granted us the license."

An egalitarian might say this was elitist rubbish, yet Baudelaire understood the earnest, ceaseless human striving for earthly paradise as well as any writer who ever lived. The bourgeois critics always scorned him, yet at the same time envied him his incandescent mind and his flowing yet sharply pointed prose. For those free spirits of his time who would not work for their ecstasies, he had nothing but contempt, even though he knew they expected, and would get, so much less out of life than he.

One could attribute his mistrust of human nature to physical anguish or spleen, both of which Baudelaire greatly suffered from. Gustave Flaubert's comment is perhaps most apt of all: "You can smell the yeast of Catholicism here and there." Baudelaire hated the secular venality of the Church but respected its authoritarianism and the civilizing virtues it taught. His own philosophy is often indistinguishable from the most orthodox believer's, and surely he was a very Savonarola in his fulminations.

From Baudelaire's melancholy it is interesting to turn to le bon Théo *Gautier's humorous account of his initiation into the Hashish-eaters Club, one of the stories that made him famous. In 1843 he had described a meeting with friends during which hashish was passed around—a short, agreeable experience, to judge by his brief account of it.* Three years later he expanded the squib into

---

* In the serials section of *La Presse*, July 10, 1843. Gautier was the newspaper's regular theater critic for several years in his early thirties.

*a full-length story, in which he told the world in his difficult, convoluted, allusive style what it was really like, this hashish experience they had all heard so much about.**

Théophile Gautier,
"THE HASHISH-EATERS CLUB" † (1846)

THE HÔTEL PIMODAN

ONE EVENING in December, obeying a mysterious summons composed in enigmatic terms understood only by initiates and unintelligible to anyone else, I arrived in a remote quarter, a kind of oasis of solitude in the middle of Paris, which the river, surrounding with both its arms, seems to protect against the encroachments of civilization: It was in the Hôtel Pimodan, built by Lauzun, an old mansion on the Île Saint-Louis, where the bizarre club, which I had joined a short time before, held its monthly sessions, and I was going to attend one for the first time.

Although it was only six o'clock, the night was pitch black. A fog, made thicker by the nearness of the Seine, obscured everything like torn cotton wadding, with holes at intervals made by reddish aureoles of lanterns and by filaments of light escaping from windows. The streets, covered with rain, glistened under the lamps as if they were a body of water; a cold north wind, laden with frozen rain, whipped the face, and its guttural blowing provided the treble to a symphony to which the swollen waves breaking against the arches of the bridges was the bass: The evening lacked none of winter's harsh poetry.

It was difficult, along the deserted quay, in the mass of somber buildings, to make out the house I sought, yet the cabman, rising up in his seat, was able to read, on a marble plaque with its gilt

---

* Gautier got long mileage from this story. He reprinted it in his 1851 novel *Partie carrée* (Party of Four), then again as a separate piece in the collection *Romans et Contes* (Novels and Tales) in 1863.
† "Le Club des Hachichins," *Revue des Deux Mondes* 13 (February 1, 1846): 520–535.

half gone, the name of the old hotel, meeting place of the adepts.

I lifted the sculptured knocker, the use of copper buttons for doorbells not having penetrated these distant places, and several times I heard the cord grate to no effect, but finally it gave way to a more vigorous pull, and the old rusty bolt was pulled back as the massively timbered door opened on its hinges.

Behind a yellowish, transparent pane there appeared, as I entered, the head of an old woman, the gatekeeper, outlined by a trembling candle, a ready-made painting by Skalken. The head made a peculiar grimace at me, and a thin finger, extending from the gatehouse, showed me the way.

As far as I could make out by the pale light that always falls from even the darkest sky, the courtyard I was crossing was surrounded by buildings of ancient architecture with gabled roofs; my feet felt as wet as if I had walked through a swamp, for the cracks between the paving stones were filled with grass.

The high, small-paned windows of the staircase, flamboyant against the somber façade, served as a guide and kept me on the right path.

Once I had climbed the outside steps, I found myself at the foot of one of those immense staircases built in the time of Louis XIV, on which a modern house might dance with ease. An Egyptian chimera in Lebrun's style, bestraddled by a cupid, stretched out its paws on a pedestal, and held a candle in its claws.

The stairs were not steep but had well-distributed rests and landings that attested to the genius of the old architect and the grandiose life of bygone centuries. Ascending this admirable flight, dressed in my thin evening coat, I felt as if I made a blot on the whole effect, that I was usurping a right to which I was un-entitled—the service staircase would have been good enough for me.

Paintings, most of them unframed copies of masterpieces of the Italian and Spanish schools, covered the walls, and overhead, in the shadows, were the vague outlines of a large mythological ceiling fresco.

I got to the designated floor. A Utrecht velvet drum, crumpled and stained, whose yellow braid and dented nails told of its long service, made me recognize the door.

I rang, was admitted with the usual precautions, and found myself in a large room, lit at its far end by several lamps. Entering there, one stepped back two centuries. Time, that passes so fast, seemed not to have moved in this house, and like a clock one has forgotten to wind, its hands always said the same date.

The walls, of white-painted carved wood, were half covered with darkened canvases bearing the mark of the period. On a gigantic mantelpiece stood a statue that one might have thought was stolen from the bowers of Versailles. On the ceiling, which was a dome, there writhed a sprawling allegory, painted in the style of Lemoine, which might indeed have been by him.

I advanced toward the lighted part of the room, where several human shapes moved nervously around a table, and as soon as the light reached me and I was recognized, a hearty hurrah shook the sonorous depths of the old edifice.

"It's he! It's he!" several voices cried out together. "Let's give him his portion!"

SOME MUSTARD BEFORE DINNER—A PARENTHESIS

The doctor * stood beside a sideboard on which was a tray filled with little Japanese porcelain saucers. A piece of greenish paste

---

* This may well have been Dr. Jacques-Joseph Moreau (1804–1884), an acquaintance of Gautier, who in 1845 wrote *Du hachich et de l'aliénation mentale* (On Hashish and Mental Derangement), the first such recommendation of cannabis as a therapeutic drug. Moreau de Tours, as he was known, reported his extensive use of it in mental asylums as a tranquilizer, though he apparently believed also that it was a cure for mental illness. Gautier described him in the *Presse* article: "One of my companions, Dr. ——, who has made long voyages to the East, and who is a determined hashish eater, was the first [to feel the effects of a communal dose he had administered]. Having taken a stronger dose than I, he was seeing stars on his plate and the firmament at the bottom of his soup dish. Then he turned his nose to the wall and talked to himself, laughing loudly, his eyes lit with profound jubilation."

Baudelaire came to believe that Moreau de Tours was an evil influence, and condemns him severely at the end of his 1851 essay "On Wine and Hashish, Compared."

or preserves, about the size of one's thumb, was drawn by him from a crystal vase by means of a spatula and placed beside a vermeil spoon on each saucer.

The doctor's face radiated enthusiasm, his eyes sparkled, his cheeks reddened, the veins in his temples stood out, and his dilated nostrils breathed forcefully.

"This will be deducted from your share of paradise," said he, handing me my dose.

When everyone had eaten his portion, they served coffee in the Arab style, that is, with the grounds and without sugar. Then we sat down at the table.

This inversion of culinary custom has probably surprised the reader: it is scarcely usual to have coffee before the soup course, and preserves are generally eaten only with dessert. The matter surely needs explanation.

ANOTHER PARENTHESIS

There existed once upon a time in the Orient a dreaded order of devotees commanded by a sheik who took the title of Old Man of the Mountain, or Prince of the Assassins.

The Old Man of the Mountain was obeyed without question; the Assassins, his subjects, would execute his orders with absolute devotion, whatever they might be; no danger stopped them, not even the most certain death. At a sign from their chief they would leap from the top of a tower or go stab a sovereign in his palace in the midst of his guards. . . .

By what artifices did the Old Man of the Mountain obtain such complete abnegation? By means of a wonderful drug for which he had the recipe, which had the property of inducing dazzling hallucinations. Those who took it found, on awakening from their intoxication, that real life was so sad and colorless that they would joyfully sacrifice it in order to reenter the paradise of their dreams, for every man killed in carrying out the sheik's orders, went straight to heaven, or, if he escaped, he would again be allowed to enjoy the delights of the mysterious concoction.

Now the green paste that the doctor had just distributed to us was precisely the one that the Old Man of the Mountain used to give to his fanatics without their knowledge, making them believe that he had the key to Mohammed's heaven and the three types of houris. It is hashish, from which comes hashisheen or hashish eater, the root of the word "assassin," whose fierce meaning is readily explicable by the bloody habits of the Old Man of the Mountain's followers.

Surely, people who saw me leave my house at the hour when ordinary mortals take their nourishment had no idea that I was going to the Île Saint-Louis, a virtuous and patriarchal place if ever there was one, to eat a strange dish that several centuries ago served an imposter sheik as a means to push his zealots to assassination. Nothing in my perfectly bourgeois appearance could have made me suspected of such an excess of orientalism: I seemed to be a nephew on his way to dine with his old aunt rather than one of the faithful about to taste the joys of Mohammed's heaven in the company of twelve highly French Arabs.

Before this revelation, if you had been told that in Paris in 1845, that period of stock speculation and railroads, there existed an order of hashish eaters whose history von Hammer-Purgstall * has not written, you would not have believed it, yet nothing would have been more true—as is the custom with unlikely things.

LOVE-FEAST

The meal was served in a bizarre manner, with every sort of extravagant and picturesque tableware.

Large Venetian glasses crisscrossed with milky spirals, emblazoned German goblets, Flemish stoneware mugs, slender-necked flasks still wrapped in reeds, took the place of glasses, bottles, and carafes.

The opaque porcelain of Louis Lebeuf and English flowered faience, adornment of bourgeois tables, shone by their absence;

* See p. 25n.

no two plates were alike, yet each had its own special merit:
China, Japan, and Saxony contributed samples of their finest clays
and richest colors—all a bit chipped and cracked, but of an exquisite taste.

The serving dishes were mostly Bernard de Palissy enamels or
Limoges faience and at times the carver's knife, when it got to the
bottom of a dish, would encounter a reptile, frog, or bird in relief.
The edible eel mingled its coils with those of the molded snake.

An honest philistine would have felt some fright at the sight of
these long-haired, bearded, moustached, or singularly shorn guests,
brandishing sixteenth-century daggers, Malayan krisses, or navajas,
and bending over food to which the reflections of the flickering
lamps gave a dubious appearance.

The dinner drew to an end, and already some of the more fer-
vent adepts felt the effects of the green paste. I was experiencing
a complete transposition of taste. The water I was drinking seemed
to have the savor of the most exquisite wine, the meat turned to
raspberries in my mouth, and vice versa. I could not have told a
cutlet from a peach.

My neighbors began to seem rather odd to me: they were opening wide, owlish eyes, their noses were lengthening into probos-
cises, their mouths became extremely wide, and their faces took
on supernatural colors. One of them, with a pale face in a black
beard, was in peals of laughter at an unseen spectacle; another
made unbelievable efforts to bring his glass to his lips, and his contortions to do this produced deafening jeers. Another, nervously
agitated, twiddled his thumbs with incredible agility; yet another,
leaning back in his chair, with dreamy eyes and lifeless arms, let
himself flow voluptuously into the bottomless sea of annihilation.

With my elbows on the table, I considered all this in the light
of a remnant of reason that came and went like a candle ready to
go out. A faint heat came over my limbs, and madness, like a
wave foaming against a rock that pulls back to hurl itself again,
entered and left my brain, and finally invaded it altogether. Hallucination, that strange guest, had come to live in me.

"To the drawing room!" cried one of the guests. "Don't you hear the celestial choirs? The musicians have long been at their stands." And indeed, a delightful harmony came to our ears across the tumult of conversation.

A GENTLEMAN WHO WAS NOT INVITED

The drawing room was enormous, with sculptured, gilded woodwork, a painted ceiling, and a frieze of satyrs pursuing nymphs through the rushes; it had a huge colored marble mantelpiece, and ample brocaded draperies that expressed the luxury of bygone times. Upholstered furniture, sofas, armchairs, and cushioned seats wide enough for the skirts of duchesses and marquises to be spread out with ease, received the hashish eaters in their soft, ever-open arms. A low chair by the fire made advances to me. I settled into it and surrendered with no resistance to the fantastic drug.

After several minutes my companions had vanished, one after another, leaving no trace other than their shadows on the walls, which were soon absorbed like the brown stains water makes on sand, that fade as they dry. As I was no longer conscious from then on of what the others were doing, you must now be content with the story of my simple personal impressions. Solitude reigned in the drawing room, where there were only a few doubtful beams of light; all of a sudden, a red flash passed beneath my eyelids, innumerable candles burst into light, and I felt bathed in a warm clear glow. My surroundings were the same, yet as different from before as a sketch is from a painting: everything was bigger, richer, more splendid. Reality served only as a point of departure for the magnificence of the hallucination.

I could still see no one, yet I guessed the presence of a multitude: I heard the rustling of fabrics, the creaking of shoes, voices that whispered, murmured, and lisped, stifled bursts of laughter, sounds of moving chair and table legs. Someone was bustling about with the dishes, opening and closing the doors: something unusual was happening.

An enigmatic character suddenly appeared before me. How had he come in? I do not know, yet seeing him did not frighten me. He had a nose curved like a bird's beak; his green eyes were surrounded with three brown circles, and he wiped them frequently with an immense handkerchief; a high starched white cravat strangled his thin collar and made the skin of his cheeks overflow in ruddy folds—in the knot was a visiting card with the words, "Daucas-Carota of the Golden Pot"; he wore a black coat with square tails and bunches of watch chains and fobs, and it imprisoned his body, which was thrust out like the breast of a capon. As to his legs, I must confess they were made of a bifurcated mandrake root—black, wrinkled, covered with knobs and warts—and seemed to be freshly uprooted, for bits of earth still adhered to the filaments. These legs wriggled and twisted with extraordinary activity, and when the small torso they supported stood directly facing me, the strange character burst into sobs, wiped his eyes with all his strength, and said in a most mournful voice:

"It is today that we must die laughing."

Tears as big as peas rolled down the sides of his nose.

"Laughing . . . laughing . . ." echoed a choir of discordant, nasal voices.

FANTASIA

I looked at the ceiling then and saw a crowd of bodiless heads like cherubs, and they had such comical expressions, such jovial and profoundly happy faces, that I could not help but share their hilarity. Their eyes creased, their faces widened, their nostrils flared; they had grimaces that would have made the spleen itself rejoice. These farcical masks moved about where they were, turning in opposite directions, which produced a dazzling and dizzying effect.

Bit by bit, the drawing room became filled with amazing figures such as one finds only in the etchings of Callot and the aquatints of Goya: a characteristic combination of tawdry finery on human and bestial figures; at another time, I might have been apprehensive about such a group, but there was nothing menacing in these monstrosities. It was mischievousness, not ferocity, that made their eyes sparkle. Good humor alone made them bare their immoderate fangs and pointed incisors.

As though I were the lord of the feast, each figure came one by one into the luminous circle of which I occupied the center, and with an air of grotesque solemnity, muttered witticisms in my ear, none of which I now remember, but which at the time I found enormously funny, and which prompted the maddest gaiety in me.

With each new apparition, a Homeric, Olympian, immense, deafening laugh, that seemed to resound through infinity, burst around me with thunderous rumblings. Voices, sometimes shrill, sometimes cavernous, cried:

"No, it's too funny! That's enough! My God, what fun! Funnier and funnier."

"Stop! I can't stand it anymore! Ha, ha! Ho, ho! He, he! What a good farce! What a beautiful pun!"

"Stop! I'm suffocating, strangling! Don't look at me like that! Or at least bind me with hoops, for I'm going to burst!"

Despite these half-jesting, half-entreating protestations, this amazing hilarity continued to increase, the noise grew in intensity, the floors and walls of the house, shaken by the frenetic, irresistible, implacable laughter, heaved and panted like a human chest.

Soon, instead of coming before me one by one, the grotesque phantoms assaulted me all at the same time, shaking their long clowns' sleeves, tripping over the folds of their magicians' gowns, flattening their false noses in ridiculous collisions, making the powder from their wigs fly away in clouds, and singing outlandish songs with impossible rhymes off key. All the types ever invented by the mocking spirit of nations and artists were assembled here, but multiplied tenfold, a hundredfold, in strength. It was a strange mob: the Neapolitan Pulcinella familiarly hitting the English Punch on his humped back; Harlequin from Bergamo rubbing his black snout on the floury mask of the French Paillasse, who uttered frightful cries; the Bolognese doctor throwing snuff into Father Cassandra's eyes; Tartaglia galloping about on a clown; Gilles kicking Don Spavento in the rear; and Karaghuz, armed with his obscene stick, fighting a duel with the buffoon Osco.

Farther away from me, fantasies of droll dreams confusedly fidgeted about: hybrid creatures, formless mixtures of men, beasts, and utensils; monks with wheels for feet and cooking pots for bellies; warriors, in armor made of dishes, brandishing wooden sabers in birds' claws; statesmen rendered mute by rotisserie gears; kings plunged to the waist in pepper mills like watchtowers; alchemists with heads like bellows, their limbs twisted into alembics; ribalds made from a collection of squashes with bizarre knobs —everything that a cynic might draw with a feverishly heated pencil when intoxication pushes his elbow. Everything swarmed, crawled, trotted, jumped, whistled, as Goethe says of his Walpurgis night.

In order to escape from the excessive crowding of these baroque characters, I hid in a dark corner, from which I could see them indulging in dances such as the Renaissance never knew at the time of Chicard, nor the opera under Musard, the king of the extravagant quadrille. These dancers, with an entrechat or a balancé, wrote comedies a thousand times better than Molière, Rabelais, Swift, or Voltaire, and so profoundly philosophical, satires of such great range and piquant wit, that I had to hold my sides in my corner.

Daucas-Carota, all the while wiping his eyes, was performing inconceivable pirouettes and leaps, especially for a man with a mandrake root for legs, and repeating in a ludicrously piteous tone, "It's today we must die laughing!"

All you who think you know a comic masque, if you had attended this ball produced by hashish, you would agree that the most sidesplitting comedians of our small theaters are only worth sculpting on the corners of a catafalque or tomb.

What bizarrely convulsed faces! What eyes, winking and sparkling with sarcasm under their birdlike membranes! What piggybank grins! What roughly done mouths! What humorous twelve-sided noses! What abdomens, fat with Pantagruelian jests! Through all the swarming of this unanguished nightmare, there were flashes of sudden resemblances with an irresistible effect, caricatures that would have made Daumier jealous, fantasies that would have delighted the marvelous artists of China, those Phidiases of toys and figurines.

All these visions, however, were not monstrous or burlesque; grace was also present in this carnival of forms. Near the fireplace, a small head with peachy cheeks, showing in an interminable fit of gaiety thirty-two teeth the size of grains of rice, uttered a high, vibrant, silvery, prolonged burst of laughter, embroidered with trills and organ notes that cross my eardrums, and by nervous magnetism made me commit a host of extravagances.

The joyous frenzy was at its peak; one could hear nothing but convulsive sighs and inarticulate cluckings. The laughter had lost its tone and turned to groans, while spasms followed pleasures: Daucas-Carota's refrain was about to come true. Already a few tired-out hashish eaters had rolled onto the floor with that soft clumsiness of intoxication that makes falling no danger; exclamations such as, "God, how happy I am!" "What felicity!" "I am swimming in ecstasy!" "I am in paradise!" "I am diving into depths of pleasure!" crossed, blended, and covered each other. Hoarse cries burst from oppressed chests; arms strained distractedly toward some fugitive vision; heels and backs of heads drummed on the floor. It was time to throw a drop of cold water on this burning vapor, or the boiler would burst. The human envelope, which has so little strength for pleasure and so much for pain, could not have endured a higher pressure of happiness.

One of the club members, who had not taken part in the voluptuous intoxication in order to keep watch over the fantasia and prevent those of us who might think we had wings from going through the windows, got up, opened the lid of the piano, and sat down to play. His hands, falling together, sank into the ivory of the keyboard, and a glorious chord strongly rang out, stilling all noise and changing the direction of the intoxication.

KIF

The theme attempted was, I believe, Agatha's aria from *Der Freischütz*; the heavenly melody, like a wind sweeping away misshapen clouds, soon dissipated the ridiculous visions that obsessed me. The grimacing phantoms withdrew, crawling under armchairs or hiding in the folds of the draperies, heaving little stifled sighs, and once again it seemed I was alone in the drawing room.

The great organ of Fribourg surely does not put out a greater mass of sound than a piano touched by the seer (as the sober adept is called). The notes vibrated with such power that they entered my breast like fiery arrows; soon the aria seemed to come out of myself; my fingers moved over an absent keyboard; sounds sprang out, blue and red, in electric sparks; Weber's soul was incarnate in me. The piece finished, I continued my inner improvisations in the style of the German master, and they caused me ineffable rapture. What a pity that a magic stenographer could not have transcribed those inspired melodies, heard by me alone, and which, modestly enough, I do not hesitate to place above the masterpieces of Rossini, Meyerbeer, and Félicien David!

To the rather convulsive gaiety of the beginning succeeded an indefinable well-being, a boundless calm. I was in that blessed hashish state that the Orientals call *kif*.* I no longer felt my body; the bounds of matter and mind were undone; I moved only by my will in a medium offering no resistance. It is thus, I suppose, that souls act in the world of fragrances where we go after death.

---

* *Kif* means "pleasure." In modern times, in northwest Africa, its meaning has become more specific: a mixture of chopped dried hemp and black tobacco, widely used as a mild stimulant.

A bluish mist, an Elysian dawn, reflected light from an azure grotto, formed in the room an atmosphere whose quivering outlines I could vaguely see. This atmosphere was at once cool and warm, moist, and perfumed; it enveloped me like a bath in an embrace of enervating sweetness. When I tried to move, the tender air made a thousand delightful eddies around me; a delicious languor seized my senses and threw me back on the sofa, where I sank down, limp as a discarded garment. Then I understood the pleasure felt by spirits and angels, according to their degree of perfection, in crossing ether and heaven, and how eternity might be spent in paradise.

Nothing material was mingled in this ecstasy, no terrestrial desire marred its purity. Love itself could in no way have increased it: Romeo the hashish eater would have forgotten Juliet. The poor girl, leaning out over the jasmine, would in vain have stretched forth her beautiful alabaster arms from the balcony into the night—Romeo would have stayed at the foot of the silken ladder, and though I love to distraction the angel of youth and beauty created by Shakespeare, I must admit that the prettiest girl in Verona, to a hashish eater, is not worth bothering about.

Thus, with a quiet though delighted eye, I watched the garland of ideally beautiful women who crowned the frieze with their divine nakedness; I saw the gleam of their satin shoulders, the sparkle of their silver breasts, their little rosy feet, the undulation of their opulent hips, without feeling the slightest temptation. The charming spirits that disturbed Saint Anthony would have had no power over me.

By some bizarre mystery, after several minutes of contemplation I would melt into the object I was looking at, and would myself become that object. Thus I became the nymph Syrinx, since the fresco represented Pan's pursuit of this daughter of the river Ladon. I felt all the terrors of the poor fugitive and sought to hide behind the fantastic reeds to avoid the cloven-hoofed monster.

KIF TURNS TO NIGHTMARE

During my ecstasy, Daucas-Carota had come in again. Seated like a tailor or a pasha on his neatly twisted roots, he fixed his flashing eyes on me; his beak snapped so sardonically, such a mocking air of triumph burst from his small deformed person, that I shuddered in spite of myself. Guessing my fright, he increased his contortions and grimaces, coming near me with little jumps like a wounded daddy longlegs or a legless cripple in his basket.

Then I felt a cold breath in my ear, and a familiar voice (though I could not make out to whom it belonged) said to me, ".That wretched Daucas-Carota, who sold his legs for drink, has made away with your head, and put in its place, not an ass's head like Puck gave to Bottom, but that of an elephant!"

Singularly puzzled, I went straight to the mirror, and saw that the warning was not for nothing. I could have been taken for a Hindu or Javanese idol: my forehead was higher, my nose, lengthened into a trunk, curved down my chest, my ears swept my shoulders, and to compound the annoyance, I was indigo in color, like the blue god Shiva.

Infuriated, I began to run after Daucas-Carota, who jumped about and screeched, giving every sign of extreme terror. I managed to catch him, and banged him so violently against the edge of the table that he finally gave me back my head, which he had wrapped in his handkerchief.

Satisfied with this victory, I was going to resume my place on the couch, but the same small, unknown voice said to me, "Take care, you are surrounded by enemies; invisible forces are trying to attract and hold you. You are a prisoner here: Try to leave, and you will see."

A veil was rent in twain in my mind, and it was clear to me that the club members were nothing more than cabalists and magicians who wanted to lead me to perdition.

TREADMILL

I got up with great difficulty and started toward the drawing room door, which I reached only after considerable time, for some unknown force compelled me to take one step backward out of every three. According to my calculation, it took ten years to cover the distance. Daucas-Carota followed me, sniggering and mumbling in mock commiseration, "If he keeps walking like that, when he arrives he'll be an old man."

Yet I managed to reach the next room, whose dimensions seemed greatly changed. It became longer and longer—indefinitely. The light that twinkled at the other end seemed as far away as a fixed star. I became discouraged and was going to stop when the little voice, nearly brushing me with its lips, said, "Courage! She expects you at eleven o'clock."

Calling desperately upon my soul's forces, I succeeded by an enormous effort of will in raising my feet, which took hold of the floor so that I had to uproot them like tree trunks. The monster with mandrake legs escorted me, mimicking my effort and chanting in a singsong voice, "The marble is winning! The marble is winning!"

Indeed, I felt my limbs turning to stone, the marble enveloping me up to the waist like the statue of Daphne in the Tuileries; I was stone halfway up, like the enchanted prince in the *Thousand and One Nights*. My hardened heels sounded very hard on the floor; I could have played the Commendatore in *Don Giovanni*.

Yet I had actually reached the head of the staircase, which I would try to descend; it was only half lit, and in my dream it seemed of cyclopean, gigantic size. Its top and bottom were drowned in shadows, and seemed to plunge into the twin gulfs of heaven and hell. Raising my head, I saw indistinctly, in an immense perspective, innumerable landings, one above the other, ramps leading up as to the top of the Tower of Babel; looking down, I sensed abysses of steps, whorls of spirals, overwhelming circumvolutions. This staircase must pierce the earth through and through, I said to myself as I continued my mechanical walking. I will get to the bottom the day after the Last Judgment. The figures in the paintings looked at me with an air of pity; some of them moved with painful contortions, like mutes who wanted to give important advice before it was too late. One would have said they wanted to warn me about a trap to avoid, but an inert, dismal force led me on. The steps were soft and sank beneath me, like the mysterious ladders in the Masonic initiations. The adhesive, flaccid stone gave way like a toad's belly, new landings, new steps ceaselessly appeared to my submissive feet, while those I passed resumed their places before me. I figured this intrigue lasted a thousand years. Finally, I reached the vestibule, where another persecution awaited me, no less terrifying.

The chimera that held the candle in its paws, which I had noticed on entering, was barring my way with clearly hostile intentions; its greenish eyes shone with mockery, its cunning mouth laughed wickedly; it was coming toward me almost on its belly, dragging its bronze trappings through the dust, though not out of submission; ferocious tremors shook its leonine rump, and Daucas-Carota urged it on like a dog that one wants to make fight.

"Bite him! Bite him! Marble meat for a bronze mouth, that's a capital feast!"

Without letting myself be frightened by this horrible beast, I stepped around it. A gust of cold air struck my face, and the night sky, clean of clouds, suddenly appeared above me. A scattering of stars powdered the veins of this great block of lapis lazuli with flecks of gold. I was in the courtyard.

To tell of the effect produced on me by this somber architecture, I would need the etching tool with which Piranesi scratched the black varnish from his wonderful copperplates: the courtyard had taken on the proportions of the Champ-de-Mars, and in a few hours had become ringed by giant buildings set against the horizon in a tracery of steeples, cupolas, towers, gables, and pyramids worthy of Rome and Babylon.

I was greatly surprised. I had never suspected that the Île Saint-

Louis contained so many monumental edifices, which, moreover, would have covered twenty times its actual area; and I thought, not without apprehension, of the power of those magicians who could build such structures in a single evening.

"You are the plaything of vain illusions. This courtyard is very small," murmured the voice. "It is twenty-seven paces long by twenty-five wide."

"Yes, of course," grumbled the bifurcated monster, "paces made with seven-league boots. You will never arrive at eleven o'clock: It is fifteen hundred years since you left. Half your hair is already gray. Go back upstairs, that's the wisest thing to do."

As I would not obey, the odious monster trapped me in the tangle of his legs, and using his hands as crampons, dragged me along despite my resistance, made me reclimb the stairs where I had felt such anguish, and to my great despair, reinstalled me in the drawing room from which I had so painfully escaped.

Then dizziness completely overwhelmed me, and I became insane, delirious. Daucas-Carota cut capers as high as the ceiling, saying, "Imbecile! I gave you back your head, but first I took out your brain with a spoon!" I felt a frightful sadness as, lifting my hand to the top of my head, I found it open, and then I lost consciousness.

DO NOT BELIEVE IN CHRONOMETERS

When I came to, I saw the room full of people dressed in black, who were conversing with sad looks and shaking hands with melancholy cordiality, as if stricken with a common sorrow. They were saying, "Time is dead. Henceforth there will be neither years, months, nor hours; time is dead, and we are going to its funeral."

"He was certainly old enough, but I didn't expect this development."

"He went along quite well for his age," added one of these people, whom I recognized as a painter friend of mine.

"Eternity was worn out; it was well enough to put an end to it," replied another.

"Great God!" I cried, struck by a sudden idea. "If there is no more time, when will it be eleven o'clock?"

"Never!" cried Daucas-Carota in a thundering voice, pushing his nose in my face and showing himself in his true aspect. "Never! it will always be a quarter past nine, the hands will be stopped at the minute when time ceased to be, and your punishment will be to come and look at the motionless hands, then go back to sit down again, only to begin once more, until you are walking on the bones of your heels."

A superior force impelled me, and I made the journey four or five hundred times to look at the clock face with a horrified disquiet. Daucas-Carota was seated astride the clock, and made appalling grimaces at me.

The hands did not move.

"Wretch! You have stopped the pendulum," I cried, drunk with rage.

"Not at all—it's going back and forth as usual, but suns will crumble to dust before this steel arrow has advanced the millionth of a millimeter."

"Come, now, I see we must exorcise the evil spirits: Things are turning splenetic," said the seer. "Let's make a little music. David's harp will be replaced this time by an Erard piano."

And sitting on the stool, he played melodies that had quick movements and happy aspects. This seemed greatly to annoy the mandrake man, who grew smaller, flatter, discolored, and made inarticulate moans; at last he lost all human form, and rolled onto the floor in the shape of a salsify with two taproots. The spell was broken.

"Hallelujah! Time has risen from the dead," shouted joyful, childish voices. "Now go see the clock."

The hands pointed to eleven o'clock.

"Sir, your carriage is downstairs," a servant said to me.

The dream was at an end. The hashish eaters went home, each in his own direction, like the officers after Marlborough's funeral.

With a light step, I went down the stairs that had caused me such torture, and a few minutes later I was in my room, in full reality; the last vapors raised by the hashish had vanished. My reason had come back, or at least what I call my reason for want of a better term. My lucidity was great enough for me to handle the review of a pantomime or a light comedy, or to write a few three-lettered rhyming verses.

Gérard de Nerval,
"HASHISH" * (1850)

When the long prose work Voyage en Orient *was published for the first time in 1851, Gérard de Nerval was already a well-known bohemian figure in Paris. He was for a short time part of the Hashish-eaters Club in the 1840s and was the best friend of Gautier, then its most eminent member. While he was still a child Gérard learned from his father to read Arabic and Persian, and these languages later served him well in his two years of travel in Turkey and Syria, 1843–1844.* Voyage en Orient *was the result of these years abroad, and he composed it slowly, publishing it in serial form in the* Revue des Deux Mondes *for several years before 1851. The book contains all the Oriental lore Nerval ever knew— real history, material gathered on his travels, mingled with half-remembered tales and fantastic imaginings. Modern commentators have criticized these travel tales for misrepresentation and general inaccuracy, but they constitute a work of primarily romantic imagination; the Orient of the title is a region of the mind; precision of fact seems of slight importance.*

If Nerval had had no extensive experience with hashish, he would surely have done his best to hide the fact behind his easy, self-assured prose. The contemporary scene was full of experiment-

* Gérard de Nerval, *Voyage en Orient*, 2 vols., Paris, 1850, vol. ii, pp. 59–68. (Original title: *Scènes de la vie orientale*, Paris, 1850.)

ers *with cannabis, which had quite suddenly become one of the
most exotic of romantic experiences. Nerval, whose lifelong avoca-
tion was to shock the bourgeoisie whenever possible, was the last
man to reject such experience. Shortly after* Voyage *was published
he suffered the first of three prolonged attacks of acute depression,
similar to those of Baudelaire, and hanged himself in January,
1855.*

What follows is the beginning of the story of Caliph Hakim,
the details of whose life are partly invented by Nerval. He imagines
him here disguised as an ill-dressed beggar wandering through his
kingdom. He stops one night at a tavern where some of his non-
Moslem subjects are taking hashish.*

ON THE RIGHT BANK of the Nile, some distance from the port
of Fostat and the ruins of Old Cairo, not far from Mount Mokatam
that overlooks the new city, there was, about the year 1000 of the
Christian era, which is the fourth century of the Hegira, a small
village inhabited in large part by people of the Sabian sect.†

There is a delightful view from the last houses along the river:
with its waves the Nile seems to caress the island of Roddah, to
hold it aloft, as a slave would carry a basket of flowers. On the other
bank is Giza, where just after sunset the gigantic triangular shapes
of the pyramids pierce through the violet haze at their base. The
tops of the doom palms, the sycamores, and the pharaoh figs stand
out black against this light background. Herds of water buffalo,
which the Sphinx seems to guard from afar as she lies in the plain

---

* Abu Ali al-Mansur was in A.D. 996 at the age of eleven proclaimed third
Fatimite Caliph of Egypt under the title al-Hakim bi'amr allah ("he who decides
according to the orders of God"). He ruled his large empire with cruelty and
cunning. In 1010 he sacked the Church of the Holy Sepulcher in Jerusalem,
which helped to provoke the Crusades. He later destroyed all the Christian
churches of Egypt and banished all unbelievers. In the last year of his reign
(1020) he claimed divinity, and was perhaps murdered by his sister. Some of
these facts find echoes in Nerval's account, but he sees no need to keep them in
order or to distinguish them from his own imaginary additions.
† The Sabians are mentioned in the Koran (ii. 59, v. 73, xxii. 17) and were a
semi-Christian sect, at first tolerated in Islam because they were thought to have
a written revelation. Hence they were usually not treated as cruelly as infidels.

like a watchdog, move toward their watering place in a long file, and the lights from the fishing boats poke golden stars through the dense dark along the river bank.

In the Sabian village, at the place from which one can best see this view, was a white-walled *okel*, or tavern, surrounded by carob trees, whose terrace had its foot in the water, and where every night the boatmen going up or down the Nile could see the night lamps flickering in their pools of oil.

A curious observer on a boat in the middle of the river, looking through the arcades of the *okel*, would have easily discerned the travelers and patrons inside, seated on palmwood cages in front of little tables, or on divans covered with matting, and most assuredly he would have been astonished at their strange appearance. Their extravagant gestures, succeeded by stupid immobility, the insensate laughter, the occasional inarticulate cries, by these he would have guessed that this was one of those houses where the infidels, defying the prohibition, came to intoxicate themselves with wine, *bouza* (beer), or hashish.

One evening a ship, steered with that certainty which comes from a thorough knowledge of the place, put in at the foot of the staircase whose bottom steps were in the water, and from it jumped a young man of worthy appearance, who seemed to be a fisherman, and who, climbing the steps with a firm and rapid tread, sat down in a corner of the room at a place that seemed to be his own. No one paid any attention to his arrival: He was evidently a patron.

At that same moment, from the opposite, landward door there entered a man dressed in a black woolen tunic, with uncustomarily long hair which he wore under a *takieh,* or white cap.

His sudden appearance caused some surprise. He sat down in a corner in the shadows, and soon, the general hilarity taking over, no one looked at him any longer. Though his clothes were shabby, the newcomer had no mark on his face of the uneasy humility of misery. His firmly drawn features had the severe lines of a lion's. His eyes, of a blue as somber as sapphire, had an indefinable power; they frightened and charmed at the same time.

Yusuf, the young man who came by boat, immediately felt in his heart a secret sympathy for this unknown person, whose unusual presence he had noticed. Not yet having joined in the revelry, he approached the divan where the stranger sat cross-legged.

"Brother," said Yusuf, "you seem tired; no doubt you come from far away. Would you like some refreshments?"

"Indeed," replied the stranger, "my journey was long. I came into the *okel* to rest a bit; but what can I drink here, where only forbidden things are consumed?"

"You Moslems dare to take nothing but pure water, but we of the Sabian sect may, without breaking our law, quench the thirst with the blood of the vine or the pale brew made from barley."

"And yet I see no fermented drink before you."

"Oh, I renounced that coarse sort of intoxication long ago," said Yusuf, signaling to a slave, who placed on the table two little glasses worked with silver filigree, and a box filled with a greenish paste, in which was stuck an ivory spatula. "This box contains the paradise your prophet promised his believers, and if you were not so scrupulous I would place you within an hour in the houris' arms, without making you pass over the bridge of al-Sirat," he continued, laughing.

"But this paste is hashish, unless I'm mistaken," replied the stranger, pushing away the glass in which Yusuf had put a dose of the fantastic mixture. "And hashish is forbidden."

"Everything pleasant is forbidden," said Yusuf, swallowing the first spoonful.

The stranger looked at him steadily with his dark blue eyes, and the skin of his forehead contracted so violently that his hair followed its undulations; one moment he seemed about to jump on the carefree young man and tear him to pieces, but he calmed himself, his features became smooth once again, and suddenly changing his mind he put out his hand, took up the glass, and slowly began to sample the green paste.

After several minutes the effects of the hashish began to be felt by Yusuf and the stranger: a sweet languor spread over their bodies and a vague smile came to their lips. Though they had spent scarcely half an hour seated side by side, it seemed they had known one another for a thousand years. Then the drug began to act more strongly on them, and they began to laugh, became excited, and talked with great volubility, especially the stranger, a strict observer of the prohibition, who had never tasted hashish and who felt its effects very strongly. He seemed gripped by extraordinary exaltation; swarms of new, unheard-of, inconceivable thoughts crossed his soul in fiery whirlwinds; his eyes glittered as if lit from within by the reflection of an unknown world; then his superhuman dignity righted itself, the vision darkened, and he let himself drift through the beatific fields of *kif*.

"Well, comrade," said Yusuf, seizing on this pause in the unknown man's intoxication, "what do you think of these fine pistachio preserves? Do you still curse good people like these, peaceably assembled in a low room, who want only to be happy in their own way?"

"Hashish makes man like God," replied the stranger in a slow, deep voice.

"Exactly," said Yusuf with enthusiasm. "Water drinkers can only know the coarse and material aspect of things. Hashish, in clouding the eyes of the body, enlightens those of the soul; the mind, once separated from the body, its weighty keeper, flies away like a prisoner whose jailer has fallen asleep with the key in the cell. It wanders happy and free in space and light, talking familiarly with the genii it meets, who astound with their sudden and delightful disclosures. It crosses in one easy bound through regions of indescribable happiness, all in the space of one minute that seems eternal, so quickly the sensations follow each other. I myself have a dream that reappears again and again, always the same yet always slightly different: I am returning to my boat, reeling with the splendor of my visions, and close my eyes against the constant flow of jacinths, carbuncles, emeralds, and rubies that form the background for the wondrous fantasies of hashish; as if in the very heart of the infinite I see a heavenly figure, more beautiful than all the poets' creations, who smiles at me with a piercing sweetness, then descends from heaven to me alone. Is it an angel, a fairy? I do not know. She sits by my side in the boat, the coarse wood of which instantly changes to mother-of-pearl, floating on a silver river, pushed along by perfumed breezes."

"A fortunate and peculiar vision," the stranger murmured, shaking his head.

"That is not all of it," Yusuf continued. "One night, when I had taken a weaker dose, and I had come out of my intoxication, just as the boat was passing the tip of the island of Roddah, a woman very like the one in my dreams looked at me with eyes that, though they were human, had nonetheless the brilliance of heaven; her veil, half opened, revealed in the moonlight a vest covered with precious stones. My hand reached out and touched hers; her soft skin, as smooth and fresh as a petal, and her rings, as the carvings on them grazed my skin, entirely convinced me of her reality."

"Near Roddah?" asked the stranger meditatively.

"I was not dreaming," pursued Yusuf, not noticing his improvised confidant's remark. "The hashish only brought forward a memory that had fled deep into my soul, for this divine face was known to me. Where indeed had I seen her before? In what world did we meet? What earlier life had thrown us together? There are questions I could not answer, but this strange meeting, this bizarre adventure, did not surprise me at all: it seemed entirely natural that this woman, who met my ideal so completely, should be there in my boat in the middle of the Nile, as if she had jumped out of one of those large flowers that bloom on the water's surface. Without asking for any explanation I threw myself at her feet, and as to the apparition of my dream I poured out to her all the most burning and sublime words of my exalted love. Words of immense meaning came to me, expressions that enclosed all the universe in thoughts, mysterious sentences that vibrated with the echo of vanished worlds. My soul was projected into past and future; I was convinced I had felt the love I expressed throughout all eternity.

"Even as I spoke I saw her large eyes become bright, throwing out their rays; her transparent hands extended toward me, breaking up into beams of light. I felt caught in a net of flames, and despite myself and the dream of the night before I fell backward. When I roused myself from the invincible delightful torpor that bound my body I was on the riverbank opposite Giza, leaning against a palm tree, and my slave was sleeping peacefully beside the boat, which he had pulled up onto the sand. A rosy glow fringed the horizon: It was almost dawn."

"This is a love that in no way resembles earthly love," said the stranger, not objecting in the slightest to the improbabilities of Yusuf's story, for hashish makes one credulous of all marvels.

"I have never told my incredible tale to anyone, so why have I confided in you, whom I have never seen? It's hard to explain. Some mysterious attraction draws me toward you. When you entered this room a voice cried in the depth of my soul, 'Here he is, finally.' Your arrival has calmed a secret disquiet that gives me no rest. You are he whom I have waited for without knowing it. My thoughts bound forward to meet you, and I have had to tell you all the mysteries of my heart."

"What you feel," replied the stranger, "I also feel, and I shall tell you what I have never dared admit even to myself. You have an impossible passion, I have a monstrous one; you love a phantom, I love—you will tremble—my sister! Yet a stranger thing is that I feel no remorse at this: in vain I condemn myself; I am absolved by a mysterious power that I feel in myself. My love has no earthly impurities. It is not lust that pushes me toward my sister, though she equals in beauty the phantom of my dreams; it is an indescribable attraction, an affection deep as the sea, wide as the sky, such as a god might feel. The idea of my sister marrying a man is disgusting, horrible, sacrilegious: in her spirit there is something divine that I can see through the veil of flesh. Despite the name they give it on earth, she is the bride of my immortal soul, the virgin destined for me from the earliest days of creation. Now and again I feel I can recapture across the darkness of the ages the reasons for our secret union. Things that happened before the arrival of men upon earth come to my memory, and I see myself under the golden boughs of Eden, sitting beside her, being attended by obedient spirits. If I were to marry any other woman I would debase and dissipate the soul of the world that beats in me. By the concentration of our divine blood I want to found an immortal race, a definitive god, more powerful than all those who have come until now under various names and aspects."

While Yusuf and the stranger were exchanging these extended confidences, the patrons of the *okel,* stirred by the hashish, were engaged in amazing contortions, inane laughter, ecstatic swoons, and convulsive dances, but bit by bit the hemp's strength wore off, calm returned, and they lay down on the divans in the prostrate condition that usually follows this kind of excess.

A man of patriarchal bearing, whose beard flowed over his trailing robes, came into the *okel* and went to the middle of the room. "Brothers, arise!" he said in a resounding voice. "I have just consulted the heavens; the hour is propitious to sacrifice a white cock before the Sphinx in honor of Hermes and Agathodaemon."

The Sabians got to their feet and seemed ready to follow their priest, but the stranger, hearing this proposal, colored deeply, his blue eyes turned black, terrifying lines furrowed his brow, and he uttered a low growl that made everyone start in fear, as if a real lion had fallen into their midst.

"Ungodly blasphemers! Vile beasts! Idol worshipers!" he roared in a voice of resounding thunder.

This angry explosion produced amazement in the crowd. The unknown man had such an air of authority and raised the folds of his cloak so menacingly that no one dared answer his insults.

The old man went up to him and said, "What evil do you see, brother, in sacrificing a cock, according to the ritual, to the good spirits Hermes and Agathodaemon?"

The stranger ground his teeth at the very mention of the names.

"If you do not share the Sabians' beliefs, why have you come here? Are you a follower of Jesus, or Mohammed?"

"Mohammed and Jesus are impostors!" cried the man with immense, blasphemous power.

"Then you must be of the Parsi religion. You venerate fire—"

"They are all fantasies, mockeries, lies!" said the man in the black cloak, with redoubled indignation.

"Then whom do you worship?"

"He asks me whom I worship! I worship no one, because I am God myself! The one, the true, the only God, before me the others are only shadows!"

Hearing this claim, inconceivable, unheard of, and insane, the Sabians threw themselves on the blasphemer, and would have injured him badly, but Yusuf, shielding him with his body, led him out backward onto the terrace beside the Nile, even though he protested loudly, yelling like a madman. Then, pushing it off from the bank with a vigorous kick, Yusuf maneuvered the boat into the middle of the river. Soon the current caught them up. "Where shall I take you?" Yusuf said to his friend.

"Down there, on Roddah, where you see the lights burning," replied the stranger, who had calmed down in the night air.

With a few pulls on the oars they reached the island's beach, and the man in the black cloak, before leaping onto the bank, said to his protector, offering him an ancient ring that he removed from his finger, "Wheresoever you find me again, you have only to show me this ring, and I will do for you whatever you wish." Then he walked away, disappearing through the trees that border the river. To make up for lost time Yusuf, who wanted to attend the sacrifice, began to move the boat quickly through the Nile's waters, with redoubled energy.

FRANÇOIS LALLEMAND, HASHISH * (1843)

Not much is known about François Lallemand, the author of this anonymously published treatise on social progress. He was born in the early nineteenth century, probably in Marseille, qualified as a doctor of medicine but never practiced, and was one of the first people in France to take cannabis. His book, entitled Le hachych, appeared in 1843, coincidentally the same year the Hashish-eaters Club was formed in Paris. It sold very well, according to the publisher's notice in the second edition of 1848, which was given the cumbersome title The 1848 Political and Social Revolutions Predicted in 1843, and published under Lallemand's name, identifying him as a member of the Academy of Sciences and an honorary professor at the University of Montpellier. He was not publicly heard from again.

Hashish for Lallemand is a catalyst and initiator: a means, not an end in itself. At the dinner party which begins the book, a rather mysterious doctor who had been to Egypt and Ethiopia offers hashish to everyone present as a kind of digestif. Nearly all the nations of Europe are represented at the party, and the drug soon stimulates a great deal of discussion and good feeling. The talk is almost entirely political and prepares us for the narrator's utopian dream, which forms the greatest part of the book.

This is one of the least known utopian works in French liter-

* François Lallemand, Le hachych, Paris, 1843.

*ature, from an era when many were written. It is concerned with
the need for social and political change and projects the European
situation in 1843 a hundred years into the future. As the narrator
is told of the European federation of 1943, he understands that
men have become more aware of their societal responsibilities and
everyone feels free, for there is no more despotic government, co-
lonialist oppression, or war. The European congress has thoroughly
reformed, and of course improved, the tax system, the professions,
and the universities; the aristocracy and police have been abolished;
and day-care centers, curiously enough, have been established
everywhere. Yet cannabis exists no more as a refuge or palliative.
Its function in the author's day was to stimulate "political ecstasies,"
dreams about the perfect society. When that comes about, there is
no more need for drugs, dreams, or dreamers.*

*The book opens as the narrator's manuscript is discovered on a
steamship by a public-spirited gentleman who decides he must share
it with the world.*

THE END of last September I left Naples on the steamer *Eurotas*,
which had just arrived from Marseille. She was forced to leave
again so quickly in order to replace the *Minos*, whose boiler broke
down as soon as she had left port.

The *Eurotas* had scarcely gained the high seas when I felt ill
and wanted to lie down outside in the fresh air in order to prevent
seasickness. As I pulled toward me the mattress of my deck chair
to spread it out, a great roll of paper fell at my feet. It was carelessly
tied with a string, and had probably been put under the pillow
and forgotten by the passenger who had had the chair before me.

After assuring myself that the packet belonged to none of the
voyagers present, I untied the cord and glanced at several sheets.
They contained only a few notes that were very hard to read,
rather incoherent, and filled with crossed-out words. The captain
informed me that the occupant of my deck chair was a pale and
melancholy young man, who was probably suffering, because his
head was wrapped in a bandage and he had the mark of a severe

contusion on his right cheek. He wrote every minute after leaving Marseille, only going to sleep when the ship had passed Gaeta and was nearly to Naples. It was therefore necessary to wake him up long after everyone else had disembarked. But the captain could tell me no more, since the list of passengers who came from Marseille had been left in Naples, according to the rule, and because the young man had not said a word to anyone, even at meals, so immersed was he in his subject.

In the few moments of respite allowed me by the sea, I read over several of these sheets, and they soon piqued my curiosity. As I wanted to look them over at my greater ease, I begged the captain to trust me with them. Since he knew me he gladly consented, on the condition that I would give them all back as soon as they were asked for.

Since that time I never heard a word about the pale and melancholy young man with the bandaged head, and I am not the man to keep the goods of another. But to whom should I give a lost object, when the owner is unknown and no one claims it? Obviously, to the person it was destined for. So I have decided to give up these notes to the public, for I must suppose they were written for the public, and in any case, whatever belongs to no one must come finally to the community. Moreover, there are so many souls in pain who might have need of hashish to console them for present and future prospects. I cannot leave them in ignorance of the fantastic ecstasies they can enjoy if they use it with pure intentions.

Though these notes were hastily thrown onto paper by a dreamer who was scarcely in his senses, I want them to be printed as they are (though without the crossing out or the carets) without allowing any changes, deletions, or additions under whatever pretext.

This type of publication might raise some claim from either the author or his heirs, so here is my name and address:
ὁ Γέρμανος,* 20, rue Paradis, Marseille.

* * *

* That is, Lallemand.

Since I have nothing better to do and the sea is calm, I want to take this opportunity to preserve my memories of last night, while they are still deeply engraved on my mind. There is much consolation and truth for me in this brilliant and prophetic phantasmagoria that happened before my eyes with so much neatness and precision. Let me first establish the facts, then follow their strange unwinding. Let me begin at the beginning.

I am at a dinner party at Dr. Cauvière's. As always, the meal is delicate rather than splendid, and the guests, more choice than numerous, come from most of the countries of Europe. A frank, good-hearted discussion, covering approximately the following ideas:

In the press, absence of a generally agreed upon, humanitarian goal, or at least a patriotic one; no principle able to fix uncertain ideas, or bring together divergent opinions, or use all the effort thrown away in sterile bickering. Among those in power, a niggling, nearsighted egotism, ignorance of the masses' most urgent needs; unpopularity and weakness within, timidity without, intrigue and corruption in place of power and dignity. In parliament, a total lack of philanthropy or any public spirit; no broad vision, no foresight, not even any strong will, no intelligence in governmental management. In the bourgeoisie, greedy preoccupations, narrow and evil ideas, without significance or future; fear of foreigners without, fear of the proletariat within, fear of government above, fear of competition below. Among the people, always deceived, always devoted to generous ideas yet always suspect, among the people there is no feeling for the power that ignores, no confidence in those who exploit instead of enlighten, no consolation in the present, and no faith in the future.

These unhappy ideas, often chased away by the natural gaiety of the party, came back obstinately again and again, and finally led to a great difference of opinion about the condition of the other nations of Europe, who had all one or two representatives at the table. We drank to the holy cause of democracy, to the brotherhood of all peoples, and then we left the table for coffee.

One of the guests, Dr. Lebon, asked if he might be allowed to take, instead of mocha, an infusion of hashish.

"An infusion of hashish!" everyone cried. "And what is hashish? A new kind of tea? Can it be that tea that's brought in by caravan? Is it a kind of cocoa?"

"It's nothing like that at all," replied Dr. Lebon. "Anyway, you may judge for yourselves, because I've brought with me, according to my custom, an ample provision." And he removed from his pocket a paper packet filled with a kind of fodder, with serrated leaves, mixed with seeds and broken stems.

"But it's only hemp," said a botanist. "It has just the same shape, look, and smell. Those seeds, leaves, and little bits of stem, even though they're broken up, very much resemble our hemp."

"That's very true," replied Dr. Lebon. "It is even probable that hashish is nothing other than our hemp plant, whose properties are weakened in the north. At least that's the opinion of the scientists from the Egyptian Expedition,* and what seems to confirm that theory is the superiority of the hashish of Syria and Abyssinia over that of the Nile Delta. We know how much soil, temperature, humidity, and cultivation can change the appearance, and especially the properties of plants. Moreover, everyone knows the properties of ordinary hemp. It is thus probable that hashish is a very near neighbor to our cannabis or, to say it even better, an early model of ours."

"And what pleasure can you find in such a drug?"

"What pleasure? Without hashish, I should have died of melancholy a hundred times."

"Really! But why?"

"Compromised in political affairs, I contrived to escape from France and reached Egypt under a false name. A few typically French indiscretions reached the ears of our consul there. He gave me a warning in a paternal fashion and sent me on a kind of mission

* It was believed that Albert Sonnerat, one of the principal physicians on Napoleon's Egyptian Expedition (1798–1799), was the first to introduce hashish into France.

to Abyssinia. I spent three years in upper Egypt, in Nubia, Sennar, Darfur, Kordofan, and Abyssinia. I brought back many pieces of information, which I gathered in the hope of being useful to science and especially to my dear country, if men of good will and intelligence ever come forward to take care of her commerce and prosperity. There is much good to be done with very little effort, provided one does it quickly and energetically.

"Always preoccupied with my absence from my country, and pursued by memories of my family at home, wounded by the appalling spectacle of our unintelligent and cowardly politics, whose effects I had seen more closely than you and whose repercussions I had strongly felt, I often fell into a depression that would have led me to stagnation or suicide if I had not been reanimated by the delicious visions that hashish brought me. The Abyssinians taught me how to use it, and the constant direction of my ideas gave me dreams very different from theirs; moreover, I always took it straight, unmixed. Instead of erotic visions or war-like furies, I experienced political ecstasies.

"The most constant and remarkable property of hashish is to exalt the dominant ideas of the person who has taken it, to make him see in the clearest way his most complicated plans come to fruition without difficulty, his dearest projects realized without obstacle, to furnish him with the precise intuition he seeks. Finally, it lets him taste in thought the absolute possession of everything according to his wishes and habitual passions, and according to the direction of his thoughts at the moment the hashish acts on him. This is what explains the different effects one hears spoken of, because the effects greatly vary according to the individual and his momentary disposition.

"Hashish is put into every confection, electuary, and opiate—all more or less aphrodisiac—that the *magoun,* the druggist of the Sudan, sells to his clients. It comes as pastes, tablets, boluses, conserves, jellies, and so forth. But in all these preparations it is mixed with opium, ginger, and cinnamon, not to mention cantharides.

As for myself, I never take it but in an infusion, so as to get its unadulterated effects.

"However, one can smoke it, either pure or mixed with sweet tobacco; its effects are exactly the same, only a bit weaker and you don't have to wait so long for them. It is even enough, if one is very impressionable and does not have the habit of smoking hashish, to stay for a while among a few people smoking it for the vapor to work, probably by pulmonary absorption. Also, the use of hashish is general and very ancient in the Orient, despite the rigorous measures used in all ages by local authorities against trading in it. The steps taken by the Pasha of Egypt against hashish are not particularly efficacious, and the same applies to the prohibition in Algeria and all along the African coast."

"But why do they forbid it?"

"Because it produced a terrific exaltation in those who nourish projects of vengeance; because, when it is abused, it ends by acting on the health; and all those who need consolation always come back to it with increasing passion. For them it becomes an irresistible need. Our soldiers on the Egyptian Expedition, deprived of all communication with France, began to take it despite the standing orders of the chief general. But what do you want? It's the sovereign remedy for melancholy, discouragement, and every kind of disappointment. I thought I would still need it in France for some time to come, and that is why I brought back an ample provision, and I offer you some of it. Try it, even if only out of curiosity. What risk is there? A small dose, a single cup of this precious infusion, can give you only gaiety and consolation. Your most delightful wishes will become transformed, for the moment, into realities: you will possess the gift of second sight; you will be raised to the rank of prophets."

A few took the suggestion of Dr. Lebon, and even drank with him several cups of the infusion he had just prepared, either because they were curious, and led on by his example, or because they had the same cares and political preoccupations as he. Others simply smoked the hashish pure, or mixed with the tobacco. I thought it prudent to do as these did, in spite of the pain which the demoralization of the country caused me. I was on guard because of my nervous condition, and I wanted to be able to observe what happened with the others.

Someone sitting near the narrator suddenly cries out that he has just then invented a new electrical engine capable of driving all machines. Everyone is astonished at his sudden statement and at the accomplished, elegant way in which he utters it.

Vanderbrook had lived for years among galvanic and electrical apparatus; he dreamed only of their application as motors. Absorbed in his meditations and silent by nature, he had not yet uttered a word.

"Don't be fooled," Dr. Lebon said to me, "that's the effect of the hashish: he took three cups of it, one after another. Listen to his flow of words! What a neatness of ideas! He sees every detail of his machine. He has found what he has been seeking for such a long time."

A professor of zoology speaks up, describing the internal organization of prehistoric animals. He explains everything clearly and convincingly, replying to objections in advance. Then young Demos the Greek rises, "inspired like a Quaker, and begins to express the humanitarian ideas that flow from his heart." The whole subject of his long speech is love of humanity, and how it should exceed all other human feeling—love of children, spouse, family, country, God. Demos continues for a long time, covering the whole of French and European revolutionary history from 1789 up to the failure of the Lyon workers' occupation of 1834. He speaks as a man of the common people fighting against the bourgeoisie, clergy, and aristocracy.

At the end of his impassioned speech, the discussion became noisy, confused, and eventually impossible to follow. Dr. Lebon then said to me with a triumphant air, "No doubt there is much irregularity in the linking of all these ideas, but that exists in every real improvisation, and it's the basis of the thought that we must judge. And certainly, sir, without hashish, these thoughts would never have surfaced at all, or at any rate with the deep sincerity that makes them convincing. During the dinner, you know, Demos remained silent; even the champagne didn't bring him out. Now, won't you try a little cup of this heavenly infusion?"

"Thank you, thank you, but I have a very nervous constitution, and for the past hour I've been breathing in all this thick smoke. I already have a burning head and feel rather agitated. I need some fresh air and sleep."

"That's the effect of the tobacco mixed with hashish, but this will set you up—swallow it quickly and get your hat. I'll drive you home."

I drank it straight down and we left. Dr. Lebon took me to the Hôtel Beauveau and continued to outline for me his plans for reform, his political ideas, his hopes for the near future. Then I went with him to the Hôtel United States, then he came back home with me. Finally, after I know not how many comings and goings, he came up to my room, shook my hand with great warmth, and said before leaving, "There are things which one may believe as if one had seen them, because they are inevitable. In the meantime, may you have dreams which console you for the present."

As soon as I went to bed I felt a great beating in the arteries in the side of my head that was resting on the pillow. I turned over several times to stop this annoying noise, all the while thinking of what I had just seen and heard: My mind went back to Egypt with my new friend, Dr. Lebon. I dreamed of beautiful Abyssinian women, of hunting ostriches and giraffes, of golden sands washing the banks of the Red Sea. Then my imagination took me off to India, Tibet, China, and Japan. My ideas swarmed around me without my being aware of them, and I slept—or rather I passed the night under the influence of hashish, in an intermediate state between waking and sleeping.

After passing over the islands of the Straits Settlements and Java, the English colonies of Australia, Tasmania, and New Zealand, and the whole of Oceania, I arrived in America by way of California. I crossed the Rocky Mountains on a railway, then over the Great Lakes. I was present at the recognition of two new states, those of Wisconsin and Jowa [sic], which ceased being simple territories in order to become stars of the Union. I was one of the first to pass through the Panama Canal. Finally, after visiting the Cape of Good Hope, Timbuctu, and the Mountains of the Moon, I journeyed down the White Nile and saw the cataracts.

This was written before 1843. The railroad did not cross the Rockies until 1869; Iowa joined the Union in 1846, Wisconsin in 1848; and the Panama Canal was not even begun by Lesseps until 1881. The Americans completed it in 1914. The narrator is dreaming through time as well as space.

He then returns to Marseille on a huge automatic boat with no crew. He is amazed to find everything in France much changed since he left on his imaginary journey. People wear strange clothes, everything works by electricity. His friends are no longer living at their accustomed houses. He has passed through a century, and has arrived at Marseille on July 27, 1943. Everything has improved: social mobility and communication, political consciousness, even food and drink. France, Italy, and Spain have become one country, and everything in Europe breathes peace and enlightenment. In fact, the whole world has arrived at utter perfection by following the new doctrines of "political religion." In a crowd on the Canebierre * he sees his friend Dr. Cauvière and runs up to him, but it is really the doctor's grandson, who invites him home to dinner and tells him how the miracles he witnesses have come to pass. They discuss each country in the world, and measure its progress

---

* The principal street of Marseille. The name is Provençal, and analogous to the French chènevière: hemp field, or windbreak of growing hemp.

and its democratic successes. At one point his host, incredulous at his odd guest's naive questions, remarks,

"You ASKED ME a little while ago whether we were really in the year 1943. What am I supposed to think of you and your questions? You must have slept like Epimenides."

"Really, sir, I must be under the influence of some strange illusion, something like that produced by hashish."

"Hashish!" replied my host, looking at me severely. "Hashish is the drug of Oriental slaves. The free man does not need to look for consolation in such things."

It came to me that I had let slip something foolish, and I hastened to bow deeply in sign of agreement. Then, to get out of the embarrassment, I added interrogatively:

"What about the Rhineland?"

And so it goes. They discuss almost every country in the world, and review once again the history of France. Every ruler of the country, the Bourbons, the republicans, the Napoleons, have failed to understand what the people can do unaided, so tyranny has constantly given way before enlightened self-leadership. Colonialism and the greed causing it are no more, and all the people in the world now live in peace. Finally, the two men come to discuss democratic developments in Oceania.

"For you to understand what there is left for me to explain, we need to have before us the great map of Oceania. Please take it from the drawer in front of you. There . . . slowly . . . pull it back a little more . . . that great roll, yes . . . very good . . . pull again . . ."

I thought the legs of my chair were slipping, then I felt the most violent shock imaginable, and a thousand stars swam before my eyes. Apparently I passed out for rather a long time, for it was broad daylight when I came to. I was very cold, stretched out on the floor of my room, half covered by the blanket, and I had lost

124 / TALES OF HASHISH

much blood through the nose. When I had completely recovered my senses, I realized that I had thrown myself out of bed while trying to remove from its drawer that immense cursed map of Oceania—that is to say my blanket, which I still held in both hands as in my dream.

I rang: the alarm sounded throughout the house. Everyone was shocked when they saw my pallor and the great quantity of blood I'd lost; but Dr. Cauvière, who had come to say good-bye, assured me that the hemorrhage was caused by the tearing of the mucous membrane which lines the spongy ethmoid bone. "A triply fortunate circumstance," he added, "in that the fracture of this thin bone probably made a brain hemorrhage unlikely, in that your great nosebleed has prevented a flow of blood into the brain cavity, and stopped any infection that might have developed there."

While he was telling me all these happy things, I recalled the features, voice, phrases, smile, and even the gestures of the man, his grandson, who had taught me so many things the previous night. I couldn't help saying to him a little bitterly, "You'd better take good care of me, Doctor, because you were the one who did this to me." And I told him about the effects the hashish had produced on me.

Since I had to leave that day, in spite of the remonstrances of the good doctor, I hastened to put myself into a safe corner of the steamboat, in order to get down my recollections on paper as quickly as possible. As to deeper reflections suggested by this immense phantasmagoria, I shall still be able to recollect them when I need to. I am dropping with fatigue, and afraid of overtiring my poor head.

The man who has found the manuscript adds in a postscript:

The rest of the manuscript is indecipherable. The only readable sentence is this one: "In spite of my fall, I will often go back to hashish." Moreover, there is no trace of a signature other than a zigzag extending to the bottom of the last page, apparently indicating the author's strong desire to stretch out and sleep.

ALEXANDRE DUMAS PÈRE, "SINBAD THE SAILOR" * (1844)

Apart from his three novels about the Musketeers, The Count of
Monte Cristo *(1844) is Dumas's (1802–1870) best-known work
among the 1,200 volumes he claimed he wrote and the 270 that
were published as his complete works. Although he was a lifelong
republican, his background and interests were solidly middle class,
and the bourgeoisie loved his novels and plays, which mostly described adventure and intrigue among the aristocracy. Throughout
most of his life, he moved in a society of actresses and countesses,
and for a while was even a friend of King Louis Philippe, but he
befriended few writers. He met Gautier, Baudelaire, and Nerval,
but they shunned him at first as impossibly vulgar and bourgeois,
while he, whose work for the theater made him many times rich,
always had a horror of "garret dwellers."*

*He was, then, not a member of the Hashish-eaters Club, nor
intimate with any of its members. His immensely long* Mes Mémoires *(1852–1854), in which he recounts spicy stories from his own
life and those of his friends, contains no mention of cannabis indulgence by anyone. And yet he wrote this chapter of Monte Cristo,
perhaps the greatest description of the cannabis experience in any*

* From Chapters 31–32 of *Le comte de Monte-Cristo,* Paris, 1844.

*language: it is fluent and attractive and shows no uneasiness about
the subject. To achieve these effects, Dumas took the course, highly
unusual for him, of rewriting the end of the chapter three times.
It is not known to what extent he was helped by research—he may
not have done any. His imagination was always prodigious, and
this account of the effects of hashish sounds quite authentic: It
contains the real poetry of ecstasy.*

*Edmond Dantès, a sailor from Marseille, is suspected of being
a Bonapartist, and in 1815 is imprisoned without trial in the Château d'If, where he spends six years in misery and increasing madness. One day he meets a fellow prisoner, the Abbé Faria, who is a
scholar and the sole heir to the treasures of the Spada family, which
are in the grottoes of the Mediterranean island of Monte Cristo.
Dantès effects an escape, and finally reaches the island, where he
discovers the immense treasure, hidden since 1498, and his fortune
is assured. As the years pass he adopts several disguises, among
which are Lord Wilmot, traveling English nobleman, and Sinbad
the Sailor, a persona he assumes whenever he is on Monte Cristo,
where he has converted the treasure grotto into an oriental fantasy.
Here he receives guests, all the while plotting his revenge on the
individuals who wronged him and the society that allowed it to
happen.*

*In this chapter Dumas constructs and exploits a classic psycho-
logical situation: the hidden cave filled with wonders which, once
one has been there, cannot be found again. The addition of hashish
was the perfect, contemporary touch, an exotic means of distancing
Dantès from the reader just as Dantès distances himself from his
guest Franz, a young nobleman, who has what he calls "an adventure out of the* Thousand and One Nights."

"His excellency awaits you," said a voice from behind, which
Franz recognized as that of the sentinel. He was accompanied by
two of the yacht's crew. In reply, Franz drew his handkerchief

from his pocket and presented it to the man who had spoken to him. Without a word they bandaged his eyes with a care that showed their apprehension that he might commit some indiscretion, then they made him swear that he would make no attempt whatever to raise the blindfold. He swore it. Then the two men each took an arm, and he was walked away, guided by them and preceded by the sentinel. After they had gone about thirty steps he perceived the appetizing odor of the roasting goat, and knew that he was passing the bivouac; then they led him on for fifty steps more, evidently going in the direction forbidden to Gaetano, a prohibition he now could understand. Presently, by a change in the air he sensed they were going underground; in a few seconds he heard a crackling, and it seemed to him the air changed again, becoming soft and perfumed. Finally he felt his feet touch a thick, soft carpet, and his guides let go of him.

There was a moment of silence, then a voice in excellent French, though with a foreign accent, said, "You are welcome, monsieur. You may now remove your blindfold." As may be imagined, Franz did not wait for this invitation to be repeated, but took off the handkerchief and found himself standing before a man from thirty-eight to forty years old, dressed in a Tunisian costume, a red cap with a long blue silk tassel, a vest of black cloth embroidered all over with gold, dark red pantaloons, large and full, gaiters of the same color, embroidered like the vest in gold, and yellow slippers. He had a splendid cashmere wrapped around his waist, and a small scimitar, sharp and curved, was passed through his belt.

Although of an almost livid pallor, this man had a remarkably handsome face; his eyes were penetrating and sparkling, his nose, straight and almost in line with his brow, exhibited the Greek type in all its purity, and his teeth, white as pearls, were well set off by the black moustache that covered them. But his paleness was strange. One might have thought he had been closed up a long time in a tomb, and was unable to recover the healthy color of living people. He was not very tall, but very well formed, and like the men of the South, he had small hands and feet.

But what astonished Franz, who had treated Gaetano's description as foolishness, was the splendor of the furnishings around him. The entire chamber was lined with crimson Turkish brocade worked with flowers of gold. In a recess was a kind of divan, and over it was a stand of Arabian swords with silver scabbards and jeweled handles; from the ceiling hung a lamp of Venetian glass, of a beautiful shape and color, while one's feet rested on a Turkish carpet, in which they sank to the instep. Tapestries were hung in front of the door by which Franz had entered, and in front of another door, leading into a second room that seemed brilliantly lit.

The host left Franz for a moment absorbed in his surprise, and moreover gave him look for look, not once taking his eyes off him. "Monsieur," he said at length, "I ask a thousand pardons for the precautions required for your introduction here, but as most of the time this island is deserted, if the secret of this place were discovered, I should doubtless on my return find my little apartment in a rather bad state, which would be exceedingly annoying not for the loss it might cause me, but because I should not have the certainty I have now of being able to separate myself at my pleasure from the rest of mankind. Let me now try to make you forget this temporary unpleasantness, and offer you what you no doubt did not expect to find here—a tolerable supper and rather comfortable beds."

"Goodness! My dear host," replied Franz, "make no apologies for that. I always thought they blindfolded those who enter enchanted palaces—like Raoul in *The Huguenots;* and really, I have nothing to complain about, for what you show me is a sequel to the wonders of the *Thousand and One Nights.*"

"Alas, I will say with Lucullus, 'If I had known of the honor of your visit, I would have been prepared for it.' But such as is my hermitage, it is all at your disposal; such as is my supper, it is yours to share if you will. Ali, are we ready?"

At the same moment the tapestry parted, and a Nubian, black as ebony, and dressed in a plain white tunic, made a sign to his master that they might enter the dining room.

"Now," said the unknown man to Franz, "I do not know if you are of my opinion, but I think nothing is more annoying than to remain for two or three hours face to face with a person without knowing by what name or title to call him. Please observe that I respect the laws of hospitality too much to ask you your name or title. I only ask you to give me a name by which I might address you. As for myself, that I might put you at your ease, I may tell you that I am generally called Sinbad the Sailor."

"And I," replied Franz, "will tell you, as I only require the wonderful lamp to put me in Aladdin's situation, that I see no reason why, for the time being, I should not be called Aladdin. This will keep us in the Orient, where I am tempted to think I have been conveyed by some good genie's power."

"Well then, Signor Aladdin," replied this curious host, "you have heard that our meal is ready; will you now trouble yourself to enter the dining room, your humble servant going first to show you the way?" With these words, lifting the tapestry, Sinbad preceded his guest. Franz proceeded from one enchantment to another; the table was splendidly covered, and once convinced of this important point, he let his eyes wander about. The dining room was no less beautiful than the sitting room he had just left: it was entirely of marble, with antique bas-reliefs of the greatest cost, and at the two ends of the hall, which was oblong, there were two magnificent statues carrying baskets on their heads. Each basket contained pyramids of magnificent fruit: there were pineapples from Sicily, pomegranates from Malaga, oranges from the Balearic Isles, peaches from France, and dates from Tunis. As to the supper, it consisted of a roast pheasant surrounded by Corsican blackbirds, a boar's ham in jelly, a quarter of a kid à la tartare, a magnificent turbot, and a gigantic lobster. In the intervals between the principal dishes there were smaller ones containing various dainties. The dishes were of silver, and the plates of Japanese porcelain.

Franz rubbed his eyes to assure himself that he was not dreaming. Ali alone was present to wait on table, and acquitted himself very well. The guest complimented his host on the servant.

"Yes," he replied, performing the honors of the supper with the greatest ease and grace, "yes, he is a poor devil much devoted to me, who does his best. He remembers that I saved his life, and as he thinks well of his head, or so it appears, he feels some gratitude to me for having preserved it for him."

Ali approached his master, took his hand, and kissed it.

"And would it be too indiscreet, Signor Sinbad," said Franz, "to ask you under what circumstances you performed that fine deed?"

"Oh, God, it's a very simple matter," replied the host. "It seems the fellow had wandered nearer to the harem of the Bey of Tunis than it was permitted a gentleman of his color to do, so that he was condemned by the bey to have his tongue cut out, and his hand and head cut off—the tongue the first day, the hand the second, and the head the third. I always had a desire to have a mute in my service, so I waited until his tongue had been cut out, and then proposed to the bey that he should give him to me in exchange for a beautiful double-barreled gun which, it seemed to me, had excited his highness's desire the previous evening. He hesitated a moment, so intent was he on finishing the poor devil. But I added to the gun an English hunting knife, with which I had shattered his highness's yataghan, so the bey yielded, and agreed to forgive the hand and head, but on condition that he should never again set foot in Tunis. This was an unnecessary condition, for whenever the miscreant catches a glimpse of the shores of Africa, from however far away, he runs below, and can be made to reappear only when we are out of sight of the third part of the globe."

Franz remained mute and pensive for a while, not knowing what to think of the cruel humor with which his host had told the tale. "And like the honorable sailor whose name you have assumed," he said, to change the conversation, "you pass your life in traveling?"

"Yes. It is a fulfillment of a vow I made at a time when I never thought I would ever be able to accomplish it," said the unknown man with a smile. "I made some others also like that one, which I hope I may fulfill in their turn."

Although Sinbad uttered these words with the greatest coolness, his eyes darted gleams of a strange ferocity.

"You have suffered a great deal, monsieur?" said Franz.

Sinbad started and looked fixedly at him. "What makes you think that?"

"Everything," replied Franz, "your voice, your look, your pallor, and even the very life you lead."

"I! I live the happiest life I ever heard of—the real life of a pasha. I am king of all creation. I am pleased with a place, and stay there; I get tired of it, and leave. I am free as a bird, and have wings like one. My attendants obey me at the slightest signal. From time to time I amuse myself by taking away from human justice some bandit it is searching for, some criminal it pursues. Then I have my own justice, high and low, without respite or appeal, which condemns or absolves, and which no one ever sees. Ah, if you could taste my life, you would never want another, and would never return to the world unless you had some great project to accomplish there."

"Some vengeance, for instance?" said Franz.

The unknown man fixed on the young man one of those looks that plunge into the depths of heart and thought. "And why vengeance?" he asked.

"Because," replied Franz, "you seem to me to be a man who, persecuted by society, has a terrible account to settle with it."

"Well," said Sinbad, with his strange laugh that showed his white, sharp teeth, "you have not guessed correctly. Such as you see me, I am a sort of philanthropist, and one day perhaps I shall go to Paris to compete with M. Appert and the man in the Little Blue Cloak."

"And will that be the first time you will have made that journey?"

"Oh, my God, yes. I must seem to you not at all curious, but I assure you that it is not my fault I have delayed it so long; I shall get to it one day."

"And do you propose to make this journey soon?"

"I do not know yet. It depends on circumstances subject to uncertainties."

"I should like to be there at the time you come, and I will try to repay you as well as I can for your liberal hospitality at Monte Cristo."

"I would accept your offer with pleasure," replied the host, "but unfortunately, if I go there, it will perhaps be incognito."

Meanwhile the supper went ahead, and appeared to have been supplied solely for Franz, for the unknown man scarcely touched one or two dishes of the splendid feast to which his unexpected guest did such ample justice. Then Ali brought on the dessert, or rather took the baskets from the statues' heads and placed them on the table. Between the two baskets he placed a small vermeil cup, closed with a lid of the same metal. The respect with which Ali had carried this cup piqued Franz's curiosity. He raised the lid and saw a kind of greenish paste that looked like preserved angelica, but which was entirely unknown to him. He replaced the lid, as ignorant of what the cup contained as he was before he had lifted it, and then, glancing at his host, he saw him smile at his disappointment.

"You cannot guess what sort of eatable is contained in that little vase, and that intrigues you, doesn't it?"

"I confess it does."

"Well, then, those green preserves are nothing less than the ambrosia that Hebe served at the table of Jupiter."

"But," replied Franz, "this ambrosia, in passing through human hands, has no doubt lost its heavenly name to assume a human one.

In vulgar language, what do you call this thing—for which, in any case, I do not feel any great desire?"

"Ah, thus is our material origin truly revealed!" cried Sinbad. "We frequently pass so near to happiness without seeing it, without really looking at it; or even if we do, we still do not recognize it. Are you a practical man, and is gold your god? Then taste this, and the mines of Peru, Gujerat, and Golconda are open to you. Are you a man of imagination, a poet? Then taste this, and the boundaries of possibility disappear, the fields of infinite space will be open to you: you will walk about, free in heart and mind, into the boundless realms of reverie. Are you ambitious, do you run after the grandeur of the earth? Only taste this, and in an hour you will be a king, not of some petty kingdom hidden in a corner of Europe, like France, Spain, or England, but a king of the world, of the universe, of creation. Your throne will be established on that mountain to which Jesus was taken by Satan, and without being obliged to do homage to the devil, without having to kiss his claw, you will be sovereign master of all the kingdoms of the earth. Is it not tempting, what I offer you? And is it not an easy thing, since it is only to do thus? Look!" With these words he uncovered the little vermeil cup containing the substance so highly praised, took a teaspoonful of the magic preserves, raised it to his lips, and savored it slowly, with his eyes half shut and his head bent backward. Franz did not disturb him while he ate his favorite dish, but when he had finished, he inquired:

"What, then, is this precious preparation?"

"Did you ever hear," asked his host, "of the Old Man of the Mountain, who attempted to assassinate Philip Augustus?"

"Of course I have."

"Well, you know he reigned over a rich valley dominated by the mountain from which he derived his picturesque name. In this valley were magnificent gardens planted by Hasan-ben-Sabah, and in these gardens were isolated pavilions. Into these pavilions he admitted his chosen ones, and there, says Marco Polo, he had them eat a certain herb, which transported them to Paradise to the midst of ever-blooming shrubs, ever-ripe fruit, and ever-fresh virgins. Now, what these happy young men took for reality was only a dream, but it was a dream so soft, voluptuous, and enthralling, that they sold themselves body and soul to him who gave it to them, and obeyed his orders as if they were God's own. They went to the ends of the earth to strike down their destined victims, and would die under torture without a word, believing that the death they suffered was only a transition to that life of delights of which the holy herb, now served before you, had given them a foretaste."

"Then," cried Franz, "it is hashish! I know it, by name at least."

"You have said the magic word, Signor Aladdin, it is hashish—the best and purest hashish made in Alexandria; the hashish of Abu-Gor, celebrated maker, unique man, the man to whom a palace should be built with this inscription: 'A grateful world to the merchant of happiness.'"

"Do you know," said Franz, "I have a great inclination to judge for myself the truth or exaggeration of your praises."

"Judge for yourself, my guest; judge, but do not keep yourself to a single experience. As in everything else, we must habituate the senses to every new impression, gentle or violent, sad or joyous. There is a struggle in nature against this divine substance—nature is not made for joy, and clings to pain. Nature, vanquished, must yield in the combat: reality must yield to dream, and then the dream reigns as master. Then the dream becomes life, and life becomes the dream. But what a difference there is in this transfiguration, in comparing the pains of actual existence to the joys of fictitious existence! You wish to live no more, but to dream forever. When you leave your own world to return to that of others, you seem to leave a Neapolitan springtime for a Lapland winter—to leave paradise for earth, heaven for hell! Taste the hashish, my guest, taste it!"

Franz's only reply was to take a spoonful of the wonderful paste, about as much as his host had eaten, and he raised it to his mouth.

"The devil!" he said after swallowing the divine confection. "I do not know if the result will be as agreeable as you describe, but the thing does not seem to me as delicious as you claim."

"Because your palate has not reached the sublimity of the substance it tastes. Tell me, the first time you tasted oysters, tea, porter, truffles, and everything else you now like, did you like them then? Can you comprehend how the Romans stuffed their pheasants with asafetida, and the Chinese eat swallows' nests? Well, it's the same with hashish: only eat it for a full week, and nothing in the world will seem to you to equal the delicacy of this flavor that now seems tasteless and nauseating. Let us now go into the next room —that is, into your room—and Ali will bring us coffee and tobacco."

They both got up, and while he who called himself Sinbad— and whom we have occasionally so named, so that, like his guest, we might have some title by which to distinguish him—gave some orders to his servant, Franz entered the adjoining room. It was more simply yet no less richly furnished. It was round, and a large divan completely encircled it. Divan, walls, ceiling, floor, were all spread with magnificent hides, as soft and downy as the richest carpets. There were skins of the lions of the Atlas, with their powerful manes, skins of the Bengal tigers, with their glowing stripes, skins of Cape panthers, joyously spotted like the one that appeared to Dante, skins of Siberian bears and Norwegian foxes, and all these skins were strewn in profusion one on the other, so that it seemed like walking over the thickest grass, or lying on the softest bed.

Both laid themselves down on the divan, where chibouks with jasmine tubes and amber mouthpieces were within reach, and all prepared so that there was no need to smoke the same pipe twice. Each took one, and Ali lit them, then retiring to prepare the coffee. There was a moment of silence, during which Sinbad gave himself up to thoughts that seemed to occupy him ceaselessly, even in the midst of his conversation, and Franz abandoned himself to that mute reverie into which one almost sinks when smoking excellent tobacco, which seems to lift with the smoke all the mind's troubles, and to give back in exchange all the soul's dreams.

Ali brought in the coffee.

"How will you take it?" inquired the unknown man. "In the French or Turkish way, strong or weak, sugared or not, filtered or boiled? It is your choice; it is ready in all ways."

"I will take Turkish coffee," replied Franz.

"And you are right!" cried his host. "It shows you have a penchant for the Oriental life. Ah, those Orientals—they are the only ones who know how to live. As for me," he added with one of those singular smiles which did not escape the young man's attention, "when I have done my business in Paris, I shall go and die in the East, and if you want to see me again, you must come find me in Cairo, Baghdad, or Isfahan."

"Heavens!" said Franz, "that would be the easiest thing in the world—for I feel eagle's wings sprouting on me, and with these wings I could tour the world in twenty-four hours."

"Ah, that's the hashish operating. Well, open your wings, and fly into superhuman regions. Fear nothing—we are watching over you, and if your wings, like those of Icarus, melt in the sun, we are here to catch you."

He then said some words in Arabic to Ali, who made a gesture of obedience and withdrew, but still remained near. As to Franz, a strange transformation was taking place in him. All the bodily fatigue of the day, all the preoccupation of mind which the events of the evening had brought on, disappeared as in the first moment of repose, when we are still sufficiently conscious to be aware of coming sleep. His body seemed to acquire an immaterial lightness; his mind brightened in a remarkable manner; his senses seemed to double their powers. The horizon continued to expand, but not that somber horizon over which a vague terror hovers, and which he had seen before he slept, but a blue, transparent, vast horizon, with all the blue of the ocean, all the beams of the sun, all the perfumes of the softest breeze. Then, in the midst of the songs of his sailors, songs so clear and resounding that they would have made a divine harmony if one could have taken down their notes, he saw the island of Monte Cristo appear, no longer as a threatening rock in the middle of the waves, but as an oasis lost in the desert. Then, as the boat approached, the songs became more numerous, for an enchanting and mysterious harmony rose to God from this island, as if some nymph like Lorelei or some enchanter like Amphion wanted to attract a soul there, or to build there a city.

At length the boat touched the shore, but without effort, without shock, as lips touch lips; and he entered the grotto while the delightful music still played. He descended, or rather seemed to descend, several steps, inhaling the fresh and balmy air, like that which is supposed to be around Circe's grotto, formed of such perfumes as set the mind to dreaming, and from such fires as burn the very senses; and he saw again all that he had seen before his sleep, from Sinbad, his fantastic host, to Ali, the mute servant. Then all seemed to fade away and become confused before his eyes, like the last shadows of a magic lantern before it is extinguished, and he was again in the room with the statues, lit only by one of those dim, antique lamps that watch in the dead of night over sleep or pleasure. They were the same statues, rich in form, beauty, and poetry, with magnetic eyes, wanton smiles, and flowing hair. They were Phryne, Cleopatra, and Messalina, those three great courtesans. Then amidst these immodest shades there glided, like a pure ray, like a Christian angel descending on Olympus, a chaste figure, a calm shadow, a soft vision, which seemed to veil its virgin brow against these marble impurities. Then it seemed to him that these three statues brought together their several loves into a love for a single man, and that was he; then they approached the bed on which he was dreaming, their feet hidden under their long white tunics, their throats bare, hair flowing like waves, and striking poses which the gods themselves could not resist, but which saints withstood. Their gazes were inflexible and ardent like the snake's on the bird, and then he gave away before these looks, which were as painful as an iron grip and as voluptuous as a kiss. It seemed to Franz that he closed his eyes, and that in his last look around he saw the modest statue completely veiled; then, his eyes closing to all reality, his senses opened themselves to receive the strangest of all impressions.

Then there was untrammeled lust, unceasing love, such as the prophet promised his elect. Then all the stony mouths opened, all the breasts grew hot, so much so that for Franz, submitting for the first time to the empire of hashish, this love was almost a pain, this lust a torture, and at last he felt at his thirsty mouth these statues' lips, soft and cold as the skin of a serpent. But the more his arms tried to push away this unknown love, the more his senses gave in to the charm of the mysterious dream, so that after a struggle for which he would have given his soul, he abandoned himself unreservedly, and finally fell back, panting, weary, drained of energy, under the kisses of these marble mistresses and the enchantment of this fantastic dream.

When Franz returned to himself, exterior objects seemed just another part of his dream. He thought he was in a sepulcher into which barely penetrated, like a look of pity, a small ray of sunlight. He stretched forth his hand and touched stone; he pulled himself up to a sitting posture, and found himself lying on his burnoose on a bed of dry heather that was very soft and fragrant. The vision was all gone, and as if the statues had been only shades coming from their tombs during his dream, they had vanished at his waking.

He advanced several steps toward the point from which the light came, and to all the excitement of his dream succeeded the calm of reality. He found he was in a grotto, went toward the opening, and through an arched doorway saw a blue sea and an azure sky. The air and water shone in the beams of the morning sun; on the shore the sailors were sitting, talking and laughing, and ten feet into the sea the boat was gracefully riding at anchor. Then he enjoyed for a little while the fresh breeze on his brow and heard the faint noise of the waves that came to the beach and left on the rocks a lace of foam as white as silver. He abandoned himself for some time without reflection or thought to the divine charm which is in the things of nature, especially when one comes out of a fantastic dream; then gradually this outer life, so calm, pure, and grand, showed him the unreality of his dream, and memories began to return to him.

He recalled his arrival on the island, his presentation to a smuggler chief, an underground palace full of splendor, an excellent supper, and a spoonful of hashish. It seemed, however, even in the face of broad daylight, that at least a year had elapsed since all these things had happened, so vivid was the impression made on his imagination by the dream, and so strong a hold had it taken of his mind. Thus every now and then his fancy saw amid the sailors, seated on a rock, or on the boat, moving with its motion, one of those shades which had starred his night with their looks and kisses. Otherwise, his head was perfectly clear and his body completely rested. There was no heaviness in his brain; on the contrary, he felt a general well-being, a faculty for absorbing the pure air and bright sunshine more vividly than ever.

He went gaily up to the sailors, who rose as soon as they saw him, and the captain went up to him, saying, "Signor Sinbad has left us his compliments for your excellency, and desires us to express the regret he feels at not being able to take his leave from you in person; but he trusts you will excuse him when you learn that a very important business matter calls him to Malaga."

"So then, Gaetano," said Franz, "all this, then, is reality. There exists a man who received me on this island, showed me royal hospitality, and has departed while I was asleep?"

"He exists in such reality that you may see his little yacht with all her sails spread, and if you will use your spyglass, you will probably recognize your host in the midst of his crew."

So saying, Gaetano stretched out his arm toward a small vessel that was making sail toward the southern point of Corsica. Franz took out his glass, adjusted it, and directed it toward the place indicated. Gaetano was not mistaken. At the stern stood the mysterious stranger, looking toward the shore, and holding a spyglass in his hand. He was dressed exactly as he had been on the previous evening, and waved his handkerchief as a sign of farewell. Franz returned the salute by taking out his handkerchief and shaking it in the same way. After a second a light cloud of smoke was seen at the stern. It rose gracefully into the air as it expanded, then the small explosion reached Franz. "There, do you hear?" observed Gaetano. "He is bidding you adieu." The young man took his carbine and fired it in the air, but without any hope that the noise could travel the distance separating the yacht from the shore.

"What are your excellency's orders?" said Gaetano.

"First of all, light me a torch."

"Ah, yes, I understand," replied the captain. "You want to find the entrance to the underground palace. With pleasure, excellency, if that would amuse you, and I will get you the torch you ask for. But I have also had the idea you have, and two or three times the same fancy has come over me, but finally I gave it up. Giovanni, light a torch," he added, "and bring it to his excellency."

Giovanni obeyed. Franz took it and entered the grotto, followed by Gaetano. He recognized the place where he had slept by the bed of heather still pressed down, but he passed his torch in vain over all the surface of the grotto. He saw nothing except a few traces of smoke, suggesting that others before him had bootlessly attempted the same thing. Yet he did not leave a foot of this granite wall, as impenetrable as the future, without examining it closely; he did not see a crack without sticking into it the blade of his hunting knife, nor any projecting point on which he did not push, in the hope that it would give way. But all his efforts were futile, and he lost two hours in the search with no results. At the end of that time he gave it up, and Gaetano was triumphant.

BAYARD TAYLOR,
"A SLIGHT EXPERIENCE
OF HASHEESH" (1855)

Though his name and works are not much remembered today, Bayard Taylor (1825–1878) was a very famous travel writer in mid-nineteenth-century America. Views Afoot (1846), a journal of a two-year walking tour of Europe, was his first great success. After a trip to the California gold fields, described in Eldorado *(1850), he set off for two more years of travel to Africa, the Middle East, and the Orient.*

His insightful curiosity at all he saw, plus an ingenuous, straightforward, and comprehensive style made his descriptions of faraway lands and exotic experiences very appealing to Americans. Whatever traveling they did then was mostly within their new land, and they loved writers who looked at the rest of the world with wide-open American eyes.

Taylor's two reports of eating hashish are the first by an American; and though his excessive experience in Damascus seems particularly grim, it was probably not his last. His home base was New York from the time he was nineteen, where a close friend in his bohemian circle was the younger writer, Fitz Hugh Ludlow (see p. 172), who had a lifelong involvement with all forms of cannabis.

In his later years, however, Taylor turned to alcohol in typically great quantities, all the while turning out fifteen volumes of poetry, including a translation of Faust *and an official Centennial Ode in*

1876. He died as minister to Germany, where he was also greatly admired, far removed from the days he describes here.

A new perception of cannabis is apparent in the writing of this American and in the pieces that follow. The self-assured, sophisticated tone of the French hashish eaters is missing, and questions of morality and propriety arise. The Americans mostly describe their hashish experiences in the first person, and their aim seems to be more to educate and warn than to amuse.

WHILE IN EGYPT, I had frequently heard mention of the curious effects produced by *hasheesh*, a preparation made from the *cannabis indica*. On reaching Siout, I took occasion to buy some, for the purpose of testing it. It was a sort of paste, made of the leaves of the plant, mixed with sugar and spices. The taste is aromatic and slightly pungent, but by no means disagreeable. About sunset, I took what Achmet considered to be a large dose, and waited half an hour without feeling the slightest effect. I then repeated it, and drank a cup of hot tea immediately afterwards. In about ten minutes, I became conscious of the gentlest and balmiest feeling of rest stealing over me. The couch on which I sat grew soft and yielding as air; my flesh was purged from all gross quality, and became a gossamer filigree of exquisite nerves, every one tingling with a sensation which was too dim and soft to be pleasure, but which resembled nothing else so nearly. No sum could have tempted me to move a finger. The slightest shock seemed enough to crush a structure so frail and delicate as I had become. I felt like one of those wonderful sprays of brittle spar which hang for ages in the unstirred air of a cavern, but are shivered to pieces by the breath of the first explorer.

As this sensation, which lasted but a short time, was gradually fading away, I found myself infected with a tendency to view the most common objects in a ridiculous light. Achmet was sitting on one of the provision chests, as was his custom of an evening. I thought: was there ever any thing so absurd as to see him sitting on that chest? and laughed immoderately at the idea. The turban worn by the captain next put on such a quizzical appearance that I chuckled over it for some time. Of all turbans in the world it was the most ludicrous. Various other things affected me in like manner, and at last it seemed to me that my eyes were increasing in breadth. "Achmet," I called out, "how is this? my eyes are precisely like two onions." This was my crowning piece of absurdity. I laughed so loud and long at the singular comparison I had made, that when I ceased from sheer weariness the effect was over. But on the following morning my eyes were much better, and I was able to write, for the first time in a week.

The Visions of Hasheesh *

DURING MY STAY in Damascus, that insatiable curiosity which leads me to prefer the acquisition of all lawful knowledge through the channels of my own personal experience, rather than in less satisfactory and less laborious ways, induced me to make a trial of the celebrated *Hasheesh*—that remarkable drug which supplies the luxurious Syrian with dreams more alluring and more gorgeous than the Chinese extracts from his darling opium pipe. The use of Hasheesh—which is a preparation of the dried leaves of the *cannabis indica*—has been familiar to the East for many centuries. During the Crusades, it was frequently used by the Saracen warriors to stimulate them to the work of slaughter, and from the Arabic term of *"Hashasheën,"* or Eaters of Hasheesh, as applied to them, the word "assassin" has been naturally derived. An infusion of the same plant gives to the drink called *"bhang,"* which is in common use throughout India and Malaysia, its peculiar properties. Thus prepared, it is a more fierce and fatal stimulant than the paste of sugar and spices to which the Turk resorts, as the food of his voluptuous evening reveries. While its immediate effects seem to be more potent than those of opium, its habitual use, though attended with ultimate and permanent injury to the system, rarely results in such

* Bayard Taylor, "The Visions of Hasheesh," *Pictures of Palestine, Asia Minor, Sicily, and Spain: Or, The Lands of the Saracen* (London, 1855), pp. 133–148.

utter wreck of mind and body as that to which the votaries of the latter drug inevitably condemn themselves.

A previous experience of the effects of hasheesh—which I took once, and in a very mild form, while in Egypt—was so peculiar in its character, that my curiosity, instead of being satisfied, only prompted me the more to throw myself, for once, wholly under its influence. The sensations it then produced were those, physically, of exquisite lightness and airiness—mentally, of a wonderfully keen perception of the ludicrous, in the most simple and familiar objects. During the half hour in which it lasted, I was at no time so far under its control, that I could not, with the clearest perception, study the changes through which I passed. I noted, with careful attention, the fine sensations which spread throughout the whole tissue of my nervous fibre, each thrill helping to divest my frame of its earthy and material nature, until my substance appeared to me no grosser than the vapors of the atmosphere, and while sitting in the calm of the Egyptian twilight, I expected to be lifted up and carried away by the first breeze that should ruffle the Nile. While this process was going on, the objects by which I was surrounded assumed a strange and whimsical expression. My pipe, the oars which my boatmen plied, the turban worn by the captain, the water-jars and culinary implements, became in themselves so inexpressibly absurd and comical, that I was provoked into a long fit of laughter. The hallucination died away as gradually as it came, leaving me overcome with a soft and pleasant drowsiness, from which I sank into a deep, refreshing sleep.

My companion and an English gentleman, who, with his wife, was also residing in Antonio's pleasant caravanserai—agreed to join me in the experiment. The dragoman of the latter was deputed to procure a sufficient quantity of the drug. He was a dark Egyptian, speaking only the *lingua franca* of the East, and asked me, as he took the money and departed on his mission, whether he should get hasheesh *"per ridere, o per dormire?"* "Oh, *per ridere*, of course," I answered; "and see that it be strong and fresh." It is customary with the Syrians to take a small portion immediately before the evening meal, as it is thus diffused through the stomach and acts more gradually, as well as more gently, upon the system. As our dinner-hour was at sunset, I proposed taking hasheesh at that time, but my friends, fearing that its operation might be more speedy upon fresh subjects, and thus betray them into some absurdity in the presence of the other travellers, preferred waiting until after the meal. It was then agreed that we should retire to our room, which, as it rose like a tower one story higher than the rest of the building, was in a manner isolated, and would screen us from observation.

We commenced by taking a tea-spoonful each of the mixture which Abdallah had procured. This was about the quantity I had taken in Egypt, and as the effect then had been so slight, I judged that we ran no risk of taking an over-dose. The strength of the drug, however, must have been far greater in this instance, for whereas I could in the former case distinguish no flavor but that of sugar and rose leaves, I now found the taste intensely bitter and repulsive to the palate. We allowed the paste to dissolve slowly on our tongues, and sat some time, quietly waiting the result. But, having been taken upon a full stomach, its operation was hindered, and after the lapse of nearly an hour, we could not detect the least change in our feelings. My friends loudly expressed their conviction of the humbug of hasheesh, but I, unwilling to give up the experiment at this point, proposed that we should take an additional half spoonful, and follow it with a cup of hot tea, which, if there were really any virtue in the preparation, could not fail to call it into action. This was done, though not without some misgivings, as we were all ignorant of the precise quantity which constituted a dose, and the limits within which the drug could be taken with safety. It was now ten o'clock; the streets of Damascus were gradually becoming silent, and the fair city was bathed in the yellow lustre of the Syrian moon. Only in the marble court-yard below us, a few dragomen and *mukkairee* lingered under the lemon-trees, and beside the fountain in the centre.

I was seated alone, nearly in the middle of the room, talking with my friends, who were lounging upon a sofa placed in a sort of alcove, at the farther end, when the same fine nervous thrill, of which I have spoken, suddenly shot through me. But this time it was accompanied with a burning sensation at the pit of the stomach; and, instead of growing upon me with the gradual pace of healthy slumber, and resolving me, as before, into air, it came with the intensity of a pang, and shot throbbing along the nerves to the extremities of my body. The sense of limitation—of the confinement of our senses within the bounds of our own flesh and blood—instantly fell away. The walls of my frame were burst outward and tumbled into ruin; and, without thinking what form I wore—losing sight even of all idea of form—I felt that I existed throughout a vast extent of space. The blood, pulsed from my heart, sped through uncounted leagues before it reached my extremities; the air drawn into my lungs expanded into seas of limpid ether, and the arch of my skull was broader than the vault of heaven. Within the concave that held my brain, were the fathomless deeps of blue; clouds floated there, and the winds of heaven rolled them together, and there shone the orb of the sun. It was—though I thought not of that at the time—like a revelation of the mystery of omnipresence. It is difficult to describe this sensation, or the rapidity with which it mastered me. In the state of mental exaltation in which I was then plunged, all sensations, as they rose, suggested more or less coherent images. They presented themselves to me in a double form: one physical, and therefore to a certain extent tangible; the other spiritual, and revealing itself in a succession of splendid metaphors. The physical feeling of extended being was accompanied by the image of an exploding meteor, not subsiding into darkness, but continuing to shoot from its centre or nucleus—which corresponded to the burning spot at the pit of my stomach—incessant adumbrations of light that finally lost themselves in the infinity of space. To my mind, even now, this image is still the best illustration of my sensations, as I recall them; but I greatly doubt whether the reader will find it equally clear.

My curiosity was now in a way of being satisfied; the Spirit (demon, shall I not rather say?) of Hasheesh had entire possession of me. I was cast upon the flood of his illusions, and drifted helplessly whithersoever they might choose to bear me. The thrills which ran through my nervous system became more rapid and fierce, accompanied with sensations that steeped my whole being in unutterable rapture. I was encompassed by a sea of light, through which played the pure, harmonious colors that are born of light. While endeavoring, in broken expressions, to describe my feelings to my friends, who sat looking upon me incredulously—not yet having been affected by the drug—I suddenly found myself at the foot of the great Pyramid of Cheops. The tapering courses of yellow limestone gleamed like gold in the sun, and the pile rose so high that it seemed to lean for support upon the blue arch of the sky. I wished to ascend it, and the wish alone placed me immediately upon its apex, lifted thousands of feet above the wheat-fields and palm-groves of Egypt. I cast my eyes downward, and, to my astonishment, saw that it was built, not of limestone, but of huge square plugs of Cavendish tobacco! Words cannot paint the overwhelming sense of the ludicrous which I then experienced. I writhed on my chair in an agony of laughter, which was only relieved by the vision melting away like a dissolving view; till, out of my confusion of indistinct images and fragments of images, another and more wonderful vision arose.

The more vividly I recall the scene which followed, the more carefully I restore its different features, and separate the many threads of sensation which it wove into one gorgeous web, the more I despair of representing its exceeding glory. I was moving over the Desert, not upon the rocking dromedary, but seated in a barque made of mother-of-pearl, and studded with jewels of surpassing lustre. The sand was of grains of gold, and my keel slid through them without jar or sound. The air was radiant with excess of light, though no sun was to be seen. I inhaled the most delicious perfumes; and harmonies, such as Beethoven may have heard in dreams, but never wrote, floated around me. The atmosphere itself was light, odor, music; and each and all sublimated beyond anything the sober senses are capable of receiving. Before me—for a thousand leagues, as it seemed—stretched a vista of rainbows, whose colors gleamed with the splendor of gems—arches of living amethyst, sapphire, emerald, topaz, and ruby. By thousands and tens of thousands, they flew past me, as my dazzling barge sped down the magnificent arcade; yet the vista still stretched as far as ever before me. I revelled in a sensuous elysium, which was perfect, because no sense was left ungratified. But beyond all, my mind was filled with a boundless feeling of triumph. My journey was that of a conqueror—not of a conqueror who subdues his race, either by Love or by Will, for I forgot that Man existed—but one victorious over the grandest as well as the subtlest forces of Nature. The spirits of Light, Color, Odor, Sound, and Motion were my slaves; and, having these, I was master of the universe.

Those who are endowed to any extent with the imaginative faculty, must have at least once in their lives experienced feelings which may give them a clue to the exalted sensuous raptures of my triumphal march. The view of a sublime mountain landscape, the hearing of a grand orchestral symphony, or of a choral upborne by the "full-voiced organ," or even the beauty and luxury of a cloudless summer day, suggests emotions similar in kind, if less intense. They took a warmth and glow from that pure animal joy which degrades not, but spiritualizes and ennobles our material part, and which differs from cold, abstract, intellectual enjoyment, as the flaming diamond of the Orient differs from the icicle of the North. Those finer senses, which occupy a middle ground between our animal and intellectual appetites, were suddenly developed to a pitch beyond what I had ever dreamed, and being thus at one and the same time gratified to the fullest extent of their preternatural capacity, the result was a single harmonious sensation, to describe which human language has no epithet. Mahomet's Paradise, with its palaces of ruby and emerald, its airs of musk and cassia, and its rivers colder than snow and sweeter than honey, would have been a poor and mean terminus for my arcade of rainbows. Yet in the character of this paradise, in the gorgeous fancies of the Arabian Nights, in the glow and luxury of all Oriental poetry, I now recognize more or less of the agency of hasheesh.

The fullness of my rapture expanded the sense of time; and though the whole vision was probably not more than five minutes in passing through my mind, years seemed to have elapsed while I shot under the dazzling myriads of rainbow arches. By and by the rainbows, the barque of pearl and jewels, and the desert of golden sand, vanished; and, still bathed in light and perfume, I found myself in a land of green and flowery lawns, divided by hills of gently undulating outline. But, although the vegetation was the richest of earth, there were neither streams nor fountains to be seen; and the people who came from the hills, with brilliant garments that shone in the sun, besought me to give them the blessing of water. Their hands were full of branches of the coral honeysuckle, in bloom. These I took; and, breaking off the flowers one by one, set them in the earth. The slender, trumpet-like tubes immediately became shafts of masonry, and sank deep into the earth; the lip of the flower changed into a circular mouth of rose-colored marble, and the people, leaning over its brink, lowered their pitchers to the bottom with cords, and drew them up again, filled to the brim, and dripping with honey.

The most remarkable feature of these illusions was, that at the time when I was most completely under their influence, I knew myself to be seated in the tower of Antonio's hotel in Damascus, knew that I had taken hasheesh, and that the strange, gorgeous and ludicrous fancies which possessed me, were the effect of it. At the very same instant that I looked upon the Valley of the Nile from the pyramid, slid over the Desert, or created my marvellous wells in that beautiful pastoral country, I saw the furniture of my room, its mosaic pavement, the quaint Saracenic niches in the walls, the painted and gilded beams of the ceiling, and the couch in the recess before me, with my two companions watching me. Both sensations were simultaneous, and equally palpable. While I was most given up to the magnificent delusion, I saw its cause and felt its absurdity most clearly. Metaphysicians say that the mind is incapable of performing two operations at the same time, and may attempt to explain this phenomenon by supposing a rapid and incessant vibration of the perceptions between the two states. This explanation, however, is not satisfactory to me; for not more clearly does a skilful musician with the same breath blow two distinct musical notes from a bugle, than I was conscious of two distinct conditions of being in the same moment. Yet, singular as it may seem, neither conflicted with the other. My enjoyment of the visions was complete and absolute, undisturbed by the faintest doubt of their reality; while, in some other chamber of my brain, Reason sat coolly watching them, and heaping the liveliest ridicule on their fantastic features. One set of nerves was thrilled with the bliss of the gods, while another was convulsed with unquenchable laughter at that very bliss. My highest ecstacies could not bear down and silence the weight of my ridicule, which, in its turn, was powerless to prevent me from running into other and more gorgeous absurdities. I was double, not "swan and shadow," but rather, Sphinx-like, human and beast. A true Sphinx, I was a riddle and a mystery to myself.

The drug, which had been retarded in its operation on account of having been taken after a meal, now began to make itself more powerfully felt. The visions were more grotesque than ever, but less agreeable; and there was a painful tension throughout my nervous system—the effect of over-stimulus. I was a mass of transparent jelly, and a confectioner poured me into a twisted mould. I threw my chair aside, and writhed and tortured myself for some time to force my loose substance into the mould. At last, when I had so far succeeded that only one foot remained outside, it was lifted off, and another mould, of still more crooked and intricate shape, substituted. I have no doubt that the contortions through which I went, to accomplish the end of my gelatinous destiny, would have been extremely ludicrous to a spectator, but to me they were painful and disagreeable. The sober half of me went into fits of laughter over them, and through that laughter, my vision shifted into another scene. I had laughed until my eyes over-flowed profusely. Every drop that fell, immediately became a large loaf of bread, and tumbled upon the shop-board of a baker in the bazaar at Damascus. The more I laughed, the faster the loaves fell, until such a pile was raised about the baker, that I could hardly see the top of his head. "The man will be suffocated," I cried, "but if he were to die, I cannot stop!"

My perceptions now became more dim and confused. I felt that I was in the grasp of some giant force; and, in the glimmering of my fading reason, grew earnestly alarmed, for the terrible stress under which my frame labored increased every moment. A fierce and furious heat radiated from my stomach throughout my system; my mouth and throat were as dry and hard as if made of brass, and my tongue, it seemed to me, was a bar of rusty iron. I seized a pitcher of water, and drank long and deeply; but I might as well have drunk so much air, for not only did it impart no moisture, but my palate and throat gave me no intelligence of having drunk at all. I stood in the centre of the room, brandishing my arms convulsively, and heaving sighs that seemed to shatter my whole being. "Will no one," I cried in distress, "cast out this devil that has possession of me?" I no longer saw the room nor my friends, but I heard one of them saying, "It must be real; he could not counter-feit such an expression as that. But it don't look much like pleasure." Immediately afterwards there was a scream of the wildest laughter, and my countryman sprang upon the floor, exclaiming, "O, ye gods! I am a locomotive!" This was his ruling hallucination; and, for the space of two or three hours, he continued to pace to and fro with a measured stride, exhaling his breath in violent jets, and when he spoke, dividing his words into syllables, each of which he brought out with a jerk, at the same time turning his hands at his sides, as if they were the cranks of imaginary wheels. The Englishman, as soon as he felt the dose beginning to take effect, prudently retreated to his own room, and what the nature of his visions was, we never heard, for he refused to tell, and, moreover, enjoined the strictest silence on his wife.

By this time it was nearly midnight. I had passed through the
Paradise of Hasheesh, and was plunged at once into its fiercest
Hell. In my ignorance I had taken what, I have since learned,
would have been a sufficient portion for six men, and was now pay-
ing a frightful penalty for my curiosity. The excited blood rushed
through my frame with a sound like the roaring of mighty waters.
It was projected into my eyes until I could no longer see; it beat
thickly in my ears, and so throbbed in my heart, that I feared the
ribs would give way under its blows. I tore open my vest, placed
my hand over the spot, and tried to count the pulsations; but
there were two hearts, one beating at the rate of a thousand beats
a minute, and the other with a slow, dull motion. My throat, I
thought, was filled to the brim with blood, and streams of blood
were pouring from my ears. I felt them gushing warm down my
cheeks and neck. With a maddened, desperate feeling, I fled from
the room, and walked over the flat, terraced roof of the house.
My body seemed to shrink and grow rigid as I wrestled with the
demon, and my face to become wild, lean and haggard. Some
lines which had struck me, years before, in reading Mrs. Brown-
ing's "Rhyme of the Duchess May," flashed into my mind:—

"And the horse, in stark despair, with his front hoofs poised in air,
     On the last verge, rears amain;
And he hangs, he rocks between—and his nostrils curdle in—
And he shivers, head and hoof, and the flakes of foam fall off;
     And his face grows fierce and thin."

That picture of animal terror and agony was mine. I was the horse,
hanging poised on the verge of the giddy tower, the next moment
to be borne sheer down to destruction. Involuntarily, I raised my
hand to feel the leanness and sharpness of my face. Oh horror!
the flesh had fallen from my bones, and it was a skeleton head that
I carried on my shoulders! With one bound I sprang to the parapet,
and looked down into the silent courtyard, then filled with the
shadows thrown into it by the sinking moon. Shall I cast myself

down headlong? was the question I proposed to myself; but though the horror of that skeleton delusion was greater than my fear of death, there was an invisible hand at my breast which pushed me away from the brink.

I made my way back to the room, in a state of the keenest suffering. My companion was still a locomotive, rushing to and fro, and jerking out his syllables with the disjointed accent peculiar to a steam-engine. His mouth had turned to brass, like mine, and he raised the pitcher to his lips in the attempt to moisten it, but before he had taken a mouthful, set the pitcher down again with a yell of laughter, crying out: "How can I take water into my boiler, while I am letting off steam?"

But I was now too far gone to feel the absurdity of this, or his other exclamations. I was sinking deeper and deeper into a pit of unutterable agony and despair. For, although I was not conscious of real pain in any part of my body, the cruel tension to which my nerves had been subjected filled me through and through with a sensation of distress which was far more severe than pain itself. In addition to this, the remnant of will with which I struggled against the demon, became gradually weaker, and I felt that I should soon be powerless in his hands. Every effort to preserve my reason was accompanied by a pang of mortal fear, lest what I now experienced was insanity, and would hold mastery over me for ever. The thought of death, which also haunted me, was far less bitter than this dread. I knew that in the struggle which was going on in my frame, I was borne fearfully near the dark gulf, and the thought that, at such a time, both reason and will were leaving my brain, filled me with an agony, the depth and blackness of which I should vainly attempt to portray. I threw myself on my bed, with the excited blood still roaring wildly in my ears, my heart throbbing with a force that seemed to be rapidly wearing away my life, my throat dry as a potsherd, and my stiffened tongue cleaving to the roof of my mouth—resisting no longer, but awaiting my fate with the apathy of despair.

My companion was now approaching the same condition, but as the effect of the drug on him had been less violent, so his stage of suffering was more clamorous. He cried out to me that he was dying, implored me to help him, and reproached me vehemently, because I lay there silent, motionless, and apparently careless of his danger. "Why will he disturb me?" I thought; "he thinks he is dying, but what is death to madness? Let him die; a thousand deaths were more easily borne than the pangs I suffer." While I was sufficiently conscious to hear his exclamations, they only provoked my keen anger; but after a time, my senses became clouded, and I sank into a stupor. As near as I can judge, this must have been three o'clock in the morning, rather more than five hours after the hasheesh began to take effect. I lay thus all the following day and night, in a state of gray, blank oblivion, broken only by a single wandering gleam of consciousness. I recollect hearing François' voice. He told me afterwards that I arose, attempted to dress myself, drank two cups of coffee, and then fell back into the same death-like stupor; but of all this, I did not retain the least knowledge. On the morning of the second day, after a sleep of thirty hours, I awoke again to the world, with a system utterly prostrate and unstrung, and a brain clouded with the lingering images of my visions. I knew where I was, and what had happened to me, but all that I saw still remained unreal and shadowy. There was no taste in what I ate, no refreshment in what I drank, and it required a painful effort to comprehend what was said to me and return a coherent answer. Will and Reason had come back, but they still sat unsteadily upon their thrones.

My friend, who was much further advanced in his recovery, accompanied me to the adjoining bath, which I hoped would assist in restoring me. It was with great difficulty that I preserved the outward appearance of consciousness. In spite of myself, a veil now and then fell over my mind, and after wandering for years, as it seemed, in some distant world, I awoke with a shock, to find myself in the steamy halls of the bath, with a brown Syrian polishing my limbs. I suspect that my language must have been rambling and incoherent, and that the menials who had me in charge understood my condition, for as soon as I had stretched myself upon the couch which follows the bath, a glass of very acid sherbet was presented to me, and after drinking it I experienced instant relief. Still the spell was not wholly broken, and for two or three days I continued subject to frequent involuntary fits of absence, which made me insensible, for the time, to all that was passing around me. I walked the streets of Damascus with a strange consciousness that I was in some other place at the same time, and with a constant effort to reunite my divided perceptions.

Previous to the experiment, we had decided on making a bargain with the shekh for the journey to Palmyra. The state, however, in which we now found ourselves, obliged us to relinquish the plan. Perhaps the excitement of a forced march across the desert, and a conflict with the hostile Arabs, which was quite likely to happen, might have assisted us in throwing off the baneful effects of the drug; but all the charm which lay in the name of Palmyra and the romantic interest of the trip, was gone. I was without courage and without energy, and nothing remained for me but to leave Damascus.

Yet, fearful as my rash experiment proved to me, I did not regret having made it. It revealed to me deeps of rapture and of suffering which my natural faculties never could have sounded. It has taught me the majesty of human reason and of human will, even in the weakest, and the awful peril of tampering with that which assails their integrity. I have here faithfully and fully written out my experience, on account of the lesson which it may convey to others. If I have unfortunately failed in my design, and have but awakened that restless curiosity which I have endeavored to forestall, let me beg all who are thereby led to repeat the experiment upon themselves, that they be content to take the portion of hasheesh which is considered sufficient for one man, and not, like me, swallow enough for six.

"THE HASHEESH EATER" * (1856)

This anonymous story is a strange one indeed. There is nothing fictional or pretended about it, nothing of the Oriental fantasy so popular at the time. The narrator intends it as a solemn warning to others who might be led into the cannabis trap. The innocents of his acquaintance think it is wonderfully fascinating stuff, and are all for trying some as soon as it arrives in a box of presents from Turkey. (The United States Customs Service of the time would not have minded.) But Edward, the hero, has barely escaped with his life, he says, from a self-made hashish prison. He was one of those Westerners for whom the freedom of the Orient was disastrous: he had taken the drug in Damascus for "four or five years" on a daily basis, had finally caught a fever, and was saved almost at the last minute by an old school friend, who sent him back to Connecticut, where the action of his story takes place.

The anxieties of persecution, the overwhelming guilt that Edward feels remind us a little of Ludlow toward the end of his story.† It is amazing how strong the feeling was against a drug that

---

* Anonymous, "The Hasheesh Eater," *Putnam's Monthly Magazine* 8 (Sept. 1856): 233–239.
† See *The Hasheesh Eater* by Fitz Hugh Ludlow, p. 172.

had only very recently been heard of in the New World. These American pioneers were breaking a strong taboo, rooted in the American Protestant ethic of self-denial, against all forms of intoxication. Indeed, Edward cannot even obtain forgiveness for his sins from "the human and crucified Jesus of Nazareth," who in one of his paranoid visions condemns him to eternal suffering.

The pain of rejection ends with these visions, and the destruction of the hashish, the source of his renewed trouble, finally calms Edward's mind. This intense little story, with its themes of restraint and guilt, certainly had an appeal to a great number of Americans, an appeal probably no less strong today than it was a century ago.

It was at Damascus that I took my first dose of hasheesh, and laid the foundations of that habit which, through the earlier years of my manhood, imprisoned me like an enchanted palace. It was surely a worthy spot on which to build up such an edifice of hallucinations as I did there erect and cement around my soul by the daily use of this weed of insanity. Certainly no other spot could be so worthy, unless it were Bagdad, the marvelous city of the marvelous Sultan, Haroun al Rashid. I need not tell the reasons: every one can imagine them; every one, at least, who knows what Damascus is; much more every one who has been there. It was among shadowy gardens, filled with oriental loungers, and in Saracenic houses, gay as kaleidoscopes with gilding and bright tintings, that I made myself the slave of the hasheesh. It was surrounded by objects so suitable for dream-work, that, by the aid of this wizard of plants, I fabricated that palace of alternating pleasure and torture which was for years my abiding place. In this palace I sometimes reveled with a joy so immense that I may well call it multitudinous; or I ran and shrieked it through its changeful spaces with an agony which the pen of a demon could not describe suitably; surrounded, chased, overclouded by all the phantasms of mythology or the Arabian Nights; by every strange, ludicrous, or horrible shape that ever stole into my fancy, from books of romance or tales of spectredom.

It is useless to think of relating, or even mentioning, the visions which, during four or five years passed through my drugged brain. A library would not suffice to describe them all: many, also, were indistinct in their first impressions, and others have so mingled together with time, that I cannot now trace their individual outlines. As the habit grew upon me, too, my memory gradually failed, and a stupor crept over me which dulled the edges of all events, whether dreams or realities. A dull confusion surrounded me at all times, and I dropped down its hateful current, stupid, indifferent, unobserving, and never thoroughly awake except when a fresh dose of the plant stimulated my mind into a brief consciousness of itself and its surroundings. The habit and its consequences naturally deepened my morbid unsociability of temper, and sunk me still more fixedly in the hermit-like existence which I had chosen. For some years I made no acquaintance with the many European travelers who pass through Syria; and I even, at last, got to avoid the presence of my listless oriental companions—keeping up no intimacy except with those who, like myself, daily wandered through the saharas and oases of hasheesh dreamland. Never before did I so completely give myself up to my besetting sin; for a sin I now consider it to cast off one's moorings to humanity; to fly from one's fellow-beings and despise, at once, their good will and their censure.

A terrible fever at last came to my relief and saved me by dragging me, as it were, through the waters of death. While the sickness continued, I could not take the hasheesh; and when I recovered, I had so far gained my self-control, that I resolved to fling the habit aside forever. I am ashamed to confess that it was partly the urgings of an old friend which supported me to this pitch of real heroism. He was a young physician from my own city, and we had been companions and often room-mates through school and college, although it was by the merest accident that he met me in Beirut a few days before my seizure. Two months he watched by me, and then perfected his work by getting me on board the steamer for Marseilles, and starting me well homeward. I shall have to speak of him again; but I cannot give his name, further than to call him Doctor Harry, the pet title by which he was known in his own family.

I reached Marseilles, hurried through France, without passing more than a night even at Paris, and sailed for New York in a Havre steamer. In less than a month after I stepped from the broken columns which lie about the landing place of Beirut, I was strolling under the elms of my native city in Connecticut. The spell was broken by this time, and its shackles fallen altogether both from mind and body. I felt no longing after the hasheesh; and the dreary languor which once seemed to demand its restorative energy had disappeared; for my constitution was vigorous, and I was still several years under thirty. But such chains as I had worn, could not be carried so long without leaving some scars behind them. The old despotism asserted itself yet in horrible dreams, or in painful reveries which were almost as vivid, and as difficult to break as dreams. These temporary illusions generally made use of two subjects, as the scaffolds on which to erect their troublesome cloud-castles: first, the scenery and personages of my old hasheesh visions; second, the incidents of my journey homeward. I was not at all surprised to find myself haunted by sultans, Moors, elephants, afreets, rocs, and other monstrosities of the Arabian Nights; but it did seem unreasonable that I should be plagued, in the least degree, by the reminiscences of that wholesome, and, on the whole, pleasant flight from the land of my captivity. The rapidity and picturesqueness of the transit had impressed themselves on my imagination; and I now journeyed in spirit, night after night, and sometimes day after day, without rest and without goal; hurried on by an endless succession of steamers, diligences and railroad trains, all driven at their utmost speed; beholding oceans of foam, immeasurable snow mountains, cities of many leagues in extents and population, whose multitudes obstructed my passage. But these illusions, whether sleeping or waking, were faint and mild compared with my old hasheesh paroxysms, and they grew rapidly weaker as time passed onward. The only thing which seriously and persistently annoyed me was an idea that my mind was slightly shaken. I vexed myself with minute self-examinations on this point, and actually consulted a physician as to whether some of my mental processes did not indicate incipient insanity. He replied in the best manner possible: he laughed at me, and forbade my pursuing those speculations.

All this time I amused myself in society, and even worked pretty faithfully at my legal profession. I shall say nothing of my cases, however, for, like most young lawyers, I had very few of them; all the fewer, doubtless, because long residence abroad had put me back in my studies. But I must speak at some length of my socialities, inasmuch as they soon flung very deep roots into my heart, and mingled themselves there with the poisonous decay of my former habit.

The first family whose acquaintance I renewed, on reaching home, was that of my dear friend, Doctor Harry. His father, the white-headed old doctor, and his dignified, kindly mother, greeted me with a heartiness that was like enthusiasm. I had been a schoolfellow of their absent son; and more than that I had very lately seen him; and more still, I spoke of him with warm praise and gratitude. They treated me with as much affection as if it were I who had saved Harry's life, and not Harry who had saved mine. A reception equally cordial was granted me by the doctor's two daughters: Ellen and Ida. Ellen, whom I knew well, was twenty-three years old, and engaged to be married. She was the same lively, nervous, sentimental thing as of old; wore the same long black ringlets, and tossed her head in the same flighty style. Ida, four years younger than her sister, was almost a stranger to me; for she was a mere child when I first became a beau, and had been transferred from the nursery to the boarding-school without attracting my student observation. She was quite a novelty, therefore, a most attractive novelty also—the prettiest, unobtrusive style of woman that ever made an unsought conquest. *I* was the conquest, not the only conquest that she ever made, indeed; but the only one that she ever deigned to accept. I could not resist the mild blue eyes, the sunny brown hair, the sweet blonde face, and the dear little coral mouth. She had the dearest little expression in her mouth when she was moved; a pleading, piteous expression that seemed to beg and entreat without a spoken word; an expression that was really infantine, not in silliness, but in an unutterable pathetic innocence. Well, she quite enslaved me, so that in three months I was more her captive than I had ever been to the hasheesh, even in the time of my deepest enthrallment.

I would not, however, offer myself to her until I had written to Doctor Harry, and asked him if he could permit his little sister to become the wife of the hasheesh eater. His reply was not kinder than I expected, but it was more cordial, and fuller of confidence. He knew little, in comparison with myself, of the strength of that old habit; nothing at all of the energy with which it can return upon one of its escaped victims. He was sure that I had broken its bonds; sure that I never would be exposed to its snares again; sure that I would resist the temptation, were it to come ever so powerful. Yes, he was quite willing that I should marry Ida; he would rejoice to meet me at his home as his brother. I might, if I chose, tell my history to his father, and leave the matter to him: but that was all that honor could demand of me, and even that was not sternly necessary.

I did as Harry directed, and related to the old physician all my dealings with the demon of hasheesh. Like a true doctor, he was immensely interested in the symptoms, and plunged into specula-tions as to whether the diabolical plant could not be introduced with advantage into the materia medica. No astonishment at my rashness; no horror at my danger; no grave disapproval of my weak wickedness; no particular rejoicing at what I considered my wonderful escape. And when, a few days after, I asked him if he could surrender his child to such a man as I, he laughed heartily, and shook both my hands with an air of the warmest encouragement. I felt guilty at that moment, as well as happy; for it seemed as if I were imposing upon an unsuspecting ignorance, which could not and would not be enlightened. Nor did Ida say *no* any more than the others, although she made up a piteous little face when I took her hand, and looked as if she thought I had no right to ask her for so much as her whole self. So I was engaged to Ida, and was happier than all the hasheesh eaters from Cairo to Stamboul.

It was about a month after our engagement, and two months before the time fixed for our marriage, that a box reached us from Smyrna. It contained a quantity of Turkish silks, and other presents from Harry to his sisters, besides the usual variety of nargeelehs, chibouks, tarbooshes, scimitars, and so forth, such as young travelers usually pick up in the East. The doctor and I opened the packages, while Ellen, Ida, and their mother skipped about in delight from wonder to wonder. Among the last things came a small wooden box, which Ellen eagerly seized upon, declaring that it contained attar of roses. She tore off the cover, and displayed to my eyes a mass of that well-remembered drug, the terrible hasheesh. "What is it?" she exclaimed, "Is this attar of roses? No it isn't. What is it, Edward? Here, you ought to know."

"It is hasheesh," I said, looking at it as if I saw an afreet or a ghoul.

"Well, what is hasheesh? Is it good to eat? Why, what are you staring at it so for? Do you want some? Here, eat a piece. I will if you will."

"Bless me!" exclaimed the doctor, dropping a Persian dagger and coming hastily forward. "Is that the real hasheesh? Bless me, so that is hasheesh, is it? Dear me, I must have a specimen. What is the ordinary dose for an adult, Edward?"

I took out a bit as large as a hazelnut, and held it up before his eyes. He received it reverently from my hands, and surveyed it with a prodigious scientific interest. "Wife," said he, "Ellen, Ida, this is hasheesh. This is an ordinary dose for an adult."

"Well, what is hasheesh?" repeated Ellen, tossing her ringlets as a colt does his mane. "Father! what is it? Did you ever take any, Edward?"

"Yes," mumbled the doctor, examining the lump with microscopic minuteness; "Edward is perfectly acquainted with the nature of the drug; he has made some very interesting experiments with it."

"Oh, take some, Edward," cried Ellen. "Come, that's a good fellow. Here, take this other bit. Let's take a dose all round."

"No, no," said Ida, catching her sister's hand. "Why, you imprudent child! Better learn a little about it before you make its acquaintance. Tell us, Edward, what does it do to people?"

I told them in part what it had done to me; that is, I told them what mighty dreams and illusions it had wrapped around me; but I could not bring myself to narrate before Ida how shamefully I had been its slave. When I had finished my story, Ellen broke forth again: "Oh, Edward, take a piece, I beg of you. I want to see you crazy once. Come, you are sane enough in a general way; and we should all enjoy it so to see you make a fool of yourself for an hour or two."

She put the morsel to my lips and held it there until Ida pushed her hand away, almost indignantly. I looked at my little girl, and, although she said nothing, I saw on her mouth that piteous, pleading expression which appeared to me enough to move angels or demons. It moved me, but not sufficiently; the smell of the hasheesh seemed to sink into my brain; the thought of the old visions came up like a wave of intoxication. Still I refused; two or three times that afternoon I refused; but in the evening, Ellen handed me the drug again. "It is the last time," I said to myself; and taking it from her hand I began to prepare it. The doctor stood by, nervous with curiosity, and urged caution; nothing more than caution; that was the whole of his warning. Ida looked at me in her imploring way, but said nothing; for she only suspected, and did not at all comprehend the danger.

I swallowed the drug while they all stood silent around me; and I laughed loudly, with a feeling of crazed triumph, as I perceived the well-remembered savor. My little girl caught my sleeve with a look of extremest terror; the doctor quite as eagerly seized my pulse and drew out his repeater. "Oh, what fun!" said Ellen. "Do you see any thing now, Edward?"

Of course I saw nothing as yet; for, be it known, that the effect of the hasheesh is not immediate; half an hour or even an hour must elapse before the mind can fully feel its influence. I told them so, and I went on talking in my ordinary style until they thought that I had been jesting with them, and had taken nothing. But forty minutes had not passed before I began to feel the usual symptoms, the sudden nervous thrill, followed by the whirl and prodigious apparent enlargement of the brain. My head expanded wider and wider, revolving with inconceivable rapidity, and enlarging in space with every revolution. It filled the room—the house —the city; it became a world, peopled with the shapes of men and monsters. I spun away into its great vortex, and wandered about its expanses as about a universe. I lost all perception of time and space, and knew no distinction between the realities around me, and the phantasmata which sprung in endless succession from my brain. Ida and the others occasionally spoke to me; and once I thought that they kneeled around and worshiped me; while I, from behind a marble altar, responded like a Jupiter. Then night descended, and I heard a voice saying: "Christ is come, and thou art no more a divinity."

The altar disappeared at that instant, and I came back to this present century, and to my proper human form. I was in the doctor's house, standing by a window, and gazing out upon a moonlit street filled with promenading citizens. Beside me was a sofa upon which Ida lay and slept, with her head thrown back, and her throat bared to the faint silvery brilliance which stole through the gauze curtains. I stooped and kissed it passionately; for I had never before seen her asleep, nor so beautiful; and I loved her as dearly in that moment as I had ever done when in full possession of my sanity. As I raised my head, her father opened a door and looked into the room. He started forward when he saw me; then he drew back, and I heard him whisper to himself: "She is safe enough, he will not hurt her."

The moment he closed the door a window opened, and a voice muttered: "Kill her, kill her, and the altar and the adoration shall be yours again;" to which innumerable voices from the floor, and the ceiling and the four walls responded: "Glory, glory in the highest to him who can put himself above man, and to him who fears not the censure of man!"

I drew a knife from my pocket, and opened it instantly; for a mighty persuasion was wrought in me by those promises. "I will kill her," I said to myself, "dearly as I love her; for the gift of Divinity outweighs the love of woman or the wrath of man."

I bent over her and placed the knife to her throat without the least pity or hesitation, so completely had all love, all nobleness, all humanity, been extingushed in me by the abominable demon of hasheesh. But suddenly she awoke, and fixed on me that sweet, piteous, startled look which was so characteristic of her. It made me forget my purpose for one moment, so that, with a lunatic inconsistency, I bent my head and kissed her hand as gently as I had ever done. Then the demoniac whisper, as if to recall my wandering resolution, swept again through the eglantines of the window: "Kill her, kill her, and the altar and the adoration shall be yours again."

She did not seem to hear it; for she stretched out her hands to give me a playful push backwards, while, closing her eyes again, she sank back to renewed slumber. Then, in the height of my drugged insanity, in the cold fury of my possession, I struck the sharp slender blade into her white throat once, and once more, with quick repetition, into her heart. "Oh, Edward, you have killed me!" she said, and seemed to die with a low moan, not once stirring from her position on the sofa.

I took no further notice of her; I did not see her in fact after the blow; for the smoke of sacrifices rose around me, obscuring the room; and once more I stood in divine elevation above a marble altar. There were giant colonnades on either side, sweeping forward to a monstrous portal, through which I beheld countless sphinxes facing each other adown an interminable avenue of granite. Before me, in the mighty space between the columns, was a multitude of men, all bowing with their faces to the earth, while priests chanted anthems to my praise as the great Osiris. But suddenly, before I could shake the temple with my nod, I saw one in the image of Christ enter the portal and advance through the crowd to the foot of my altar. It was not Christ the risen and glorified; but the human and crucified Jesus of Nazareth. I knew him by his grave sweetness of countenance; I knew him still better by his wounded hands and bloody vestments. He beckoned me to descend and kneel before him; and when I would have called on my worshipers for aid, I found that they had all vanished; so that I was forced to come down and fall at his pierced feet in helpless condemnation. Then he passed judgment upon me, saying: "Forasmuch as thou hast sought to put thyself above man, all men shall abhor and shun thee."

He disappeared, and when I rose the temple had disappeared also, with every trace of that mighty worship by which I had been for a moment surrounded. Then did my punishment commence; nor did it cease throughout a seeming eternity; for, in order to complete it, time was reversed, and I could live in bygone ages; so that I ran through the whole history of the world, and was avoided with loathing by every generation. First I stood near the garden of Eden, and saw a hideous man hurrying by it, alone, with a bloody mark on his forehead. "This is Cain," I said to myself; "this is a wicked murderer, also, and he will be my comrade."

I ran toward him confidently, eagerly, and with an intense long-

ing for companionship; but when he saw me he covered his face
and fled away from me, with incomparable swiftness, shrieking:
"Save me, O God, from this abominable wretch!"

After that, I hastened wildly over earth, across many countries,
and through many successive ages, alone always, avoided always,
an object of fear, of horror, of incredible detestation. Every one
that saw me, knew me, and fled from my presence, even to certain
death, if that were necessary, to evade my contact. I saw men of
Gomorrah rush back into the flames of their perishing city, when
they beheld me coming humbly to meet them. Egyptians, who had
barely escaped from the Red Sea, leaped again into the foaming
waters as I ran toward them along the shore. Everywhere that I
went, populations, even of mighty cities, scattered from my track,
like locusts rising in hurried flight before the feet of a camel. The
loneliest shipwrecked sailor, on the most savage island of the sea,
fled from his hut of reeds, and plunged into untracked and serpent-
haunted marshes at the sight of my supplicating visage. Unable to
obtain the companionship of men, I at last sought that of wild
beasts and reptiles—of the gods of ancient mythology, and the
monsters of fairydom; but, all to no purpose. The crocodiles buried
themselves in the midcurrent of the Nile, as I stealthily approached
its banks. I unavailingly chased the terrified speed of tigers and
anacondas through the stifling heat of the jungles of Bengal. Mem-
non arose from his throne, and hid himself in the clouds, when
he saw me kneeling at his granite feet. I followed in vain the
sublime flight of Odin over the polar snows and ice-islands of both
hemispheres. Satyrs hid from me; dragons and gorgons avoided me.
The very ants and insects disappeared from my presence, taking
refuge in dead trunks, and in the bowels of the earth. My punishment was constant and fearful—it was greater than I could bear;
yet, I bore it for ages. I tried in many ways to escape from it by
death; but always unsuccessfully. I sought to fling myself down
precipices, but an unseen power drew me back; I endeavored to
drown myself in the sea, but the billows upheld me, like a feather.

It was not remorse that prompted me to these attempts at self-destruction. Remorse, penitence, and every other noble emotion had been swallowed up in mere anguish under the dreadfulness of my punishment. Sometimes I could not believe that all this was a reality, and struggled with wild, but useless ragings to break the dreadful presence of horror. At other times I felt convinced of its perfect truth; because I saw that the punishment was exactly suited to the offense, and that it reproved, with astonishing directness, that unsocial and almost misanthropic spirit which I had so long encouraged by my habits of life and temper of thought. Thus, dragging about with me a ghastly immortality, I wandered through miserable year after year, through desolation after desolation, until I stood once more on the deck of the steamer to Marseilles. Now I again performed my journey homeward, passing, as before, through a succession of steamers, railroads, and diligences. But the steamers were empty; for the passengers and sailors leaped overboard at my appearance; and the vessel reeled on unguided, through wild, lonely seas that I knew not. Just in the same manner, every one fled before me from the rail-cars; and, through deserted plains and valleys, I arrived, at headlong speed, in great cities, as the only passenger. My diligence journeys were performed without companion, or conductor, or postillion, in shattering vehicles, drawn by horses which flew in the very lunacy of fright. Paris was a solitude when I entered it—without man, and without inhabitant, and without beast—silence in its streets, in its galleries, and in its palaces—the sentinels all fled from the gates, and the children from the gardens.

At last I arrived at the entrance of my native city; and now I hoped that in presence of this familiar spot my vision would break; but it did not, and so I paused in a most miserable stupor of despair. It was early dawn, and the sky was yet gray; nor had many people arisen from their sleep. I heard dogs barking in the streets, and birds singing in the orchards; but, as always, neither the one race nor the other ventured near the spot where I stood. I sat down behind a thicket, where I could see the road, but could not be seen from it, and wept for an hour over my terrible misery. It was the first time that tears had come to soften my terrible punishment; for, hitherto my anguish had been desperate and sullen, or wild and blasphemous; but now I wept easily, with some feeling of tender penitence, and speechless supplication. I looked wistfully down the street, longing to enter the town, yet dreading to see the universal terror which I knew would spread through the inhabitants at the moment I stepped in among them.

At last persons began to pass me; chiefly, I believe, workmen, or market people; but among them were some whose faces I had seen before. I cannot describe the thrill of tremulous, fearful, painful pleasure with which I looked from so near upon these familiar human countenances. How I longed, yet dreaded, to have one of them turn his eyes upon me. At last I said to myself: "These people know of my crime; perhaps they will not fly from me, and will only kill me."

I stepped out suddenly in front of a couple of ruddy countrymen, who were driving a market-cart from the city, and fell on my knees, with my hands uplifted toward their faces. For a moment they stared at me in ghastly horror, then, wheeling their rearing horse, they lashed him into violent flight. I rose in desperation, in fury, and with the steps of a greyhound, leaped after them through streets now resonant with human footsteps. Oh, the wild terror! oh, the agonized shrieking! oh, the wide confusion! and oh, the swift vanishing of all life which marked my passage! I hastened on, panting, stamping, screaming, foaming in the uttermost extremity of despair and anguish, until I reached the house where my darling had once lived. As I neared the steps, I saw a person whom I knew to be Harry. He did not shriek and fly at my approach, but met me and looked me steadily in the face. His eyes, at first, were full of inquiry; but, in a moment, he seemed to gather the whole truth from my visage; and then, with a terrible tremor of abhorrence, he drew a pistol from his bosom. "It is right, Harry," I said; "kill me, as I killed her."

But with a quick motion which I could not arrest, he placed the muzzle to his own temples, drew the trigger, and fell a disfigured corpse at my feet. I howled as if I were a wild beast, and sprang over him into the door-way. I saw Ellen and her father and mother flying with uplifted hands out of the other end of the passage. I did not follow them, but turned into the parlor where I had committed my crime; and there, to my amazement, I saw Ida lying on the sofa in the same position in which I had left her; her head fallen backward, her eyes closed, her throat hidden by her long hair, and her hands clasped upon her bosom. On the floor lay my knife still open, just as it had fallen. I picked it up and passed my finger over the keen edge of the blade muttering: "Now, I know that all this is real; now I can kill myself, for this is the time and the place to die."

Just as I was placing the knife to my throat, I saw a sweet smile stealing over Ida's lips. She has become a seraph, I thought, and is smiling to see the eternal glory. But, suddenly, as I looked at her for this last time, she opened her eyes on me, and over her mouth stole that sweet pleading expression which was the outward sign of her gentle spirit. "Stop, Edward!" she cried, earnestly; and springing up, she caught my hand firmly, although I could feel that her own trembled. In that moment, my horrible dream began to fade from me, and I gazed around no longer utterly blinded by the hazes of the hasheesh demon. She was not harmed, then! No, and I was not her murderer; no, and I had not been the loathing of mankind. Nothing of the whole scene had been real, except her slumber on the sofa, and the knife which I held in my hand. I flung it fiercely from me; for I thought of what I might have done with it had my madness been only a little more persistent and positive. Then, struck by a sudden thought, half suspicion and half comprehension, I ran to the front door-way. Harry was not, indeed, lying there in his blood; but he was there, nevertheless, upright and in full health; and we exchanged a delighted greeting before the rest of the family could reach him.

"Why, Harry," said the doctor, in the parlor again, "that was a most interesting substance you sent us—that hasheesh. I have made an extraordinary experiment with it upon Edward here. He muttered wonders for an hour or two in my study. He then went to sleep, and I missed him about two minutes ago. I really had no idea that he had come to."

That closing dream of crime and punishment, then, had passed through my brain in less than two minutes; and I had been standing by the sleeping form of my little girl all the time that I seemed to be wandering through that eternity of horror.

"What!" said Harry, "has Edward gone back to the hasheesh again?"

"Yes," I replied; "but I have taken my last dose, my dear fellow. With your permission, Doctor, I will pitch that infernal drug into the fire."

"Really," said the doctor, "I—I—don't know. I should like to reserve a few doses for experiments."

"Oh! don't throw it away," urged Ellen. "It is *such* fun. Edward has been saying *such* queer things."

"Where is it?" asked Harry resolutely. "I will settle that question."

"It is in the fire, brother," replied Ida. "I threw it there half an hour ago."

I raised the little girl's hand to my lips and kissed it; and since then I have taken no other hasheesh than such as that.

FITZ HUGH LUDLOW, THE HASHEESH EATER (1857)

The author of this remarkable book * calls himself a Pythagorean, by which he means two things at least: first, his belief that hashish enables the soul to move in and out of the body, and second, that he professes a true but unacceptable doctrine that makes him feel, like the early followers of Pythagoras, scorned and abused. Ludlow firmly believed that eating hashish was good for his mind and soul, and that any consequent bodily deterioration or derangement were well worth enduring. Nothing else he did in his thirty-four-year existence (1836–1870) attracted nearly so much attention as The Hasheesh Eater, *which he wrote at nineteen and published two years later. The book was a great curiosity and success in 1857, going through four printings that year in both the United States and Britain. America in the mid-1850s was experiencing a literary flourishing never seen before and hardly since. Much was published that strict Christians did not consider edifying, Ludlow's book included.*

That a young man, the son of a clergyman, should take a fancy

---

* Anonymous, *The Hasheesh Eater, Being Passages from the Life of a Pythagorean* (New York, Harper and Brothers, 1857), pp. 15–60, 65–75, 146–153, 169–172, 227–232, 269–284, 368–371.

to hallucination-producing substances was not at all inconceivable in the America of the 1850s, though writing about them did cause eyebrows to be raised. Along with laudanum, cannabis preparations had been freely available from apothecaries in America for decades, generally in the form of tinctures of varying strengths and qualities. In the 1840s the alcohol-based Robinson's Life Extract began to be manufactured. It was very strong, of reliable quality, and dominated the market for many years. Opium addicts were not unheard of in early America, but there is no record before Taylor (see p. 141) and Ludlow of Americans taking cannabis for its mind-altering qualities. In the greater freedom of manners prevailing then in America, anyone had the right to purchase drugs, and that included the right to experiment with them, yet the anonymity of The Hasheesh Eater testifies to Ludlow's strong feeling that his daily habit outraged propriety. Though he is rarely unwilling to discuss his favorite drug with friends and relatives, guilt is apparent everywhere in the book. It may be merely the result of Ludlow's paranoia, or really engendered by his society's strictures against any form of intoxication, or both, but it contrasts strongly with the nonchalant, sybaritic indulgence of the hashish eaters of Paris. That city, as described by Gautier (see p. 86), is as full of genies as an enchanted Arabian palace; Ludlow's Poughkeepsie is always just a small American town, where neighbors might peek from behind the curtains at Reverend Ludlow's self-conscious son passing by.

Ludlow owed a great and obvious debt to Thomas De Quincey, whose Confessions of an English Opium Eater had been world-famous since its appearance in 1821–1822. The Hasheesh Eater does not parody the earlier work, but is rather a faithful imitation, at an awed distance, of De Quincey's "dream-pictures" and "impassioned prose." Ludlow parades his learning far more than De Quincey, is quite his equal in self-involvement, but cannot match the Englishman's authoritative tone, depth of introspection, and clarity of description. Hashish works on Ludlow in much the same way opium affected De Quincey: at first a passport to exotic lands, it then be-

comes a trap, a horror, and finally a powerful instrument for self-knowledge. One can sense in both writers their disheartened awareness that the stoic societies they address can never approve what they describe, and both crave acceptance as well as vindication. Despite his heavily rhetorical style, Ludlow's hashish experiments, reported with such dread earnestness, were a great leap into unknown territory. His courage still seems palpable more than a century later.

At the beginning of his story, the narrator is about to call on a friend, a doctor who has been a regular source of stimulants for him.

THE NIGHT ENTRANCE

About the shop of my friend Anderson the apothecary there always existed a peculiar fascination, which early marked it out as my favorite lounging-place. In the very atmosphere of the establishment, loaded as it was with a composite smell of all things curative and preventive, there was an aromatic invitation to scientific musing, which could not have met with a readier acceptance had it spoken in the breath of frankincense. The very gallipots grew gradually to possess a charm for me as they sat calmly ranged upon their oaken shelves, looking like a convention of unostentatious philanthropists, whose silent bosoms teemed with every variety of renovation for the human race. A little sanctum at the inner end of the shop, walled off with red curtains from the profane gaze of the unsanative, contained two chairs for the doctor and myself, and a library where all the masters of physic were grouped, through their sheep and paper representatives, in more friendliness of contact than has ever been known to characterize a consultation of like spirits under any other circumstances. Within the limits of four square feet, Pereira and Christison condensed all their stores of wisdom and research, and Dunglison and Brathwaite sat cheek by jowl beside them. There stood the Dispensatory, with the air of a business-like office, wherein all the specifics of the materia medica had been brought together for a scientific conversazione, but, becoming enamored of each other's society, had resolved to stay, overcrowded though they might be, and make an indefinite sitting of it. In a modest niche, set apart like a vestibule from the apartments of the medical gentlemen, lay a shallow case, which disclosed, on the lifting of a cover, the neatly-ordered rank of tweezers, probe, and lancet, which constituted my friend's claim to the confidence of the plethoric community; for, although unblessed with metropolitan fame, he was still no "Cromwell guiltless of his country's blood." *

Here many an hour have I sat buried in the statistics of human life or the history of the make-shifts for its preservation. Here the details of surgical or medical experiment have held me in as complete engrossment as the positions and crises of romance; and here especially, with a disregard to my own safety which would have done credit to Quintus Curtius,† have I made upon myself the trial of the effects of every strange drug and chemical which the laboratory could produce. Now with the chloroform bottle beneath my nose have I set myself careering upon the wings of a thrilling and accelerating life, until I had just enough power remaining to restore the liquid to its place upon the shelf, and sink back into the enjoyment of the delicious apathy which lasted through the few succeeding moments. Now ether was substituted for chloroform, and the difference of their phenomena noted, and now some other exhilarant, in the form of an opiate or stimulant, was the instrument of my experiments, until I had run through the whole gamut of queer agents within my reach.

In all these experiences research and not indulgence was my object, so that I never became the victim of any habit in the prosecution of my headlong investigations. When the circuit of all the accessible tests was completed, I ceased experimenting, and

* Thomas Gray, "Elegy Written in a Country Church-Yard," l. 60.
† Quintus Curtius Rufus was a first-century biographer of Alexander the Great, but was not known for impetuosity.

sat down like a pharmaceutical Alexander, with no more drug-worlds to conquer.

One morning, in the spring of 185-, I dropped in upon the doctor for my accustomed lounge.

"Have you seen," said he, "my new acquisitions?"

I looked toward the shelves in the direction of which he pointed, and saw, added since my last visit, a row of comely pasteboard cylinders inclosing vials of the various extracts prepared by Tilden & Co. Arranged in order according to their size, they confronted me, as pretty a little rank of medicinal sharp-shooters as could gratify the eye of an amateur. I approached the shelves, that I might take them in review.

A rapid glance showed most of them to be old acquaintances. "Conium, taraxacum, rhubarb—ha! what is this? Cannabis Indica?" "That," answered the doctor, looking with a parental fondness upon his new treasure, "is a preparation of the East Indian hemp, a powerful agent in cases of lock-jaw." On the strength of this intro-duction, I took down the little archer, and, removing his outer verdant coat, began the further prosecution of his acquaintance. To pull out a broad and shallow cork was the work of an instant, and it revealed to me an olive-brown extract, of the consistency of pitch, and a decided aromatic odor. Drawing out a small portion upon the point of my penknife, I was just going to put it to my tongue, when "Hold on!" cried the doctor; "do you want to kill yourself? That stuff is deadly poison." "Indeed!" I replied; "no, I can not say that I have any settled determination of that kind"; and with that I replaced the cork, and restored the extract, with all its appurtenances, to the shelf.

The remainder of my morning's visit in the sanctum was spent in consulting the Dispensatory under the title "Cannabis Indica." The sum of my discoveries there may be found, with much addi-tional information, in that invaluable popular work, Johnston's Chemistry of Common Life. This being universally accessible, I will allude no further to the result of that morning's researches than to mention the three following conclusions to which I came. First, the doctor was both right and wrong; right, inasmuch as a sufficiently large dose of the drug, if it could be retained in the stomach, would produce death, like any other narcotic, and the ultimate effect of its habitual use had always proved highly injurious to mind and body; wrong, since moderate doses of it were never immediately deadly, and many millions of people daily employed it as an indulgence similarly to opium. Second, it was the hasheesh referred to by Eastern travelers, and the subject of a most graphic chapter from the pen of Bayard Taylor, which months before had moved me powerfully to curiosity and admiration. Third, I would add it to the list of my former experiments.

In pursuance of this last determination, I waited till my friend was out of sight, that I might not terrify him by that which he considered a suicidal venture, and then quietly uncapping my little archer a second time, removed from his store of offensive armor a pill sufficient to balance the ten grain weight of the sanctorial scales. This, upon the authority of Pereira and the Dispensatory, I swallowed without a tremor as to the danger of the result.

Making all due allowance for the fact that I had not taken my hasheesh bolus fasting, I ought to experience its effects within the next four hours. That time elapsed without bringing the shadow of a phenomenon. It was plain that my dose had been insufficient.

For the sake of observing the most conservative prudence, I suffered several days to go by without a repetition of the experiment, and then, keeping the matter equally secret, I administered to myself a pill of fifteen grains. This second was equally ineffectual with the first.

Gradually, by five grains at a time, I increased the dose to thirty grains, which I took one evening half an hour after tea. I had now almost come to the conclusion that I was absolutely unsusceptible of the hasheesh influence. Without any expectation that this last experiment would be more successful than the former ones, and indeed with no realization of the manner in which the drug affected those who did make the experiment successfully, I went to pass the evening at the house of an intimate friend. In music and conversation the time passed pleasantly. The clock struck ten, reminding me that three hours had elapsed since the dose was taken, and as yet not an unusual symptom had appeared. I was provoked to think that this trial was as fruitless as its predecessors.

Ha! what means this sudden thrill? A shock, as of some unimagined vital force, shoots without warning through my entire frame, leaping to my fingers' ends, piercing my brain, startling me till I almost spring from my chair.

I could not doubt it. I was in the power of the hasheesh influence. My first emotion was one of uncontrollable terror—a sense of getting something which I had not bargained for. That moment I would have given all I had or hoped to have to be as I was three hours before.

No pain any where—not a twinge in any fibre—yet a cloud of unutterable strangeness was settling upon me, and wrapping me impenetrably in from all that was natural or familiar. Endeared faces, well known to me of old, surrounded me, yet they were not with me in my loneliness. I had entered upon a tremendous life which they could not share. If the disembodied ever return to hover over the hearth-stone which once had a seat for them, they look upon their friends as I then looked upon mine. A nearness of place, with an infinite distance of state, a connection which had no possible sympathies for the wants of that hour of revelation, an isolation none the less perfect for seeming companionship.

Still I spoke; a question was put to me, and I answered it; I even laughed at a bon mot. Yet it was not my voice which spoke; perhaps one which I once had far away in another time and another place. For a while I knew nothing that was going on externally, and then the remembrance of the last remark which had been made returned slowly and indistinctly, as some trait of a dream will return after many days, puzzling us to say where we have been conscious of it before.

A fitful wind all the evening had been sighing down the chimney; it now grew into the steady hum of a vast wheel in accelerating motion. For a while this hum seemed to resound through all space. I was stunned by it—I was absorbed in it. Slowly the revolution of the wheel came to a stop, and its monotonous din was changed for the reverberating peal of a grand cathedral organ. The ebb and flow of its inconceivably solemn tone filled me with a grief that was more than human. I sympathized with the dirge-like cadence as spirit sympathizes with spirit. And then, in the full conviction that all I heard and felt was real, I looked out of my isolation to see the effect of the music on my friends. Ah! we were in separate worlds indeed. Not a trace of appreciation on any face.

Perhaps I was acting strangely. Suddenly a pair of busy hands, which had ben running neck and neck all the evening with a nimble little crochet-needle over a race-ground of pink and blue silk, stopped at their goal, and their owner looked at me steadfastly. Ah! I was found out—I had betrayed myself. In terror I waited, expecting every instant to hear the word "hasheesh." No, the lady only asked me some question connected with the previous conversation. As mechanically as an automaton I began to reply. As I heard once more the alien and unreal tones of my own voice, I became convinced that it was some one else who spoke, and in another world. I sat and listened; still the voice kept speaking. Now for the first time I experienced that vast change which hasheesh makes in all measurements of time. The first word of the reply occupied a period sufficient for the action of a drama; the last left me in complete ignorance of any point far enough back in the past to date the commencement of the sentence. Its enunciation might have occupied years. I was not in the same life which had held me when I heard it begun.

And now, with time, space expanded also. At my friend's house one particular arm-chair was always reserved for me. I was sitting in it at a distance of hardly three feet from the centre-table around which the members of the family were grouped. Rapidly that distance widened. The whole atmosphere seemed ductile, and spun endlessly out into great spaces surrounding me on every side. We were in a vast hall, of which my friends and I occupied opposite extremities. The ceiling and the walls ran upward with a gliding motion, as if vivified by a sudden force of resistless growth.

Oh! I could not bear it. I should soon be left alone in the midst of an infinity of space. And now more and more every moment increased the conviction that I was watched. I did not know then, as I learned afterward, that suspicion of all earthly things and persons was the characteristic of the hasheesh delirium.

In the midst of my complicated hallucination, I could perceive that I had a dual existence. One portion of me was whirled unresistingly along the track of this tremendous experience, the other sat looking down from a height upon its double, observing, reasoning, and serenely weighing all the phenomena. This calmer being suffered with the other by sympathy, but did not lose its self-possession. Presently it warned me that I must go home, lest the growing effect of the hasheesh should incite me to some act which might frighten my friends. I acknowledged the force of this remark very much as if it had been made by another person, and rose to take my leave. I advanced toward the centre-table. With every step its distance increased. I nerved myself as for a long pedestrian journey. Still the lights, the faces, the furniture receded. At last, almost unconsciously, I reached them. It would be tedious to attempt to convey the idea of the time which my leave-taking consumed, and the attempt, at least with all minds that have not passed through the same experience, would be as impossible as tedious. At last I was in the street.

Beyond me the view stretched endlessly away. It was an unconverging vista, whose nearest lamps seemed separated from me by leagues. I was doomed to pass through a merciless stretch of space. A soul just disenthralled, setting out for his flight beyond the farthest visible star, could not be more overwhelmed with his newly-acquired conception of the sublimity of distance than I was at that moment. Solemnly I began my infinite journey. Before long I walked in entire unconsciousness of all around me. I dwelt in a marvelous inner world. I existed by turns in different places and various states of being. Now I swept my gondola through the moonlit lagoons of Venice. Now Alp on Alp towered above my view, and the glory of the coming sun flashed purple light upon the topmost icy pinnacle. Now in the primeval silence of some unexplored tropical forest I spread my feathery leaves, a giant fern, and swayed and nodded in the spice-gales over a river whose waves at once sent up clouds of music and perfume. My soul changed to a vegetable essence, thrilled with a strange and unimagined ecstasy. The palace of Al Haroun could not have brought me back to humanity.

I will not detail all the transmutations of that walk. Ever and anon I returned from my dreams into consciousness, as some well-known house seemed to leap out into my path, awaking me with a shock. The whole way homeward was a series of such awakings and relapses into an abstraction and delirium until I reached the corner of the street in which I lived.

Here a new phenomenon manifested itself. I had just awaked for perhaps the twentieth time, and my eyes were wide open. I recognized all surrounding objects, and began calculating the distance home. Suddenly, out of a blank wall at my side a muffled figure stepped into the path before me. His hair, white as snow, hung in tangled elf-locks on his shoulders, where he carried also a heavy burden, like unto the well-fitted sack of sins which Bunyan places on the back of his pilgrim. Not liking his manner, I stepped aside, intending to pass around him and go on my way. This change of our relative position allowed the blaze of a neighboring street-lamp to fall full on his face, which had hitherto been totally obscured. Horror unspeakable! I shall never, till the day I die, forget that face. Every lineament was stamped with the records of a life black with damning crime; it glared upon me with ferocious wickedness and a stony despair which only he may feel who is entering on the retribution of the unpardonable sin. He might have sat to a demon painter as the ideal of Shelley's Cenci. I seemed to grow blasphemous in looking at him, and, in an agony of fear, began to run away. He detained me with a bony hand, which pierced my wrist like talons, and, slowly taking down the burden from his own shoulders, laid it upon mine. I threw it off and pushed him away. Silently he returned and restored the weight. Again I repulsed him, this time crying out, "Man, what do you mean?" In a voice which impressed me with the sense of wickedness as his face had done, he replied, "You *shall* bear my burden with me," and a third time laid it on my shoulders. For the last time I hurled it aside, and, with all my force, dashed him from me. He reeled backward and fell, and before he could recover his disadvantage I had put a long distance between us.

Through the excitement of my struggle with this phantasm the effects of the hasheesh had increased mightily. I was bursting with an uncontrollable life; I strode with the thews of a giant. Hotter and faster came my breath; I seemed to pant like some tremendous engine. An electric energy whirled me resistlessly onward; I feared for myself lest it should burst its fleshly walls, and glance on, leaving a wrecked frame-work behind it.

At last I entered my own house. During my absence a family connection had arrived from abroad, and stood ready to receive my greeting. Partly restored to consciousness by the naturalness of home-faces and the powerful light of a chandelier which shed its blaze through the room, I saw the necessity of vigilance against betraying my condition, and with an intense effort suppressing all I felt, I approached my friend, and said all that is usual on such occasions. Yet recent as I was from my conflict with the supernatural, I cast a stealthy look about me, that I might learn from the faces of the others if, after all, I was shaking hands with a phantom, and making inquiries about the health of a family of hallucinations. Growing assured as I perceived no symptoms of astonishment, I finished the salutation and sat down.

It soon required all my resolution to keep the secret which I had determined to hold inviolable. My sensations began to be terrific— not from any pain that I felt, but from the tremendous mystery of all around me and within me. By an appalling introversion, all the operations of vitality which, in our ordinary state, go on unconsciously, came vividly into my experience. Through every thinnest corporeal tissue and minutest vein I could trace the circulation of the blood along each inch of its progress. I knew when every valve opened and when it shut; every sense was preternaturally awakened; the room was full of a great glory. The beating of my heart was so clearly audible that I wondered to find it unnoticed by those who were sitting by my side. Lo, now, that heart became a great fountain, whose jet played upward with loud vibrations, and, striking upon the roof of my skull as a gigantic dome, fell back with a splash and echo into its reservoir. Faster and faster came the pulsations, until at last I heard them no more, and the stream became one continuously pouring flood, whose roar resounded through all my frame. I gave myself up for lost, since judgment, which still sat unimpaired above my perverted senses, argued that congestion must take place in a few moments, and close the drama with my death. But my clutch would not yet relax from hope. The thought struck me, Might not this rapidity of circulation be, after all, imaginary? I determined to find out.

Going to my own room, I took out my watch, and placed my hand upon my heart. The very effort which I made to ascertain the reality gradually brought perception back to its natural state. In the intensity of my observations, I began to perceive that the circulation was not as rapid as I had thought. From a pulseless flow it gradually came to be apprehended as a hurrying succession of intense throbs, then less swift and less intense, till finally, on comparing it with the second-hand, I found that about 90 a minute was its average rapidity. Greatly comforted, I desisted from the experiment. Almost instantly the hallucination returned. Again I dreaded apoplexy, congestion, hemorrhage, a multiplicity of nameless deaths, and drew my picture as I might be found on the morrow, stark and cold, by those whose agony would be redoubled by the mystery of my end. I reasoned with myself; I bathed my forehead—it did no good. There was one resource left: I would go to a physician.

With this resolve, I left my room and went to the head of the staircase. The family had all retired for the night, and the gas was turned off from the burner in the hall below. I looked down the stairs: the depth was fathomless; it was a journey of years to reach the bottom! The dim light of the sky shone through the narrow panes at the sides of the front door, and seemed a demon-lamp in the middle darkness of the abyss. I never could get down! I sat me down despairingly upon the topmost step.

Suddenly a sublime thought possessed me. If the distance be infinite, I am immortal. It shall be tried. I commenced the descent, wearily, wearily down through my league-long, year-long journey. To record my impressions in that journey would be to repeat what I have said of the time of hasheesh. Now stopping to rest as a traveler would turn aside at a wayside inn, now toiling down through the lonely darkness, I came by-and-by to the end, and passed out into the street.

UNDER THE SHADOW OF ESCULAPIUS

On reaching the porch of the physician's house, I rang the bell, but immediately forgot whom to ask for. No wonder; I was on the steps of a palace in Milan—no (and I laughed at myself for the blunder), I was on the staircase of the Tower of London. So I should not be puzzled through my ignorance of Italian. But whom to ask for? This question recalled me to the real bearings of the place, but did not suggest its requisite answer. Whom shall I ask for? I began setting the most cunning traps of hypothesis to catch the solution of the difficulty. I looked at the surrounding houses; of whom had I been accustomed to think as living next door to them? This did not bring it. Whose daughter had I seen going to school from this house but the very day before? Her name was Julia—Julia—and I thought of every combination which had been made with this name from Julia Domna down to Giulia Grisi. Ah! now I had it—Julia H.; and her father naturally bore the same name. During this intellectual rummage I had rung the bell half a dozen times, under the impression that I was kept waiting a small eternity. When the servant opened the door she panted as if she had run for her life. I was shown up stairs to Dr. H.'s room, where he had thrown himself down to rest after a tedious operation. Locking the door after me with an air of determined secrecy, which must have conveyed to him pleasant little suggestions of a design upon his life, I approached his bedside.

"I am about to reveal to you," I commenced, "something which I would not for my life allow to come to other ears. Do you pledge me your eternal silence?"

"I do; what is the matter?"

"I have been taking hasheesh—Cannabis Indica, and I fear that I am going to die."

"How much did you take?"

"Thirty grains."

"Let me feel your pulse." He placed his finger on my wrist and counted slowly, while I stood waiting to hear my death-warrant. "Very regular," shortly spoke the doctor; "triflingly accelerated. Do you feel any pain?" "None at all." "Nothing the matter with you; go home and go to bed." "But—is there—is there—no—danger of—apoplexy?" "Bah!" said the doctor; and, having delivered himself of this very Abernethy-like * opinion of my case, he lay down again. My hand was on the knob, when he stopped me with, "Wait a minute; I'll give you a powder to carry with you, and if

* John Abernethy (1764–1831), British physician, noted for his persuasive expression of opinions.

you get frightened again after you leave me, you can take it as a sedative. Step out on the landing, if you please, and call my servant."

I did so, and my voice seemed to reverberate like thunder from every recess in the whole building. I was terrified at the noise I had made. I learned in after days that this impression is only one of the many due to the intense susceptibility of the sensorium as produced by hasheesh. At one time, having asked a friend to check me if I talked loudly or immoderately while in a state of fantasia among persons from whom I wished to conceal my state, I caught myself shouting and singing from very ecstasy, and reproached him with a neglect of his friendly office. I could not believe him when he assured me that I had not uttered an audible word. The intensity of the inward emotion had affected the external through the internal ear.

I returned and stood at the foot of the doctor's bed. All was perfect silence in the room, and had been perfect darkness also but for the small lamp which I held in my hand to light the preparation of the powder when it should come. And now a still sublimer mystery began to enwrap me. I stood in a remote chamber at the top of a colossal building, and the whole fabric beneath me was steadily growing into the air. Higher than the topmost pinnacle of Bel's Babylonish temple—higher than Ararat—on, on forever into the lonely dome of God's infinite universe we towered ceaselessly. The years flew on; I heard the musical rush of their wings in the abyss outside of me, and from cycle to cycle, from life to life I careered, a mote in eternity and space. Suddenly emerging from the orbit of my transmigrations, I was again at the foot of the doctor's bed, and thrilled with wonder to find that we were both unchanged by the measureless lapse of time. The servant had not come.

"Shall I call her again?" "Why, you have this moment called her." "Doctor," I replied solemnly, and in language that would have seemed bombastic enough to any one who did not realize what

I felt, "I will not believe you are deceiving me, but to me it appears as if sufficient time has elapsed since then for all the Pyramids to have crumbled back to dust." "Ha! ha! you are very funny tonight," said the doctor; "but here she comes, and I will send her for something which will comfort you on that score, and reestablish the Pyramids in your confidence." He gave the girl his orders, and she went out again.

The thought struck me that I would compare *my time* with other people's. I looked at my watch, found that its minute-hand stood at the quarter mark past eleven, and, returning it to my pocket, abandoned myself to my reflections.

Presently I saw myself a gnome imprisoned by a most weird enchanter, whose part I assigned to the doctor before me, in the Domdaniel caverns, "under the roots of the ocean." Here, until the dissolution of all things, was I doomed to hold the lamp that lit that abysmal darkness, while my heart, like a giant clock, ticked solemnly the remaining years of time. Now, this hallucination departing, I heard in the solitude of the night outside the sound of a wondrous heaving sea. Its waves, in sublime cadence, rolled forward till they met the foundations of the building; they smote them with a might which made the very topstone quiver, and then fell back, with hiss and hollow murmur, into the broad bosom whence they had arisen. Now through the street, with measured tread, an armed host passed by. The heavy beat of their footfall and the grinding of their brazen corslet-rings alone broke the silence, for among them all there was no more speech nor music than in a battalion of the dead. It was the army of the ages going by into eternity. A godlike sublimity swallowed up my soul. I was overwhelmed in a fathomless barathrum of time, but I leaned on God, and was immortal through all changes.

And now, in another life, I remembered that far back in the cycles I had looked at my watch to measure the time through which I passed. The impulse seized me to look again. The minute-hand stood half way between fifteen and sixteen minutes past eleven. The watch must have stopped; I held it to my ear; no, it was still going. I had traveled through all that immeasurable chain of dreams in thirty seconds. "My God!" I cried, "I am in eternity." In the presence of that first sublime revelation of the soul's own time, and her capacity for an infinite life, I stood trembling with breathless awe. Till I die, that moment of unveiling will stand in clear relief from all the rest of my existence. I hold it still in unimpaired remembrance as one of the unutterable sanctities of my being. The years of all my earthly life to come can never be as long as those thirty seconds.

Finally the servant reappeared. I received my powder and went home. There was a light in one of the upper windows, and I hailed it with unspeakable joy, for it relieved me from a fear which I could not conquer, that while I had been gone all familiar things had passed away from earth. I was hardly safe in my room before I doubted having ever been out of it. "I have experienced some wonderful dream," said I, "as I lay here after coming from the parlor." If I had not been out, I reasoned that I would have no powder in my pocket. The powder was there, and it steadied me a little to find that I was not utterly hallucinated on every point. Leaving the light burning, I set out to travel to my bed, which gently invited me in the distance. Reaching it after a sufficient walk, I threw myself down.

One day, about the hour of noon, a little more than a week after my first experiment, I rolled twenty grains of hasheesh into a pill and swallowed it, saying as I did so, "Here is the final test for the sake of science." The afternoon lay before me unoccupied by any especial appointment, and, after dining, I threw myself down upon a lounge to await the result of the dose. The day was soft and hazy, and its influence lay so nepenthe-like upon my eyelids, that before long, without knowing it, I fell asleep. It was tea-time when I awoke, and I had not experienced any visions. A friend of mine joined me at the table, and when we pushed back our chairs, he proposed that we should take a walk. Every thing above, below, around us united in the invitation. It was one of those evenings when the universal sense of balminess makes all outdoors as home-like and delicious as the cheeriest winter fireside can be, with its enlivenment of ruddy blaze, and its charm of sheltered privacy. The very soul seems turned inside out for an airing, and we are almost ashamed of ourselves for ever preferring rafters to the sky, and fleeing from the presence of Nature to find a home.

Through all the streets that ran toward the west the sun was sending a thrill of light from his good-by place on the horizon, and the pavements were a mosaic of dancing leaf-shadows and golden polygons, forever shifting as the trees quivered over us in the gentlest of southern winds. Arm-in-arm with Dan, I strolled down the checkered avenue, and more and more luxuriant grew the sunset as we came gradually out of the environment of houses and breathed the air of the open country. The suburbs of P——* are very beautiful. If the stranger knows it and remarks it, it is not because he is smitten with the mere novelty of his view. There are few landscapes which will bear so frequent beholding—few whose admirers so soon and lastingly become their lovers. Were there any jealousy in my love for that, my own home-scenery, I know no season which would ever have given me more pangs for fear of a rival than the one of which I speak, for the earth and sky were fair around us, even with a human fascination. Of my companion let me say that which any man of varying moods will realize to be one of the highest eulogies that can be passed upon a friend. Dan was one of those choice spirits whom you are always glad to have beside you, whatever may be your feeling. He belonged to that rare and sensitive order of beings who can never become uncongenial to one who has once been in sympathy with them. How many a time, most valued and longed-for one, have I tested this in thee! How often, in this very intuitive perception of our accordance, have I felt the proof that friendship is as inborn a

* Poughkeepsie, N.Y., where Ludlow grew up.

principle in hearts as the quality of their harmony in tones of a chord.

There is a road running south from the suburbs of P—— which in many respects affords one of the most delightful walks which can be imagined. On the one hand, for a long distance, a terraced embankment rises luxuriantly green through all the days of summer, and crowned with picturesque rusurban cottages. On the other, a broad table-land stretches away to the abrupt banks of the Hudson, dotted over all its surface with clumps of healthful trees and embowered villas. Here and there, through the fringes of shade which skirt the brink, delicious views of the river break upon the eye, with a background of mountains, still unsubdued by labor, rising in primeval freshness from the other side. Under the tutelar protection of their evening shadows the farther water lay, at the season of which I speak, like a divine child asleep, watched by an eternal nurse.

Along this road we traveled arm-in-arm, so filled and overcome with the beauty of the view that we read each other's feelings and went silently. Perhaps we had come half a mile from the town when, without the smallest premonition, I was smitten by the hasheesh thrill as by a thunderbolt. Though I had felt it but once in life before, its sign was as unmistakable as the most familiar thing of daily life. I have often been asked to explain the nature of this thrill, and have as often tried to do it, but no analogue exists which will represent it perfectly, hardly even approximately. The nearest resemblance to the feeling is that contained in our idea of the instantaneous separation of soul and body. Very few in the world have ever known before absolute death what state accompanies this separation, yet we all of us have an idea more or less distinct of that which it must be when it arrives. Even on this vague conception I throw myself for the sake of being understood with more confidence than I would dare to give to the most thorough description that I could elaborate.

The road along which we walked began slowly to lengthen. The

hill over which it disappeared, at the distance of half a mile from
me, soon came to be perceived as the boundary of the continent
itself. But for the infinite loveliness of the sky, and waters, and
fields, I should have been as greatly terrified with the increasing
mystery of my state as I had been at the commencement of my first
experience. But a most beautiful sunset was dying in the west, the
river was tinged by it, the very zenith clouds were bathed in it, and
the world beneath seemed floating in a dream of rosy tranquility.
My awakened perceptions drank in this beauty until all sense of
fear was banished, and every vein ran flooded with the very wine
of delight. Mystery enwrapped me still, but it was the mystery of
one who walks in Paradise for the first time.

Could I keep it from Dan? No, not for a moment. I had no
remembrance of having taken hasheesh. The past was the property
of another life, and I supposed that all the world was reveling in
the same ecstasy as myself. I cast off all restraint; I leaped into the
air; I clapped my hands, and shouted for joy. An involuntary ex-
clamation raised the mustache of the poet beside me. "What in
the world," he cried, "is the matter with you?" I could only answer,
"Bliss! bliss! unimagined bliss!" In an instant he saw all, for he
knew my former experience, and as quickly formed the resolution
of humoring me to the utmost in all my vagaries.

I glowed like a new-born soul. The well-known landscape lost
all of its familiarity, and I was setting out upon a journey of years
through heavenly territories, which it had been the longing of my
previous lifetime to behold. "My dear friend," I said, "we are about
to realize all our youthful dreams of travel. Together you and I
will wander on foot at our will through strange and beauteous
countries; our life spreads before us henceforward unoccupied by
cares, and the riches of all nature stretch onward through the immense domain we see in exultant expectancy to become the food
for our thought and the fountains of our delight. To think that
we should have been spared until this day—spared to each other,
spared for such glorious scenes! My friend, we shall travel together,

linked soul to soul, and gaining ecstasy by impartition. At night, beneath the shade of zephyr-fanned mimosas, we shall lay ourselves down to sleep on the banks of primeval Asian rivers, and Bulbul shall sing us to sleep with his most delicious madrigals. When the first auroral tinges are glassed back from the peaks of Himmaleh, we will arise, and, bathing ourselves in rock-o'er-shadowed fountains, will start again upon our immortal way. Sleep shall repeat the echoes of the day to another and unfatigued inner sense of dreams, and awaking shall be a repetition of birth into newer and still more enchanting life. On! on!"

"I will go," said my friend, "with delight." Not a shadow of incredulousness or inappreciation passed over his face, and, drawing his arm still closer through my own, I hastened onward, as delighted with his consent as I was thoroughly convinced of the reality of the presence of grand old Asia.

The peculiar time of hasheesh, already so frequently mentioned, added one more most rapturous element to my enjoyment. Through leagues of travel the shadows did not deepen around us, but the same unutterable sunset peace and beauty transfused the earth unchangeably. In watching the glories of the west at sunset in our ordinary state, they pass away from us so soon that the dying lustres have become to us almost the synonym for transition and decay. The golden masses become ruddy, the ruddy fall away to purple, the purple speedily grow black, and all this transmutation occupies no longer time than we may lean our foreheads, unfatigued, against a window-pane. In my present state of enlarged perception, Time had no kaleidoscope for me; nothing grew faint, nothing shifted, nothing changed except my ecstasy, which heightened through interminable degrees to behold the same rose-radiance lighting us up along all our immense journey. I might style my present chapter "Notes of Travel through the Champaigns of Perpetual Sunset."

From the road along which we traveled another leads back into P——, across a more precipitous hill than any we had already ascended. Into this second road we turned. Yet, from the absence of all familiar appearances in the world around me, I did not suppose that we were returning to the town, but merely that we were continuing our journey through a new and less frequented by-path. Presently we struck a plank walk, and began mounting the hill of which I have spoken.

The moment that the planks began to resound beneath our feet I realized in what part of Asia we were journeying. We were on the great wall of China. Below us stretched into grand distances the plains of Thibet. Multitudinous were the flocks that covered them; countless groups of goats and goatherds were dispersed over the landscape as far as the eye could reach. The banks of innumerable streams were dotted with picturesque tents, and every minutest detail of the view in all respects harmonized with the idea of Asiatic life. Beyond Thibet, as with clairvoyant eyes, I looked straight through and over Hindoo Koosh, and beheld Cashmere sleeping in grand shadows. The fountains of the Punjaub were unveiled, and among their spicy outflowings there gamboled, in Old-world freshness of heart, children of a primitive race whom prodigal nature had put beyond the necessity of labor. Through greenest valleys roved pairs of Oriental lovers, while above them flashed golden light from the fruit that hung in a Vallambrosa of citron-branches. Distance did not dim either scenery or countenances; every living thing was audible and visible in its rejoicing though leagues of light and shadow stretched between us. Again I leaped into the air and shouted for joy.

Along the road that skirted the outside of my Chinese wall a carriage came, drawn by a span of richly-caparisoned white horses. In it a young man and a maiden were sitting, and as they drew nearer they bowed to myself and my fellow-traveler. "Who are those?" asked Dan. "An eminent mandarin of the interior," I replied, "of the order of the Blue Button, and by name Fuh-chieng, who, with his sister, at this season every year takes the tour of the provinces, dispensing justice and examining into the state of the public works. Verily, an estimable youth. Having known him during the summer we spent together at Pekin, I feel constrained to speak with him." With a choice compliment upon my lips, worded in the most courtly Chinese with which I was conversant, I was about to rush up to the carriage and make my kow-tow, when my friend, grasping my arm, entreated me to desist, begging to know whether I were not aware that, since the year 580 B.C., when Ching-Chong was assassinated in his palanquin, it had been a criminal offense to approach within ten paces of a mandarin on his travels. "My dearest friend," I replied, "you have saved me! I am astonished at your knowledge of Chinese law, this title of which had entirely escaped my mind. With thankfulness I yield to your suggestion, and will suffer the young man to pass on." It was well that I did so, as my acquaintances in the carriage might otherwise have been terrified beyond measure by the singularity, if not by the sublimity of the dialect in which I should have addressed them.

It is possible for a man of imaginative mind, by mere suggestions of rich veins of thought, to lead a companion in the hasheesh state through visions of incomparable delight. This fact Dan had discovered in the good grace with which I instantly received his advice as to the mandarin. In our journey we came to a tall gate-post of granite, which stood at the entrance to a lawn in front of one of the suburban residences of which I have spoken. Making his manner Oriental, to suit our supposed surroundings, he said to me, "Seest thou that tower that rises into the rosy air?" In an instant I beheld the tower with such conviction of reality that I did not even think of it as a metamorphose from something else. From the battlements flaunted yellow flags gorgeous with crimson dragons, and over each corner of the turret glared a rampant hippogriff, flaming, from his forked tongue even to his anomalous tail, with scales of dazzling gold. There was revelry within; its ecstasy worded in Shemitic monosyllables, and accompanied by the mellifluous flights of gong and tom-tom. We passed on through Asia.

We now reached the summit of the hill. The broadest scope of vision which was possible was now ours. My ecstasy became so great that I seemed to cast off all shackles of flesh. The lover of beauty who should, for the first time, drink in the richness of this exalted view through the channels of the soul which are ordinarily opened, might well burst forth into singing were not reverence the stronger feeling. But when, with me, that flow of loveliness broke in through doors in the spiritual nature to which no open sesame had ever before been granted, I felt, I cried out, "Why need we, in our journey, touch the earth at all? Let us sweep through air above this expanse of beauty, and read it like the birds."

I was about to fly heavenward, chanting a triumphant hymn, when I turned and looked at Dan. He was standing sorrowfully, without means of flight. I was filled with contrition. "Dear brother of my pilgrimage," I said, "did I speak of tempting the air, forgetful that thou wast not like unto myself? Forgive me—I will not leave thee; yet, oh that thou couldst also fly! through what abysses of sublimity would we float!" Restoring myself to contentment with the airy tread of feet which hardly seemed to touch the ground, and my wish to oblivion, I again took his arm, and we voyaged as before.

Now we went singing, and I question whether Mozart ever rejoiced in his own musical creations as I did in that symphony we sang together. The tune and the words were extemporaneous, yet, by a close sympathy, he sang an accordant base to my air, and I heard delicious echoes thrown back from the dome of heaven. We sang the primal simplicity of Asia, the cradle of the nations, the grand expectancy of the younger continents, looking eastward to their mysterious mother for the gift of races still treasured in her womb. On our paean were borne the praises of the golden days of Foh * and the serene prophecies of Confucius; we spoke of the rivers that for numberless centuries bore down to the eternal ocean no freight but the sere leaves of uninhabited wildernesses, whose shadows they glassed, and of fountains upon whose face no smile had rested save that of Hesper and the rising sun. I lived in

* Buddha.

what we sang: our music seemed a wondrous epic, whose pages we illustrated, not with pictures, but with living groups; the ancient days were restored before my eyes and to my ears, and I exulted in the perception with such conviction of reality that I ascribed it to no power of my own, but knew it as an exterior and universal fact.

This will be realized, perhaps, by very few who read my recital. The word for every strange phenomenon with all the world is "only imagination." Truly, this was imagination; but to me, with eyes and ears wide open in the daylight, an imagination as real as the soberest fact.

It will be remembered that the hasheesh states of ecstasy always alternate with less intense conditions, in which the prevailing phenomena are those of mirth or tranquillity. In accordance with this law, in the present instance, Dan, to whom I had told my former experience, was not surprised to hear me break forth at the final cadence of our song into a peal of unextinguishable laughter, but begged to know what was its cause, that he might laugh too. I could only cry out that my right leg was a tin case filled with stair-rods, and as I limped along, keeping that member perfectly rigid, both from fear of cracking the metal and the difficulty of bending it, I heard the rattle of the brazen contents shaken from side to side with feelings of the most supreme absurdity possible to the human soul. Presently the leg was restored to its former state, but in the interim its mate had grown to a size which would have made it a very respectable trotter for Brian Borru or one of the Titans. Elevated some few hundred feet into the firmament, I was compelled to hop upon my giant pedestal in a way very ungraceful in a world where two legs were the fashion, and eminently disagreeable to the slighted member, which sought in vain to reach the earth with struggles amusing from their very insignificance. This ludicrous affliction being gradually removed, I went on my way quietly until we again began to be surrounded by the houses of the town.

Here the phenomenon of the dual existence once more presented itself. One part of me awoke, while the other continued in perfect hallucination. The awakened portion felt the necessity of keeping in side streets on the way home, lest some untimely burst of ecstasy should startle more frequented thoroughfares. I mentioned this to Dan, who drew me into a quiet lane, by the side of which we sat down together to rest on a broad stone. By this time the sunset had nearly faded, while my attention was directed to other things, and its regency of all the beauties of the sky was replaced by that of the full moon, now at the zenith. A broad and clearly-defined halo surrounded her, and refracted her rays in such a manner as to shower them from its edge in a prismatic fringe. That vision of loveliness was the only possible one which could have recompensed me for the loss of my sunset. I gazed heavenward, as one fascinated by mystical eyes. And now the broad luminous belt began to be peopled with myriads of shining ones from the realm of Faëry, who plunged into the translucent lake of ether as into a sea, and, dashing back its silvery spray from their breasts, swam to the moon and ascended its gleaming beach.

Between this moon-island and the shore of halo now growing multitudes endlessly passed and repassed, and I could hear, tinkling down through the vacant spaces, the thrill of their gnome-laughter. I could have kept that stony seat all night, and looked speechlessly into heaven, unmoved though an armed host had passed by me on the earth, but unconsciously I closed my eyes, and was in a moment whirling on through a visionary dance, like that in which I had been borne as soon as I lay down at the time of my first experiment. Temples and gardens, pyramids and unearthly rivers, began to float along before the windows of my sense, when Dan, looking around, saw that I would become unconscious, and aroused me. Again we walked on.

And now that unutterable thirst which characterizes hasheesh came upon me. I could have lain me down and lapped dew from the grass. I must drink, wheresoever, howsoever. We soon reached home—soon, because it was not five squares off from where we sat down, yet ages, from the thirst which consumed me and the expansion of time in which I lived. I came into the house as one would approach a fountain in the desert, with a wild bound of exultation, and gazed with miserly eyes at the draught which my friend poured out for me until the glass was brimming. I clutched it—I put it to my lips. Ha! a surprise! It was not water, but the most delicious metheglin in which ever bard of the Cymri drank the health of Howell Dda. It danced and sparkled like some liquid metempsychosis of amber; it gleamed with the spiritual fire of a thousand chrysolites. To sight, to taste it was metheglin, such as never mantled in the cups of the Valhalla.

The remainder of that evening I spent in a delirium which, unlike all that had preceded it, was one of unutterable calm. Not the heavy sleep of a debauch, not the voluntary musing of the visionary, but a clarifying of all thought, and the flowing in of the richest influences from the world around me, without the toil of selecting them. I looked at the stars, and felt kindred with them; I spoke to them, and they answered me. I dwelt in an inner communion with heaven—a communion where every language is understood, rather where all speak the same language, and deeply did I realize a voice which seemed to say, as in my waking dreams I had faintly heard it murmur upon earth,

$$\Pi o\lambda\lambda a\grave{\iota}\ \mu\grave{\epsilon}\nu\ \theta\nu\eta\tau o\acute{\iota}\varsigma\ \gamma\lambda\tilde{\omega}\tau\tau a\iota,\ \mu\iota a\ \delta\dot{a}\theta\acute{a}\nu a\tau o\iota\sigma\iota\nu.^{*}$$

THE HOUR AND THE POWER OF DARKNESS

Having exhausted the supply of hasheesh which I had originally obtained from the shelves of my old lounging-place at the shop of the doctor, I procured a small jar of a preparation of the same drug by another chemist, which, I was told, was much weaker than the former. Late in the evening I took about fifty grains of the new preparation, arguing that this amount was a rational equivalent for the thirty which had before been my maximum dose.

* Indeed, many speak as mortals; one alone is immortal.

It is impossible, however, to base any calculation of the energy of hasheesh upon such a comparison. The vital forces upon which this most magical stimulant operates are too delicate, too recondite to be treated like material parts in a piece of mechanism whose power of resistance can be definitely expressed by an equation. There are certain nerves, no doubt, which the anatomist and the physician will find affected by the cannabine influence—certain functions over which its essence appears to hold peculiar regency; but we must have proceeded much farther in the science which treats of the connection between matter and mind, must know much more of those imponderable forces which, more delicate than electricity and more mysterious than the magnetic fluid, weave the delicate interacting network that joins our human duality, before we can treat that part of us affected by hasheesh as a constant in any calculation.

There are two facts which I have verified as universal by repeated experiment, which fall into their place here as aptly as they can in the course of my narrative: 1st. At two different times, when body and mind are apparently in precisely analogous states, when all circumstances, exterior and interior, do not differ tangibly in the smallest respect, the same dose of the same preparation of hasheesh will frequently produce diametrically opposite effects. Still further, I have taken at one time a pill of thirty grains, which hardly gave a perceptible phenomenon, and at another, when my dose had been but half that quantity, I have suffered the agonies of a martyr, or rejoiced in a perfect phrensy. So exceedingly variable are its results, that, long before I abandoned the indulgence, I took each successive bolus with the consciousness that I was daring an uncertainty as tremendous as the equipoise between hell and heaven. Yet the fascination employed Hope as its advocate, and won the suit. 2d. If, during the ecstasy of hasheesh delirium, another dose, however small—yes, though it be no larger than half a pea—be employed to prolong the condition, such agony will inevitably ensue as will make the soul shudder at its own possibility of endurance without annihilation. By repeated experiments, which now occupy the most horrible place upon my catalogue of horrible remembrances, have I proved that, among all the variable phenomena of hasheesh, this alone stands unvarying. The use of it directly after any other stimulus will produce consequences as appalling.

But to return from my digression. It was perhaps eight o'clock in the evening when I took the dose of fifty grains. I did not retire until near midnight, and as no effects had then manifested themselves, I supposed that the preparation was even weaker than my ratio gave it credit for being, and, without any expectation of result, lay down to sleep. Previously, however, I extinguished my light. To say this may seem trivial, but it is as important a matter as any which it is possible to notice. The most direful suggestions of the bottomless pit may flow in upon the hasheesh-eater through the very medium of darkness. The blowing out of a candle can set an unfathomed barathrum wide agape beneath the flower-wreathed table of his feast, and convert his palace of sorcery into a Golgotha. Light is a necessity to him, even when sleeping; it must tinge his visions, or they assume a hue as sombre as the banks of Styx.

I do not know how long a time had passed since midnight, when I awoke suddenly to find myself in a realm of the most perfect clarity of view, yet terrible with an infinitude of demoniac shadows. Perhaps, I thought, I am still dreaming; but no effort could arouse me from my vision, and I realized that I was wide awake. Yet it was an awaking which, for torture, had no parallel in all the stupendous domain of sleeping incubus. Beside my bed in the centre of the room stood a bier, from whose corners drooped the folds of a heavy pall; outstretched upon it lay in state a most fearful corpse, whose livid face was distorted with the pangs of assassination. The traces of a great agony were frozen into fixedness in the tense position of every muscle, and the nails of the dead man's fingers pierced his palms with the desperate clinch of one who has yielded not without agonizing resistance. Two tapers at his head, two at his feet, with their tall and unsnuffed wicks, made the ghastliness of the bier more luminously unearthly, and a smothered laugh of derision from some invisible watcher ever and anon mocked the corpse, as if triumphant demons were exulting over their prey. I pressed my hands upon my eyeballs till they ached, in intensity of desire to shut out the spectacle; I buried my head in the pillow, that I might not hear that awful laugh of diabolic sarcasm.

But—oh horror immeasurable! I beheld the walls of the room slowly gliding together, the ceiling coming down, the floor ascending, as of old the lonely captive saw them, whose cell was doomed to be his coffin. Nearer and nearer am I borne toward the corpse. I shrunk back from the edge of the bed; I cowered in most abject fear. I tried to cry out, but speech was paralyzed. The walls came closer and closer together. Presently my hand lay on the dead man's forehead. I made my arm as straight and rigid as a bar of iron; but of what avail was human strength against the contraction of that cruel masonry? Slowly my elbow bent with the ponderous pressure; nearer grew the ceiling—I fell into the fearful embrace of death. I was pent, I was stifled in the breathless niche, which was all of space still left to me. The stony eyes stared up into my own, and again the maddening peal of fiendish laughter rang close beside my ear. Now I was touched on all sides by the walls of the terrible press; there came a heavy crush, and I felt all sense blotted out in darkness.

I awaked at last; the corpse was gone, but I had taken his place upon the bier. In the same attitude which he had kept I lay motionless, conscious, although in darkness, that I wore upon my face the counterpart of his look of agony. The room had grown into a gigantic hall, whose roof was framed of iron arches; the pavement, the walls, the cornice were all of iron. The spiritual essence of the metal seemed to be a combination of cruelty and despair. Its massive hardness spoke a language which it is impossible to embody in words, but any one who has watched the relentless sweep of some great engine crank, and realized its capacity for murder, will catch a glimpse, even in the memory, of the thrill which seemed to say,

"This iron is a tearless fiend," of the unutterable meaning I saw in those colossal beams and buttresses. I suffered from the vision of that iron as from the presence of a giant assassin.

But my senses opened slowly to the perception of still worse presences. By my side there gradually emerged from the sulphureous twilight which bathed the room the most horrible form which the soul could look upon unshattered—a fiend also of iron, white hot and dazzling with the glory of the nether penetralia. A face that was the ferreous incarnation of all imaginations of malice and irony looked on me with a glare, withering from its intense heat, but still more from the unconceived degree of inner wickedness which it symbolized. I realized whose laughter I had heard, and instantly I heard it again. Beside him another demon, his very twin, was rocking a tremendous cradle framed of bars of iron like all things else, and candescent with as fierce a heat as the fiend's.

And now, in a chant of the most terrific blasphemy which it is possible to imagine, or rather of blasphemy so fearful that no human thought has ever conceived of it, both the demons broke forth, until I grew intensely wicked merely by hearing it. I still remember the meaning of the song they sang, although there is no language yet coined which will convey it, and far be it from me even to suggest its nature, lest I should seem to perpetuate in any degree such profanity as beyond the abodes of the lost no lips are capable of uttering. Every note of the music itself accorded with the thought as symbol represents essence, and with its clangor mixed the maddening creak of the forever-oscillating cradle, until I felt driven into a ferocious despair. Suddenly the nearest fiend, snatching up a pitchfork (also of white-hot iron), thrust it into my writhing side, and hurled me shrieking into the fiery cradle. I sought in my torture to scale the bars; they slipped from my grasp and under my feet like the smoothest icicles. Through increasing grades of agony I lay unconsumed, tossing from side to side with the rocking of the dreadful engine, and still above me pealed the chant of blasphemy, and the eyes of demoniac sarcasm smiled at me in mockery of a mother's gaze upon her child.

"Let us sing him," said one of the fiends to the other, "the lullaby of Hell." The blasphemy now changed into an awful word-picturing of eternity, unveiling what it was, and dwelling with raptures of malice upon its infinitude, its sublimity of growing pain, and its privation of all fixed points which might mark it into divisions. By emblems common to all language rather than by any vocal words, did they sing this frightful apocalypse, yet the very emblems had a sound as distinct as tongue could give them. This was one, and the only one of their representatives that I can remember. Slowly they began, "To-day is father of to-morrow, to-morrow hath a son that shall beget the day succeeding." With increasing rapidity they sang in this way, day by day, the genealogy of a thousand years, and I traced on the successive generations, without a break in one link, until the rush of their procession reached a rapidity so awful as fully to typify eternity itself; and still I fled on through that burning genesis of cycles. I feel that I do not convey my meaning, but may no one else ever understand it better!

Withered like a leaf in the breath of an oven, after millions of years I felt myself tossed upon the iron floor. The fiends had departed, the cradle was gone. I stood alone, staring into immense and empty spaces. Presently I found that I was in a colossal square, as of some European city, alone at the time of evening twilight, and surrounded by houses hundreds of stories high. I was bitterly athirst. I ran to the middle of the square, and reached it after an infinity of travel. There was a fountain carved in iron, every jet inimitably sculptured in mockery of water, yet dry as the ashes of a furnace. "I shall perish with thirst," I cried. "Yet one more trial. There must be people in all these immense houses. Doubtless they love the dying traveler, and will give him to drink. Good friends! water! water!" A horribly deafening din poured down on me from the four sides of the square. Every sash of all the hundred stories of every house in that colossal quadrangle flew up as by one spring. Awakened by my call, at every window stood a terrific maniac. Sublimely in the air above me, in front, beside me, on either hand, and behind my back, a wilderness of insane faces gnashed at me, glared, gibbered, howled, laughed horribly, hissed, and cursed. At the unbearable sight I myself became insane, and, leaping up and down, mimicked them all, and drank their demented spirit.

A hand seized my arm—a voice called my name. The square grew lighter—it changed—it slowly took a familiar aspect, and gradually I became aware that my room-mate was standing before me with a lighted lamp. I sank back into his arms, crying "Water! water, Robert! For the love of heaven, water!" He passed across the room to the wash-stand, leaving me upon the bed, where I afterward found he had replaced me on being awakened by hearing me leap frantically up and down upon the floor. In going for the water, he seemed to be traveling over a desert plain to some far-off spring, and I hailed him on his return with the pitcher and the glass as one greets his friend restored after a long journey. No glass for me! I snatched the pitcher, and drank a Niagara of refreshment with every draught. I reveled in the ecstasy of a drinker of the rivers of Al Ferdoos.

Hasheesh always brings with it an awakening of perception which magnifies the smallest sensation till it occupies immense boundaries. The hasheesh-eater who drinks during his highest state of exaltation almost invariably supposes that he is swallowing interminable floods, and imagines his throat an abyss which is becoming gorged by the sea. Repeatedly, as in an agony of thirst I have clutched some small vessel of water and tipped it at my lips, I have felt such a realization of an overwhleming torrent that, with my throat still charred, I have put the water away, lest I should be drowned by the flow.

With the relighting of the lamp my terrors ceased. The room was still immense, yet the iron of its structure, in the alembic of that heavenly light, had been transmuted into silver and gold.

Beamy spars, chased by some unearthly graver, supported the roof above me, and a mellow glory transfused me, shed from sunny panels that covered the walls. Out of this hall of grammarye I suddenly passed through a crystal gate, and found myself again in the world outside. Through a valley carpeted with roses I marched proudly at the head of a grand army, and the most triumphant music pealed from all my legions. In the symphony joined many an unutterable instrument, bugles and ophicleides, harps and cymbals, whose wondrous peals seemed to say, "We are self-conscious; we exult like human souls." There were roses every where—roses under foot, roses festooning the lattices at our sides, roses showering a prodigal flush of beauty from the arches of an arbor overhead. Down the valley I gained glimpses of dreamy lawns basking in a Claude Lorraine sunlight. Over them multitudes of rosy children came leaping to throw garlands on my victorious road, and singing pæans to me with the voices of cherubs. Nations that my sword had saved ran bounding through the flowery walls of my avenue to cry "Our hero—our savior," and prostrate themselves at my feet. I grew colossal in a delirium of pride. I felt myself the centre of all the world's immortal glory. As once before the ecstasy of music had borne me from the body, so now I floated out of it in the intensity of my triumph. As the last chord was dissolved, I saw all the attendant splendors of my march fade away, and became once more conscious of my room restored to its natural state.

Not a single hallucination remained. Surrounding objects resumed their wonted look, yet a wonderful surprise broke in upon me. In the course of my delirium, the soul, I plainly discovered, had indeed departed from the body. I was that soul utterly divorced from the corporeal nature, disjoined, clarified, purified. From the air in which I hovered I looked down upon my former receptacle. Animal life, with all its processes, still continued to go on; the chest heaved with the regular rise and fall of breathing, the temples throbbed, and the cheek flushed. I scrutinized the body with wonderment; it seemed no more to concern me than that of another being. I do not remember, in the course of the whole experience I have had of hasheesh, a more singular emotion than I felt at that moment. The spirit discerned itself as possessed of all the human capacities, intellect, susceptibility, and will—saw itself complete in every respect; yet, like a grand motor, it had abandoned the machine which it once energized, and in perfect independence stood apart. In the prerogative of my spiritual nature I was restrained by no objects of a denser class. To myself I was visible and tangible, yet I knew that no material eyes could see me. Through the walls of the room I was able to pass and repass, and through the ceiling to behold the stars unobscured.

This was neither hallucination nor dream. The sight of my reason was preternaturally intense, and I remembered that this was one of the states which frequently occur to men immediately before their death has become apparent to lookers-on, and also in the more remarkable conditions of trance. That such a state is possible is incontestably proved by many cases on record in which it has fallen under the observation of students most eminent in physico-psychical science.

A voice of command called on me to return into the body, saying in the midst of my exultation over what I thought was my final disenfranchisement from the corporeal, "The time is not yet." I returned, and again felt the animal nature joined to me by its mysterious threads of conduction. Once more soul and body were one.

Now that he has experienced metempsychosis, the movement of his soul out of his body, the Pythagorean has no fears of the hellfire he has seen. He continues to experiment with hashish, getting most of his friends, one by one, to try it with him. They usually feel no effects at all, but sometimes the results are thoroughly disagreeable and frightening. Realizing he is alone in his world of hashish every day, he tries several times to stop the habit, only to yield again each time to its attractions. Most of the book takes place *in the narrator's mind, but one of the physical settings is an American university patterned after Union College, where, in his senior year, Ludlow actually attempted to introduce his classmates to hashish.*

Ludlow's portentous, vatic style never deserts him, yet occasionally he strives to be funny.

THE PRINCE OF WHALES

At one time, in my ramble through the realm of incongruities, I came to the strand of the Mediterranean, and beheld an acquaintance of mine standing close beside the water. With a tourist's knapsack upon his back, and a stout umbrella in his hand, to serve the double purpose of a walking-stick, he drew near and accosted me. "Will you go with me," said he, "to make a call upon a certain old and valued friend?"

"Most willingly, if you will let me know his name."

"It is the Prophet Jonah, who still occupies submarine lodgings in a situation, to be sure, rather cold and damp, yet commanding a fine water privilege." "There is nothing," I replied, "which would please me more; but how is it to be accomplished?" "Be patient, and you shall see." Just then a slight ripple ridged the surface of the sea, bubbles appeared, and then there followed them the black muzzle of Leviathan, who, with mighty strokes, pushed toward the shore. Arriving there, his under jaw slid half way up the beach, and his upper jaw slowly rose like a trapdoor, disclosing a fearful chasm of darkness within. I looked down the throat of the beast, and beheld descending it a rickety wooden staircase, which was evidently the only feasible access to interior apartments. Hardly would I have dared to trust myself to the tumble-down passage but for the importunate hand of my companion, which pressed me along beside him through the doorway and down the steps. The monster let down his grisly portcullis behind us, and in total darkness we groped to the bottom of our way, where we emerged into the most shabby room that ever dawned upon the eyes of the visiting committee of a benevolent association.

The central figure was an unutterably lean and woebegone looking man, who, on a rush-bottomed chair, the only one in the room, sat mending his sole pair of unmentionables by the aid of a small needle-book which I was informed his mother had given him on leaving home.

"Mr. Jonah, Mr. Fitz-Gerald," said my friend, sententiously. "Very happy to know Mr. Fitz-Gerald," returned the seer; though, as I took his lank and ghostly fingers in mine, he looked the very antipodes of happy. Decayed gentleman as he was, he shuffled around to do the honors of his mansion, and offered us the chair in which he had been sitting. We refused to dispossess him, and took our seats upon the shaky pine table, which, with one battered brazen candlestick, holding an inch of semi-luminous tallow, and a dog's-eared copy of Watts's Hymns, also a gift from his mother, completed his inventory of furniture.

"How do you like your situation?" asked my friend.

"Leaky," replied Jonah; "find the climate don't agree with me. I often wish I hadn't come."

"Can't you leave here when you want to? I should think you would clear out if you find it uncomfortable," said I to our entertainer.

"I have repeatedly asked my landlord to make out his bill and let me go," replied the gentleman; "but he isn't used to casting up his prophets, and I don't know when I *shall* get off."

Just then Leviathan, from the top of the stairs, by a strange introversion looked down into his own interiors, and in a hoarse voice called out to know whether we were going to stay all night, as he wanted to put down the shutters.

"Be happy to give you a bed, gentlemen, but I sleep on the floor myself," woefully murmured the poor seer. "You mustn't neglect to call on me if you ever pass through Joppa, and—and—I ever get back myself." We wrung Jonah's hand convulsively, rattled up the crazy stairs, and ran out upon the sand just as Leviathan was about shoving off into deep water.

RESURGAM

One morning, having taken my ordinary dose without yet feeling its effect, I strolled into a bookseller's to get the latest number of Putnam's. Turning over its leaves as it lay upon the counter, the first article which detained my eyes was headed "The Hasheesh Eater." * None but a man in my circumstances can realize the intense interest which possessed me at the sight of these words.

For a while I lingered upon them with an inexplicable dread of looking further into the paper. I shut the book, and toyed with my curiosity by examining its cover, as one who receives a letter directed in some unfamiliar hand carefully scrutinizes the postmark and the envelope, and dallies with the seal before he finally breaks it open. I had supposed myself the only hasheesh-eater upon this side of the ocean; this idea of utter isolation had been one element in many of my horrors. That some one among my acquaintance had been detailing a fragment of my own experience, as viewed by him from without, was my first hypothesis. Although, in itself considered, there was nothing very improbable in the acquirement of the habit by another person, the coincidence of my having fallen upon this article, with the hasheesh force still latent within me, seemed so remarkable that I could not believe it. Then I said to myself, I will not read this paper now. I will defer it until another time; for, if its recital be one of the horrors, it may darken the complexion of my awaited vision. In pursuance of this purpose, I passed out of the shop and went down the street.

I was not satisfied. Whichever way I turned I was followed by a shadow of fascination. By an irresistible attraction I was drawn back to the counter. If the worst were there, I must know it. I

* See p. 156. Ludlow also contributed a piece to *Putnam's Monthly Magazine* entitled "The Apocalypse of Hasheesh" 8 (Dec. 1856): 625–630, almost entirely drawn from his *Hasheesh Eater.*

returned, and there, as before, lay the unsealed mystery. With a trembling hand I turned to the place; again I scrutinized the caption, to see if some unconscious illusion of a hasheesh state, which had ensued before I was aware, had not made objective the words which so many a day had stamped upon my brain. No; plainly as eyes could read them, they stood upon the page. I would read the article from beginning to end. This resolution, once formed, was shaken, but not broken, by an unavoidable glance ahead, which told me that the recital was one of agonies.

It was only a moment before I found that I was not this hasheesh-eater. Yet as, with the devouring gaze of a miser, I read, dwelt upon, and re-read every line, I found such startling analogies to my own past experience that cold drops started upon my forehead, and I exclaimed, "This man has been in my own soul." We both had been abandoned of Heaven; had climbed up into the prerogatives of Deity, thence to be cast down; had drawn the accursed knife at the whispers of a frightful temptation; had been the disowned, the abominated, the execrated of men. Should I carry the parallel further? *He had forever abandoned hasheesh.* How terribly this question shook my soul! In an instant, like some grand pageant, the glories of the enchantment streamed before my eyes. Out of the past came Memory, swinging delicious censers; upon the fragrant vapor, as it floated upward, was traced a sublimer heaven, a more beauteous earth, from the days gone by, than ever Sorcery painted upon the Fate-compelling smoke for a rapt gazer into Futurity. There the pangs of the old time had no place; all was serenity, ecstasy, revelation. Should I forego all this forever?

So help me God, I would!

The author of that article I did not know. Of his name I had not even the faintest suspicion. Yet for him I felt a sympathy; yes, though it be unworldly, an affection such as would move me to the highest office of gratitude. Into my hitherto unbroken loneliness he had penetrated; unconscious of each other's presence, we had walked the valley of awful shadows side by side. As no other man upon the earth could feel for me, he could feel. As none other could counsel me, he might counsel. For the first time in all the tremendous stretch of my spell-bound eternity heard I the voice of sympathy or saw I an exemplar of escape. Though I might never look upon his face on earth, disenthralled from the bodily I should know him immediately, for I was bound to him by ties spun from the distaff of a supernatural hand.

I returned homeward, bearing in my mind almost the exact words of that vivid and most truthful recital. So powerfully did its emotion possess me as to supplant entirely that of the drug, which did not once render itself perceptible.

There is a rich lesson of deep springs of human action taught by the old history, wherein he who in after years was to make the name of Carthage glorious among the peoples uplifted his hand of adjuration in the presence of his father. From him out of whose original fount he came, and in whose depths his earliest waves of being found their noblest, their truest echo of response, most naturally did he draw that full tide of strength which through all barriers was to bear him on until he whelmed in the deluge of inherited vengeance the territory of his foe.

No Hannibal was I, but the struggling sufferer under long soldered thrall of sorcery, groaning for a deliverance which I just dared to tempt; no Hamilcar wert thou, my father,* for the hands with which thou supportedst mine in their final vow of liberty were wet, not with the blood of war, but the tears of a most precious compassion; and as before thee, on that last night of my bondage, I took the oath which opened up my prison-doors, from thy presence I won a sustaining force of will which, through many a day of fray and weariness, was to press me on (in all reverence to the majestic memorials of past time) against a mightier, a subtler enemy than Rome!

After thus sealing my deliverance, my next step was to discover the author of the article in Putnam's, which had determined me

* The Rev. Henry G. Ludlow, a Presbyterian.

to it at first. This, through the kind courtesy of some of its presiding minds, I was in a few days enabled to do. To the author I then wrote, trusting to no other introduction than that of our common ground and the sympathies of human nature. I asked counsel upon the best means of softening the pathway of my escape, for I had seen enough in my former effort to assure me that it would be a very hard one. Moreover, the simple possession of a letter from one who had been so instrumental in originally effecting my release would be a powerful aid toward rendering it permanent.

A very short time elapsed before I received an answer to my inquiries. My anxiety could not have made it more full than it was of information and assistance; my gratitude could not have exaggerated the value of its sympathy and encouragement. But for the sacredness which to a mind of any refinement invests a correspondence of such nature, I could not refrain from here giving it publicity. It strengthened my resolution, it opened for me a cheering sky of hope, it pointed me to expedients for insuring success, it mitigated the sufferings of the present. It is, and ever will be, treasured among the most precious archives of my life.

Thus supported humanly, and feeling the ever-near incitement and sustenance of a Presence still higher, I began to feel my way out of the barathrum of my long sojourn, and its jaws closed behind me, never since then, never hereafter till there be no more help in heaven, to open for my ingress. Out of its tremendous Elysium, its quenchless Tartarus, its speechless revelations, I came slowly into a land of subdued skies and heavier atmosphere. The jet of flame and fountain grew dimmer behind me in the mists of distance; broader, in the land from which I had long wandered, before me grew the shadows of the present life. Yet among all the lights which, unobscured by vapor, from afar led me on my way, was one which gleamed with a promise that in the days hereafter, the soul, purified from the earthy, should once more, painlessly, look on the now abandoned glories of its past apocalypse.

CAVE SUCCEDANEA *

I am not aware of the existence of any in this part of the world who are now in the habit of using hasheesh. Those persons to whom, at their request, I formerly administered it, for experiment's sake, were satisfied with the one trial, upon my assuring them that any prolonged indulgence would infallibly lead to horrors.

Yet, since it is not at all impossible that these pages may meet the eye of those who, unknown to me, are incipient hasheesh-eaters, or who, having tested to the full the powers of the drug, now find its influence a slavery, yet are ignorant of the proper means of emancipation, I will not let this opportunity pass for suggesting, through a somewhat further narrative of my own case, a counsel which may chance to be salutary.

The hasheesh-eater needs particularly to resist the temptation of retreating, in the trials of his slow disenthrallment, to some other stimulus, such as liquors or opium. Against such a retreat I was warned by the same adviser whose article in the Magazine had been my prime motor to escape.

As in an early part of this narrative it has been mentioned, strong experimental tendencies had led me, long before the first acquaintance with hasheesh, to investigate the effect of all narcotics and stimulants, not so much with a view to pleasure as to the discovery of new phases of mental life. Among these researches had been opium. This drug never affected me very powerfully, not in one instance producing any thing like hallucination, but operating principally through a quiet which no external circumstances could disturb—slightly tinged, when my eyes were shut, with pleasing images of scenery. Its mild effect was probably owing to some resistant peculiarity of constitution, since I remember having once taken a dose, which I afterward learned, upon good authority, to have been sufficient to kill three healthy men, without any remarkable phenomena ensuing. Several considerations

* Roughly translated, "Watch out you don't take my place."

operated with me to prevent my making opium an habitual indulgence, besides this fact of its moderate potency. This, of itself, might not have been sufficient, since the capability which I acquired in its use of sustaining the most prolonged and severe fatigue was in my case unexampled.

In the first place, I was secured from enslavement by the terrors of De Quincey's suffering. I felt assured that he had not unmasked the half of it, since his exquisite sense of the refined and the appropriate in all communion with the public, showing itself in a thousand places throughout his works, had evidently withheld him, in his confessions, from giving to the painful intaglio that deep stroke of the graver which he thought that good taste would not permit, even under sanction of truth.

Again, a consideration of more narrow prejudice withheld me— the impossibility, if I should use opium, of concealing the fact from my associates, some of whom were physicians, and hardly any of them so unobserving as not to be attracted curiously to the peculiarities of the opium eye, complexion, and manner.

At this time the reputation of being an opium-eater was one very little desirable in the community which included me, had its further abominable consequences been recklessly put aside. It was impossible for any one known to have used the drug to make any intellectual effort whatever, speech, published article, or brilliant conversation, without being hailed satirically as Coleridge *le petit,* or De Quincey in the second edition. That this was not altogether a morbid condition of public sentiment in the microcosm where I dwelt, may be inferred from a fact which, occurring a few months before I entered it, had no doubt acted to tinge general opinion.

A certain person, in reading "The Confessions," had gathered from them (it would be hard to say how, since their author every where expresses the opium state as one whose serenity is repulsive to all action for the time being) that he should be able to excel De Quincey upon his own field if he wrote while at the height of the effect. Setting apart one evening for the English opium-eater's literary discomfiture, he drank his laudanum, and locked himself into his room alone with the awful presence of a quire of foolscap. On the following morning, his friends, knocking at the door repeatedly, received no answer, and, fearful of some accident, broke in the lock. Lo! our De Quincey *in petto* was seated in his chair, with pen in hand, and his forehead resting upon a blank mass of paper, in all the *abandon* of innocent repose!

After the final abandonment of hasheesh, however, at times, when distress had reduced me to the willingness to test any relief save that of return, I once or twice tried the effect of opium. It was invariably bad, not operating, as a renewal of the hasheesh indulgence would have done, to lift me into the former plane of pleasurable activity and interest in things about me, but singularly combining with whatever of the hasheesh force might be remaining in my system to cover me once more with the pall which made the worst parts of the old life so painful. Insane faces glared at me; dire voices of prophecy spoke to me even when wide awake; I was filled with foreboding of some impending wrathful visitation, and learned to my sorrow that I was only exchanging one bitter cup for another. As the opium-influence never approximated the authority of a fascination over me, I willingly and finally abjured it as an impossible relief.

It was some time after this that my constitution, broken down by hard work, which, corporeally, to use an intensely idiomatic term, was much more "cruel on me" than hasheesh had been at its most nerve-racking stages, demanded not only rest, but something immediately tonic. The former was easily attained by closing my connection with the educational "Knight of the Rueful Countenance"—a connection which all the while had not been chemical, like that of an acid with a base, but mechanical, like that of a force with a lever. The latter (the tonic) was to be found ultimately in exercise; but, for the sake of more instantaneous relief from debility, at the advice of a physician, I had recourse to spirits. A very short trial of their effect having convinced me that their stimulus was as dangerous as opium, I abandoned this also as a means of relief. The experiment made with it renewed, sometimes for two days together, the clarity, though not the exquisite beauty of the hasheesh visionary state, and repeated, in due succession, its ideal sufferings of night and daylight.

Thus taught that every possible stimulus of any power must invariably act as auxiliary to the partially routed forces of my foe, I called in no more treacherous helps from without, but went single-handed to the fight, armed only with patience and friendly sympathies.

Since learning this lesson, the progress into recovery has been by slow degrees, yet a progress after all. Ever and anon a return of the former suffering has made it necessary to spend half the night in walking; but the sense that every step forward was also a step, however infinitesimal, upward, is a greater relief than the possibility of once more journeying through the rosiest realms of the former hasheesh happiness. At least for the present—as a proviso to the proposition let this be added—for he who has once looked upon great glories can not but hope to behold them again, when nature is freed from all the grossness which makes them painful in the present state, and they shall come to him, not through walls which they must melt to make a passage-way, but like the sunlight, which, falling joyously and harmlessly, bathes the forehead of the little child asleep.

Though the Pythagorean is able to put aside hashish for an extended time, he still is eager to defend its use as a stimulant, and believes he owes to it his deeper understanding of truth and beauty. He prefers it to opium, he says, and though he warns the reader to beware, he clearly has not much terror of his own relapse into further hashish eating. Indeed, Ludlow's later life had few periods of hiatus. He always insisted, as he does here, that there was not as much physical deterioration connected with the habit as was popularly believed. The causes of his early death are unknown, though those who remembered him ascribed it to hashish in one way or another.

LOUISA MAY ALCOTT, "PERILOUS PLAY" * (1869)

This story of hashish eating at the seaside was published at the very peak of the career of Louisa May Alcott (1832–1888), after the first part of Little Women (1868) and before An Old-Fashioned Girl (1870). She had just won a national reputation as a preceptive novelist for young people, and her treatment of hashish in "Perilous Play" provides a look at another of her aspects—that of sophisticated narrator of contemporary manners.

There is no hint in this story, of course, about any personal experience Alcott may have had with cannabis, and none of her correspondence or contemporary biographical notes about her contain any either. But as narrator she has no strongly adverse opinion of the drug, and the story's action, from the abrupt decision in the middle of a summer garden to try hashish to the final praise of the drug by Mark, the hero, suggests that Alcott did not particularly disapprove of taking hashish as a novel pastime, or even of the odd idea of falling in love when under its influence. She is content here mainly to observe, the writer who, of all others in her time

---

* L[ouisa] M[ay] A[lcott], "Perilous Play," *Frank Leslie's Chimney Corner* viii (194), Feb. 13, 1869, reprinted in *Plots and Counterplots,* ed. M. Stern (New York, 1976).

we would consider as having set the standard of correct behavior for young men and women. The answer to this seeming paradox lies partly in our own society's belief that the illegality of cannabis reinforces its immorality. To take it was certainly not illegal in 1869, only perhaps slightly foolhardy. "Perilous Play" is a relic of a simpler age, when manners were freer than now.

One note on the form of the drug taken by Belle, Rose, Mark, and their friends: Ludlow (see p. 177) took cannabis extract and also speaks of his "bolus," by which he means a large pill or tablet of compressed hashish, to be swallowed whole or dissolved in a hot drink. This is not quite what Alcott describes. In her story the pills are "white," "bean-shaped," with a green center, and quite a number of them must be taken for any effect, according to Dr. Meredith, who offers them. They were probably pills specially made according to the doctor's prescription. He says that he gives them to patients for nervous disorders.

Nearly all his beach companions are eager to try them, yet if he offers them an exotic experience, it is one completely devoid of Taylor's and Ludlow's orientalism, and in this we get a sense of the naturalization of cannabis in nineteenth-century America.

"IF SOMEONE does not propose a new and interesting amusement, I shall die of ennui!" said pretty Belle Daventry, in a tone of despair. "I have read all my books, used up all my Berlin wools, and it's too warm to go to town for more. No one can go sailing yet, as the tide is out; we are all nearly tired to death of cards, croquet, and gossip, so what shall we do to while away this endless afternoon? Dr. Meredith, I command you to invent and propose a new game in five minutes."

"To hear is to obey," replied the young man, who lay in the grass at her feet, as he submissively slapped his forehead, and fell a-thinking with all his might.

Holding up her finger to preserve silence, Belle pulled out her watch and waited with an expectant smile. The rest of the young party, who were indolently scattered about under the elms, drew nearer, and brightened visibly, for Dr. Meredith's inventive powers were well-known, and something refreshingly novel might be expected from him. One gentleman did not stir, but then he lay within earshot, and merely turned his fine eyes from the sea to the group before him. His glance rested a moment on Belle's piquant figure, for she looked very pretty with her bright hair blowing in the wind, one plump white arm extended to keep order, and one little foot, in a distracting slipper, just visible below the voluminous folds of her dress. Then the glance passed to another figure, sitting somewhat apart in a cloud of white muslin, for an airy burnoose floated from head and shoulders, showing only a singularly charming face. Pale and yet brilliant, for the Southern eyes were magnificent, the clear olive cheeks contrasted well with darkest hair; lips like a pomegranate flower, and delicate, straight brows, as mobile as the lips. A cluster of crimson flowers, half falling from the loose black braids, and a golden bracelet of Arabian coins on the slender wrist were the only ornaments she wore, and became her better than the fashionable frippery of her companions. A book lay on her lap, but her eyes, full of a passionate melancholy, were fixed on the sea, which glittered round an island green and flowery as a summer paradise. Rose St. Just was as beautiful as her Spanish mother, but had inherited the pride and reserve of her English father; and this pride was the thorn which repelled lovers from the human flower. Mark Done sighed as he looked, and as if the sigh, low as it was, roused her from her reverie, Rose flashed a quick glance at him, took up her book, and went on reading the legend of "The Lotus Eaters."

"Time is up now, Doctor," cried Belle, pocketing her watch with a flourish.

"Ready to report," answered Meredith, sitting up and producing a little box of tortoiseshell and gold.

"How mysterious! What is it? Let me see, first!" And Belle removed the cover, looking like an inquisitive child. "Only bonbons; how stupid! That won't do, sir. We don't want to be fed with sugarplums. We demand to be amused."

"Eat six of these despised bonbons, and you *will* be amused in a new, delicious, and wonderful manner," said the young doctor, laying half a dozen on a green leaf and offering them to her.

"Why, what are they?" she asked, looking at him askance.

"Hashish; did you never hear of it?"

"Oh, yes; it's that Indian stuff which brings one fantastic visions, isn't it? I've always wanted to see and taste it, and now I will," cried Belle, nibbling at one of the bean-shaped comfits with its green heart.

"I advise you not to try it. People do all sorts of queer things when they take it. I wouldn't for the world," said a prudent young lady warningly, as all examined the box and its contents.

"Six can do no harm, I give you my word. I take twenty before I can enjoy myself, and some people even more. I've tried many experiments, both on the sick and the well, and nothing ever happened amiss, though the demonstrations were immensely interesting," said Meredith, eating his sugarplums with a tranquil air, which was very convincing to others.

"How shall I feel?" asked Belle, beginning on her second comfit.

"A heavenly dreaminess comes over one, in which they move as if on air. Everything is calm and lovely to them: no pain, no care, no fear of anything, and while it lasts one feels like an angel half asleep."

"But if one takes too much, how then?" said a deep voice behind the doctor.

"Hum! Well, that's not so pleasant, unless one likes phantoms, frenzies, and a touch of nightmare, which seems to last a thousand years. Ever try it, Done?" replied Meredith, turning toward the speaker, who was now leaning on his arm and looking interested.

"Never. I'm not a good subject for experiments. Too nervous a temperament to play pranks with."

"I should say ten would be about your number. Less than that seldom affects men. Ladies go off sooner, and don't need so many. Miss St. Just, may I offer you a taste of Elysium? I owe my success to you," said the doctor, approaching her deferentially.

"To me! And how?" she asked, lifting her large eyes with a slight smile.

"I was in the depths of despair when my eye caught the title of your book and I was saved. For I remembered that I had hashish in my pocket."

"Are you a lotus-eater?" she said, permitting him to lay the six charmed bonbons on the page.

"My faith, no! I use it for my patients. It is very efficacious in nervous disorders, and is getting to be quite a pet remedy with us."

"I do not want to forget the past, but to read the future. Will hashish help me to do that?" asked Rose with an eager look, which made the young man flush, wondering if he bore any part in her hopes of that veiled future.

"Alas, no. I wish it could, for I, too, long to know my fate," he answered, very low, as he looked into the lovely face before him.

The soft glance changed to one of cool indifference and Rose gently brushed the hashish off her book, saying, with a little gesture of dismissal, "Then I have no desire to taste Elysium."

The white morsels dropped into the grass at her feet; but Dr. Meredith let them lie, and turning sharply, went back to sun himself in Belle's smiles.

"I've eaten all mine, and so has Evelyn. Mr. Norton will see goblins, I know, for he has taken quantities. I'm glad of it, for he don't believe in it, and I want to have him convinced by making a spectacle of himself for our amusement," said Belle, in great spirits at the new plan.

"When does the trance come on?" asked Evelyn, a shy girl, already rather alarmed at what she had done.

"About three hours after you take your dose, though the time varies with different people. Your pulse will rise, heart beat quickly, eyes darken and dilate, and an uplifted sensation will pervade you generally. Then these symptoms change, and the bliss begins. I've seen people sit or lie in one position for hours, rapt in a delicious dream, and wake from it as tranquil as if they had not a nerve in their bodies."

"How charming! I'll take some every time I'm worried. Let me see. It's now four, so our trances will come about seven, and we will devote the evening to manifestations," said Belle.

"Come, Done, try it. We are all going in for the fun. Here's your dose," and Meredith tossed him a dozen bonbons, twisted up in a bit of paper.

"No, thank you; I know myself too well to risk it. If you are all going to turn hashish-eaters, you'll need someone to take care of you, so I'll keep sober," tossing the little parcel back.

It fell short, and the doctor, too lazy to pick it up, let it lie, merely saying, with a laugh, "Well, I advise any bashful man to take hashish when he wants to offer his heart to any fair lady, for it will give him the courage of a hero, the eloquence of a poet, and the ardor of an Italian. Remember that, gentlemen, and come to me when the crisis approaches."

"Does it conquer the pride, rouse the pity, and soften the hard hearts of the fair sex?" asked Done.

"I dare say now is your time to settle the fact, for here are two ladies who have imbibed, and in three hours will be in such a seraphic state of mind that 'No' will be an impossibility to them."

"Oh, mercy on us; what *have* we done? If that's the case, I shall shut myself up till my foolish fit is over. Rose, you haven't taken any; I beg you to mount guard over me, and see that I don't disgrace myself by any nonsense. Promise me you will," cried Belle, in half-real, half-feigned alarm at the consequences of her prank.

"I promise," said Rose, and floated down the green path as noiselessly as a white cloud, with a curious smile on her lips.

"Don't tell any of the rest what we have done, but after tea let us go into the grove and compare notes," said Norton, as Done strolled away to the beach, and the voices of approaching friends broke the summer quiet.

At tea, the initiated glanced covertly at one another, and saw, or fancied they saw, the effects of the hashish, in a certain suppressed excitement of manner, and unusually brilliant eyes. Belle laughed often, a silvery ringing laugh, pleasant to hear; but when complimented on her good spirits, she looked distressed, and said she could not help her merriment; Meredith was quite calm, but rather dreamy; Evelyn was pale, and her next neighbor heard her heart beat; Norton talked incessantly, but as he talked uncommonly well, no one suspected anything. Done and Miss St. Just watched the others with interest, and were very quiet, especially Rose, who scarcely spoke, but smiled her sweetest, and looked very lovely.

The moon rose early, and the experimenters slipped away to the grove, leaving the outsiders on the lawn as usual. Some bold spirit asked Rose to sing, and she at once complied, pouring out Spanish airs in a voice that melted the hearts of her audience, so full of fiery sweetness or tragic pathos was it. Done seemed quite carried away, and lay with his face in the grass, to hide the tears that would come; till, afraid of openly disgracing himself, he started up and hurried down to the little wharf, where he sat alone, listening to the music with a countenance which plainly revealed to the stars the passion which possessed him. The sound of loud laughter from the grove, followed by entire silence, caused him to wonder what demonstrations were taking place, and half resolve to go and see. But that enchanting voice held him captive, even when a boat put off mysteriously from a point nearby, and sailed away like a phantom through the twilight.

Half an hour afterward, a white figure came down the path, and Rose's voice broke in on his midsummer night's dream. The moon shone clearly now, and showed him the anxiety in her face as she said hurriedly, "Where is Belle?"

"Gone sailing, I believe."

"How could you let her go? She was not fit to take care of herself!"

"I forgot that."

"So did I, but I promised to watch over her, and I must. Which way did they go?" demanded Rose, wrapping the white mantle about her, and running her eye over the little boats moored below.

"You will follow her?"

"Yes."

"I'll be your guide then. They went toward the lighthouse; it is too far to row; I am at your service. Oh, say yes," cried Done, leaping into his own skiff and offering his hand persuasively.

She hesitated an instant and looked at him. He was always pale, and the moonlight seemed to increase this pallor, but his hat brim hid his eyes, and his voice was very quiet. A loud peal of laughter floated over the water, and as if the sound decided her, she gave him her hand and entered the boat. Done smiled triumphantly as he shook out the sail, which caught the freshening wind, and sent the boat dancing along a path of light.

How lovely it was! All the indescribable allurements of a perfect summer night surrounded them: balmy airs, enchanting moonlight, distant music, and, close at hand, the delicious atmosphere of love, which made itself felt in the eloquent silences that fell between them. Rose seemed to yield to the subtle charm, and leaned back on the cushioned seat with her beautiful head uncovered, her face full of dreamy softness, and her hands lying loosely clasped before her. She seldom spoke, showed no further anxiety for Belle, and soon seemed to forget the object of her search, so absorbed was she in some delicious thought which wrapped her in its peace.

Done sat opposite, flushed now, restless, and excited, for his eyes glittered; the hand on the rudder shook, and his voice sounded intense and passionate, even in the utterance of the simplest words. He talked continually and with unusual brilliance, for, though a man of many accomplishments, he was too indolent or too fastidious to exert himself, except among his peers. Rose seemed to look without seeing, to listen without hearing, and though she smiled blissfully, the smiles were evidently not for him.

On they sailed, scarcely heeding the bank of black cloud piled up in the horizon, the rising wind, or the silence which proved their solitude. Rose moved once or twice, and lifted her hand as if to speak, but sank back mutely, and the hand fell again as if it had not energy enough to enforce her wish. A cloud sweeping over the moon, a distant growl of thunder, and the slight gust that struck the sail seemed to rouse her. Done was singing now like one inspired, his hat at his feet, hair in disorder, and a strangely rapturous expression in his eyes, which were fixed on her. She started, shivered, and seemed to recover herself with an effort.

"Where are they?" she asked, looking vainly for the island heights and the other boat.

"They have gone to the beach, I fancy, but we will follow." As Done leaned forward to speak, she saw his face and shrank back with a sudden flush, for in it she read clearly what she had felt, yet doubted until now. He saw the telltale blush and gesture, and said impetuously, "You know it now; you cannot deceive me longer, or daunt me with your pride! Rose, I love you, and dare tell you so tonight!"

"Not now—not here—I will not listen. Turn back, and be silent, I entreat you, Mr. Done," she said hurriedly.

He laughed a defiant laugh and took her hand in his, which was burning and throbbing with the rapid heat of his pulse.

"No, I *will* have my answer here, and now, and never turn back till you give it; you have been a thorny Rose, and given me many wounds. I'll be paid for my heartache with sweet words, tender looks, and frank confessions of love, for proud as you are, you do love me, and dare not deny it."

Something in his tone terrified her; she snatched her hand away and drew beyond his reach, trying to speak calmly, and to meet coldly the ardent glances of the eyes which were strangely darkened and dilated with uncontrollable emotion.

"You forget yourself. I shall give no answer to an avowal made in such terms. Take me home instantly," she said in a tone of command.

"Confess you love me, Rose."

"Never!"

"Ah! I'll have a kinder answer, or—" Done half rose and put out his hand to grasp and draw her to him, but the cry she uttered seemed to arrest him with a sort of shock. He dropped into his seat, passed his hand over his eyes, and shivered nervously as he muttered in an altered tone, "I meant nothing; it's the moonlight; sit down, I'll control myself—upon my soul I will!"

"If you do not, I shall go overboard. Are you mad, sir?" cried Rose, trembling with indignation.

"Then I shall follow you, for I *am* mad, Rose, with love—hashish!"

His voice sank to a whisper, but the last word thrilled along her nerves, as no sound of fear had ever done before. An instant she regarded him with a look which took in every sign of unnatural excitement, then she clasped her hands with an imploring gesture, saying, in a tone of despair, "Why did I come! How will it end? Oh, Mark, take me home before it is too late!"

"Hush! Be calm; don't thwart me, or I may get wild again. My thoughts are not clear, but I understand you. There, take my knife, and if I forget myself, kill me. Don't go overboard; you are too beautiful to die, my Rose!"

He threw her the slender hunting knife he wore, looked at her a moment with a far-off look, and trimmed the sail like one moving in a dream. Rose took the weapon, wrapped her cloak closely about her, and crouching as far away as possible, kept her eye on him, with a face in which watchful terror contended with some secret trouble and bewilderment more powerful than her fear.

The boat moved round and began to beat up against wind and tide; spray flew from her bow; the sail bent and strained in the gusts that struck it with perilous fitfulness. The moon was nearly hidden by scudding clouds, and one-half the sky was black with the gathering storm. Rose looked from threatening heavens to treacherous sea, and tried to be ready for any danger, but her calm had been sadly broken, and she could not recover it. Done sat motionless, uttering no word of encouragement, though the frequent flaws almost tore the rope from his hand, and the water often dashed over him.

"Are we in any danger?" asked Rose at last, unable to bear the silence, for he looked like a ghostly helmsman seen by the fitful light, pale now, wild-eyed, and speechless.

"Yes, great danger."

"I thought you were a skillful boatman."

"I am when I am myself; now I am rapidly losing the control of my will, and the strange quiet is coming over me. If I had been alone I should have given up sooner, but for your sake I've kept on."

"Can't you work the boat?" asked Rose, terror-struck by the changed tone of his voice, the slow, uncertain movements of his hands.

"No. I see everything through a thick cloud; your voice sounds far away, and my one desire is to lay my head down and sleep."

"Let me steer—I can, I must!" she cried, springing toward him and laying her hand on the rudder.

He smiled and kissed the little hand, saying dreamily, "You could not hold it a minute; sit by me, love; let us turn the boat again, and drift away together—anywhere, anywhere out of the world."

"Oh, heaven, what will become of us!" and Rose wrung her hands in real despair. "Mr. Done—Mark—dear Mark, rouse yourself and listen to me. Turn, as you say, for it is certain death to go on so. Turn, and let us drift down to the lighthouse; they will hear and help us. Quick, take down the sail, get out the oars, and let us try to reach there before the storm breaks."

As Rose spoke, he obeyed her like a dumb animal; love for her was stronger even than the instinct of self-preservation, and for her sake he fought against the treacherous lethargy which was swiftly overpowering him. The sail was lowered, the boat brought round, and with little help from the ill-pulled oars it drifted rapidly out to sea with the ebbing tide.

As she caught her breath after this dangerous maneuver was accomplished, Rose asked, in a quiet tone she vainly tried to render natural, "How much hashish did you take?"

"All that Meredith threw me. Too much; but I was possessed to do it, so I hid the roll and tried it," he answered, peering at her with a weird laugh.

"Let us talk; our safety lies in keeping awake, and I dare not let you sleep," continued Rose, dashing water on her own hot forehead with a sort of desperation.

"Say you love me; that would wake me from my lost sleep, I think. I have hoped and feared, waited and suffered so long. Be pitiful, and answer, Rose."

"I do; but I should not own it now."

So low was the soft reply he scarcely heard it, but he felt it and made a strong effort to break from the hateful spell that bound him. Leaning forward, he tried to read her face in a ray of moonlight breaking through the clouds; he saw a new and tender warmth in it, for all the pride was gone, and no fear marred the eloquence of those soft, Southern eyes.

"Kiss me, Rose, then I shall believe it. I feel lost in a dream, and you, so changed, so kind, may be only a fair phantom. Kiss me, love, and make it real."

As if swayed by a power more potent than her will, Rose bent to meet his lips. But the ardent pressure seemed to startle her from a momentary oblivion of everything but love. She covered up her face and sank down, as if overwhelmed with shame, sobbing through passionate tears, "Oh, what am I doing? I am mad, for I, too, have taken hashish."

What he answered she never heard, for a rattling peal of thunder drowned his voice, and then the storm broke loose. Rain fell in torrents, the wind blew fiercely, sky and sea were black as ink, and the boat tossed from wave to wave almost at their mercy. Giving herself up for lost, Rose crept to her lover's side and clung there, conscious only that they would bide together through the perils their own folly brought them. Done's excitement was quite gone now; he sat like a statue, shielding the frail creature whom he loved with a smile on his face, which looked awfully emotionless when the lightning gave her glimpses of its white immobility. Drenched, exhausted, and half senseless with danger, fear, and exposure, Rose saw at last a welcome glimmer through the gloom, and roused herself to cry for help.

"Mark, wake and help me! Shout, for God's sake—shout and call them, for we are lost if we drift by!" she cried, lifting his head from his breast, and forcing him to see the brilliant beacons streaming far across the troubled water.

He understood her, and springing up, uttered shout after shout like one demented. Fortunately, the storm had lulled a little; the lighthouse keeper heard and answered. Rose seized the helm, Done the oars, and with one frantic effort guided the boat into quieter waters, where it was met by the keeper, who towed it to the rocky nook which served as harbor.

The moment a strong, steady face met her eyes, and a gruff, cheery voice hailed her, Rose gave way, and was carried up to the house, looking more like a beautiful drowned Ophelia than a living woman.

"Here, Sally, see to the poor thing; she's had a rough time on't. I'll take care of her sweetheart—and a nice job I'll have, I reckon, for if he ain't mad or drunk, he's had a stroke of lightnin', and looks as if he wouldn't get his hearin' in a hurry," said the old man as he housed his unexpected guests and stood staring at Done, who looked about him like one dazed. "You jest turn in yonder and sleep it off, mate. We'll see to the lady, and right up your boat in the morning," the old man added.

"Be kind to Rose. I frightened her. I'll not forget you. Yes, let me sleep and get over this cursed folly as soon as possible," muttered this strange visitor.

Done threw himself down on the rough couch and tried to sleep, but every nerve was overstrained, every pulse beating like a trip-hammer, and everything about him was intensified and exaggerated with awful power. The thundershower seemed a wild hurricane, the quaint room a wilderness peopled with tormenting phantoms, and all the events of his life passed before him in an endless procession, which nearly maddened him. The old man looked weird and gigantic, his own voice sounded shrill and discordant, and the ceaseless murmur of Rose's incoherent wanderings haunted him like parts of a grotesque but dreadful dream.

All night he lay motionless, with staring eyes, feverish lips, and a mind on the rack, for the delicate machinery which had been tampered with revenged the wrong by torturing the foolish experimenter. All night Rose wept and sang, talked and cried for help in a piteous state of nervous excitement, for with her the trance came first, and the after-agitation was increased by the events of the evening. She slept at last, lulled by the old woman's motherly care, and Done was spared one tormenting fear, for he dreaded the consequences of this folly on her, more than upon himself.

As day dawned he rose, haggard and faint, and staggered out. At the door he met the keeper, who stopped him to report that the boat was in order, and a fair day coming. Seeing doubt and perplexity in the old man's eye, Done told him the truth, and added that he was going to the beach for a plunge, hoping by that simple tonic to restore his unstrung nerves.

He came back feeling like himself again, except for a dull headache, and a heavy sense of remorse weighing on his spirits, for he distinctly recollected all the events of the night. The old woman made him eat and drink, and in an hour he felt ready for the homeward trip.

Rose slept late, and when she woke soon recovered herself, for her dose had been a small one. When she had breakfasted and made a hasty toilet, she professed herself anxious to return at once. She dreaded yet longed to see Done, and when the time came armed herself with pride, feeling all a woman's shame at what had passed, and resolving to feign forgetfulness of the incidents of the previous night. Pale and cold as a statue she met him, but the moment he began to say humbly, "Forgive me, Rose," she silenced him with an imperious gesture and the command "Don't speak of it; I only remember that it was very horrible, and wish to forget it all as soon as possible."

"All, Rose?" he asked, significantly.

"Yes, *all*. No one would care to recall the follies of a hashish dream," she answered, turning hastily to hide the scarlet flush that would rise, and the eyes that would fall before his own.

"I never can forget, but I will be silent if you bid me."

"I do. Let us go. What will they think at the island? Mr. Done, give me your promise to tell no one, now or ever, that I tried that dangerous experiment. I will guard your secret also." She spoke eagerly and looked up imploringly.

"I promise," and he gave her his hand, holding her own with a wistful glance, till she drew it away and begged him to take her home.

Leaving hearty thanks and a generous token of their gratitude, they sailed away with a fair wind, finding in the freshness of the morning a speedy cure for tired bodies and excited minds. They said little, but it was impossible for Rose to preserve her coldness. The memory of the past night broke down her pride, and Done's tender glances touched her heart. She half hid her face behind her hand, and tried to compose herself for the scene to come, for as she approached the island, she saw Belle and her party waiting for them on the shore.

"Oh, Mr. Done, screen me from their eyes and questions as much as you can! I'm so worn out and nervous, I shall betray myself. You will help me?" And she turned to him with a confiding look, strangely at variance with her usual calm self-possession.

"I'll shield you with my life, if you will tell me why you took the hashish," he said, bent on knowing his fate.

"I hoped it would make me soft and lovable, like other women. I'm tired of being a lonely statue," she faltered, as if the truth was wrung from her by a power stronger than her will.

"And I took it to gain courage to tell my love. Rose, we have been near death together; let us share life together, and neither of us be any more lonely or afraid?"

He stretched his hand to her with his heart in his face, and she gave him hers with a look of tender submission, as he said ardently, "Heaven bless hashish, if its dreams end like this!"

"A HASHISH-HOUSE
IN NEW YORK" * (1888)

*Taking hashish was not at all unheard of as a pastime in America
by the end of the nineteenth century. At the beginning of this
anonymous story, written as reportage, two middle-class New York
gentlemen are urbanely discussing the different forms of "narcotic
indulgence" available in their city. They agree to meet later for a
visit to a hashish-house in Hell's Kitchen, a house one of them
knows quite well. When they arrive there, they find the place
fairly packed with obviously well-connected New Yorkers, some
wearing masks, all dressed in Oriental costumes, all smoking marijuana and eating hashish. The narrator follows the customs of the
place, and has an experience that is only partly agreeable.*

The question arises of what a reader of Harper's Magazine *in
1888 would have made of all this. He might well have heard of
the opium dens of Chinatown referred to in the first paragraph,
and they were neither novel nor attractive. He might also have
concluded, if he thought about it at all, that cannabis was, as the
narrator first thought, taken "occasionally and experimentally by a*

* "A Hashish-house in New York: The Curious Adventures of an Individual
Who Indulged in a Few Pipefuls of the Narcotic Hemp," Harper's Magazine 67
(1888): 944–949.

234 /   TALES OF HASHISH

few scattered individuals." The purpose of the story seems to be to change his mind.

New York City figures prominently here. It has almost always been a city of bland façades, behind which the privileged people— those who can pay—may see sights as strange as they could wish. In New York questions of morality and propriety have invariably given way before unruffled urbanity, the genius of the place. The tone of this story may seem strangely modern for its time, but in fact it shows New York much as it always was, and is today.

We cannot be sure now whether "Boston, Philadelphia, Chicago, and especially New Orleans" had their own "hemp retreats," as the narrator's friend claims, but the description of the one in New York is clearly of a real place, where tastes for luxury and exoticism were fully satisfied.

"AND SO YOU THINK that opium-smoking as seen in the foul cellars of Mott Street and elsewhere is the only form of narcotic indulgence of any consequence in this city, and that hashish, if used at all, is only smoked occasionally and experimentally by a few scattered individuals?"

"That certainly is my opinion, and I consider myself fairly well informed."

"Well, you are far from right, as I can prove to you if you care to inform yourself more fully on the subject. There is a large community of hashish smokers in this city, who are daily forced to indulge their morbid appetites, and I can take you to a house up-town where hemp is used in every conceivable form, and where the lights, sounds, odors, and surroundings are all arranged so as to intensify and enhance the effects of this wonderful narcotic."

"I must confess that I am still incredulous."

"Well, if it is agreeable to you, meet me at the Hoffman House reading-room to-morrow night at ten o'clock, and I think I shall be able to convince you."

The above is the substance of a conversation that took place in the lobby of a down-town hotel between the writer of these lines and a young man about thirty-eight years of age, known to me for some years past as an opium-smoker. It was through his kindness that I had first gained access to and had been able to study up the subject of opium-smoking. Hence I really anticipated seeing some interesting phases of hemp indulgence, and was not disappointed.

The following evening at precisely ten o'clock I met the young man at the Hoffman House, and together we took a Broadway car up-town, left it at Forty-second Street, and walked rapidly toward the North River,* talking as we went.

"You will probably be greatly surprised at many things you will see to-night," he said, "just as I was when I was first introduced into the place by a friend. I have travelled over most of Europe, and have smoked opium in every *joint* in America, but never saw anything so curious as this, nor experienced any intoxication so fascinating yet so terrible as that of hashish."

"Are the habitués of this place of the same class as those who frequent the opium-smoking dives?"

"By no means. They are about evenly divided between Americans and foreigners; indeed, the place is kept by a Greek, who has invested a great deal of money in it. All the visitors, both male and female, are of the better classes, and absolute secrecy is the rule. The house has been opened about two years, I believe, and the number of regular habitués is daily on the increase."

"Are you one of the number?"

"I am, and find the intoxication far pleasanter and less hurtful than that from opium. Ah! here we are."

We paused before a gloomy-looking house, entered the gate, and passed up the steps. The windows were absolutely dark, and the entranceway looked dirty and desolate. Four pulls at the bell, a pause, and one more pull were followed by a few moments' silence, broken suddenly by the sound of falling chain, rasping bolt, and the grinding of a key in the lock. The outer door was

* Another name for the Hudson.

cautiously opened, and at a word from my companion we passed into the vestibule. The outer door was carefully closed by some one whom I could not distinguish in the utter darkness. A moment later the inner door was opened, and never shall I forget the impression produced by the sudden change from total darkness to the strange scene that met my eyes. The dark vestibule was the boundary line separating the cold, dreary streets and the ordinary world from a scene of Oriental magnificence.

A volume of heavily scented air, close upon the heels of which came a deadly sickening odor, wholly unlike anything I had ever smelled, greeted my nostrils. A hall lamp of grotesque shape flooded the hall with a subdued violet light that filtered through crenated disks of some violet fabric hung below it. The walls and ceilings, if ever modern, were no longer so, for they were shut in and hung by festoons and plaits of heavy cloth fresh from Eastern looms. Tassels of blue, green, yellow, red, and tinsel here and there peeped forth, matching the curious edging of variously colored bead-work that bordered each fold of drapery like a huge procession of luminous ants, and seemed to flow into little phosphorescent pools wherever the cloth was caught up. Queer figures and strange lettering, in the same work, were here and there disclosed upon the ceiling cloth.

Along one side of the hall, between two doors, were ranged huge tubs and pots of majolica-like ware and blue-necked Japanese vases, in which were plants, shrubs, and flowers of the most exquisite color and odor. Green vines clambered up the walls and across the ceiling, and catching their tendrils in the balustrades of the stairs (which were also of curious design), threw down long sprays and heavy festoons of verdure.

As my companion, who had paused a moment to give me time to look about me, walked toward the far end of the hall, I followed him, and passed into a small room on the right, where, with the assistance of a colored servant, we exchanged our coats, hats, and shoes for others more in keeping with our surroundings. First a long plush gown, quilted with silk down the front, and irregularly ornamented in bead and braid with designs of serpents, flowers, crescents, and stars, was slipped on over the head. Next a tasselled smoking-cap was donned, and the feet incased in noiseless list slippers. In any other place or under any other circumstances I should have felt ridiculous in this costume, but so in keeping was it with all I had seen, and so thoroughly had I seemed to have left my every-day self in the dark vestibule, that I felt perfectly at home in my strange dress. We next crossed the hall to a smaller room, where a young man, apparently a Frenchman, furnished us, on the payment of two dollars each, with two small pipes and a small covered bronze cup, or urn, filled with a dry green shrub, which I subsequently learned was *gunjeh* (the dried tops and leaves of the hemp plant), for smoking. My friend, on the payment of a further sum, obtained a curious little box which contained some small black lozenges, consisting of the resin of hemp, henbane, crushed datura seeds, butter, and honey, and known in India as *Majoon*, amongst the Moors as *El Mogen*.

Passing from this room we ascended the richly carpeted stairs, enarbored by vines, and paused upon a landing from which three doors opened. Upon one a pink card bore Dryden's line, "Take the good the gods provide thee." * The knob turned by my friend's hand allowed the door to swing open, and, welcomed by a spice breeze from India, we were truly in paradise.

"This," he said, in a whisper, "is the public room, where any one having pipe or lozenge, and properly attired, may enter and indulge—eat, smoke, or dream, as best suits him."

Wonder, amazement, admiration, but faintly portray my mental condition. Prepared by what I had already seen and experienced for something odd and Oriental, still the magnificence of what now met my gaze far surpassed anything I had ever dreamed of, and brought to my mind the scenes of the *Arabian Nights,* forgotten since boyhood until now. My every sense was irresistibly taken

* From "Alexander's Feast; Or, the Power of Music" (1697), l. 106.

captive, and it was some moments before I could realize that I really was not the victim of some dream, for I seemed to have wholly severed my connection with the world of today, and to have stepped back several centuries into the times of genii, fairies, and fountains —into the very heart of Persia or Arabia.

Not an inharmonious detail marred the symmetry of the whole. Beneath, my feet sank almost ankle-deep into a velvet carpet—a sea of subdued colors. Looked at closely, I found that the design was that of a garden: beds of luxurious flowers, stars and crescents, squares and diamond-shaped plots, made up of thousands of rare exotics and richly colored leaves. Here a brook, edged with damp verdure, from beneath which peeped coy violets and tiny bluebells; there a serpentine gravelled walk that wound in and out amongst the exquisite plants, and everywhere a thousand shrubs in bloom or bud. Above, a magnificent chandelier, consisting of six dragons of beaten gold, from whose eyes and throats sprang flames, the light from which, striking against a series of curiously set prisms, fell shattered and scintillating into a thousand glancing beams that illuminated every corner of the room. The rows of prisms being of clear and variously colored glass, and the dragons slowly revolving, a weird and ever-changing hue was given to every object in the room.

All about the sides of the spacious apartment, upon the floor, were mattresses covered with different-colored cloth, and edged with heavy golden fringe. Upon them were carelessly strewn rugs and mats of Persian and Turkish handicraft, and soft pillows in heaps. Above the level of these divans there ran, all about the room, a series of huge mirrors framed with gilded serpents intercoiled, effectually shutting off the windows. The effect was magnificent. There seemed to be twenty rooms instead of one, and everywhere could be seen the flame-tongued and fiery-eyed dragons slowly revolving, giving to all the appearance of a magnificent kaleidoscope in which the harmonious colors were ever blending and constantly presenting new combinations.

Just as I had got thus far in my observations I caught sight of my friend standing at the foot of one of the divans, and beckoning to me. At the same moment I also observed that several of the occupants of other divans were eying me suspiciously. I crossed to where he was, esteeming it a desecration to walk on such a carpet, and, despite my knowledge to the contrary, fearing every moment to crush some beautiful rose or lily beneath my feet. Following my friend's example, I slipped off my list foot-gear, and half reclined beside him on the divan and pillows, that seemed to reach up and embrace us. Pulling a tasselled cord that hung above our heads, my friend spoke a few words to a gaudily turbaned colored servant who came noiselessly into the room in answer to his summons, disappeared again, and in a moment returned bearing a tray, which he placed between us. Upon it was a small lamp of silver filigree-work, two globe-like bowls, of silver also, from which protruded a long silver tube and a spoon-like instrument. The latter, I soon learned, was used to clean and fill the pipes. Placing the bronze jar of hashish on the tray, my friend bade me lay my pipe beside it, and suck up the fluid in the silver cup through the long tube. I did so, and found it delicious.

"That," said he, "is tea made from the genuine coca leaf. The cup is the real *mate* and the tube a real *bombilla* from Peru.* Now let us smoke. The dried shrub here is known as *gunjeh,* and is the dried tops of the hemp plant. Take a little tobacco from that jar and mix with it, else it will be found difficult to keep it alight. These lozenges here are made from the finest Nepaul resin of the hemp, mixed with butter, sugar, honey, flour, pounded datura seeds, some opium, and a little henbane, or hyoscyamus. I prefer taking these to smoking, but, to keep you company, I will also smoke to-night. Have no fear. Smoke four or five pipefuls of the *gunjeh,* and enjoy the effect. I will see that no harm befalls you."

* There is some confusion here. Maté is a tea made from a hollylike South American tree, *Ilex paraguayensis,* also called "Paraguay tea." No drink is made from coca leaves, *Erythroxylon coca.* A bombilla is simply a reed, used here as a straw.

Swallowing two of the lozenges, my guide filled our pipes, and we proceeded to smoke, and watch the others. These pipes, the stems of which were about eighteen inches in length, were incrusted with designs in varicolored beads, strung on gold wire over a ground of some light spirally twisted tinsel, marked off into diamond-shaped spaces by thin red lines. From the stem two green and yellow silken tassels depended. A small bell-shaped piece of clouded amber formed the mouthpiece, while at the other end was a small bowl of red clay scarcely larger than a thimble. As I smoked I noticed that about two-thirds of the divans were occupied by persons of both sexes, some of them masked, who were dressed in the same manner as ourselves. Some were smoking, some reclining listlessly upon the pillows, following the tangled thread of a hashish reverie or dream. A middle-aged woman sat bolt-upright, gesticulating and laughing quietly to herself; another with lacklustre eyes and dropped jaw was swaying her head monotonously from side to side. A young man of about eighteen was on his knees, praying inaudibly; and another man, masked, paced rapidly and noiselessly up and down the room, until led away somewhere by the turbaned servant.

As I smoked, the secret of that heavy, sickening odor was made clear to me. It was the smell of burning hashish. Strangely enough, it did not seem to be unpleasant any longer, for, although it rather rasped my throat at first, I drew large volumes of it into my lungs. Lost in lazy reverie and perfect comfort, I tried to discover whence came the soft, undulating strains of music that had greeted me on entering, and which still continued. They were just perceptible above the silvery notes of a crystal fountain in the centre of the room, the falling spray from which plashed and tinkled musically as it fell from serpents' mouths into a series of the very thinnest huge pink shells held aloft by timid hares. The music seemed to creep up through the heavy carpet, to ooze from the walls, to flurry, like snow-flakes, from the ceiling, rising and falling in measured cadences unlike any music I had ever heard. It seemed to steal, now softly, now merrily, on tiptoe into the room to see whether we were awake or asleep, to brush away a tear, if tear there was, or gambol airily and merrily, if such was our humor, and then as softly, sometimes sadly, to steal out again and lose itself in the distance. It was just such music as a boatful of fairies sailing about in the clear water of the fountain might have made, or that with which an angel mother would sing its angel babe to sleep. It seemed to enter every fibre of the body, and satisfy a music-hunger that had never before been satisfied. I silently filled my second pipe, and was about to lapse again into a reverie that had become delightfully full of perfect rest and comfort, when my companion, leaning toward me, said:

"I see that you are fast approaching Hashishdom. Is there not a sense of perfect rest and strange, quiet happiness produced by it?"

"There certainly is. I feel supremely happy, at peace with myself and all the world, and all that I ask is to be let alone. But why is everything so magnificent here? Is it a whim of the proprietor, or an attempt to reproduce some such place in the East?" I asked.

"Possibly the latter; but there is another reason that you may understand better later. It is this: the color and peculiar phases of a hashish dream are materially affected by one's surroundings just prior to the sleep. The impressions that we have been receiving ever since we entered, the lights, odors, sounds, and colors, are the strands which the deft fingers of imagination will weave into the hemp reveries and dreams, which seem as real as those of every-day life, and always more grand. Hashish eaters and smokers in the East recognized this fact, and always, prior to indulging in the drug, surrounded themselves with the most pleasant sounds, faces, forms, etc."

"I see," I answered, dreamily. "But what is there behind those curtains that I see moving now and again?" The heavy curtains just opposite where we lay seemed to shut in an alcove.

"There are several small rooms there," said my companion, "shut off from this room by the curtains you see move. Each is magnificently fitted up, I am told. They are reserved for persons, chiefly ladies, who wish to avoid every possibility of detection, and at the same time enjoy their hashish and watch the inmates of this room."

"Are there many ladies of good social standing who come here?"

"Very many. Not the cream of the *demi-monde,* understand me, but *ladies.* Why, there must be at least six hundred in this city alone who are *habituées.* Smokers from different cities, Boston, Philadelphia, Chicago, and especially New Orleans, tell me that each city has its hemp retreat, but none so elegant as this."

And my companion swallowed another lozenge and relapsed into dreamy silence. I too lay back listlessly, and was soon lost in reverie, intense and pleasant. Gradually the room and its inmates faded from view; the revolving dragons went swifter and more swiftly, until the flaming tongues and eyes were merged into a huge ball of flame, that, suddenly detaching itself with a sharp sound from its pivot, went whirling and streaming off into the air until lost to sight in the skies. Then a sudden silence, during which I heard the huge waves of an angry sea breaking with fierce monotony in my head. Then I heard the fountain; the musical tinkle of the spray as it struck upon the glass grew louder and louder, and the notes longer and longer, until they merged into one clear, musical bugle note that woke the echoes of a spring morning, and broke sharp and clear over hill and valley, meadow-land and marsh, hill-top and forest. A gayly caparisoned horseman, bugle in hand, suddenly appeared above a hill-crest. Closely following, a straggling group of horsemen riding madly. Before them a pack of hounds came dashing down the hill-side, baying deeply. Before them I, the fox, was running with the speed of desperation, straining every nerve to distance or elude them. Thus for miles and miles I ran on until at last, almost dead with fright and fatigue, I fell panting in the forest. A moment more and the cruel hounds would have had me, when suddenly a little field-mouse appeared, caught me by the paw, and dragged me through the narrow entrance to her nest. My body lengthened and narrowed until I found myself a serpent, and in me rose the desire to devour my little preserver, when, as I was about to strike her with my fangs, she changed into a beautiful little fairy, tapped my ugly black flat head with her wand, and as my fangs fell to earth I resumed my human shape. With the parting words, "Never seek to injure those who endeavor to serve you," she disappeared.

Looking about I found myself in a huge cave, dark and noisome. Serpents hissed and glared at me from every side, and huge lizards and ugly shapes scrambled over the wet floor. In the far corner of the cave I saw piles of precious stones of wondrous value that glanced and sparkled in the dim light. Despite the horrid shapes about me, I resolved to secure some, at least, of these precious gems. I began to walk toward them, but found that I could get no nearer —just as fast as I advanced, so fast did they seem to recede. At last, after what seemed a year's weary journey, I suddenly found myself beside them, and falling on my knees, began to fill my pockets, bosom, even my hat. Then I tried to rise, but could not: the jewels weighed me down. Mortified and disappointed, I replaced them all but three, weeping bitterly. As I rose to my feet it suddenly occurred to me that this was in no way real—only a hashish dream. And, laughing, I said, "You fool, this is all nonsense. These are not real jewels; they only exist in your imagination." My real self arguing thus with my hashish self, which I could see, tired, ragged, and weeping, set me to laughing still harder, and then we laughed together—my two selves. Suddenly my real self faded away, and a cloud of sadness and misery settled upon me, and I wept again, throwing myself hysterically upon the damp floor of the cave.

Just then I heard a voice addressing me by name, and looking up, I saw an old man with an enormous nose bending over me. His nose seemed almost as large as his whole body. "Why do you weep, my son?" he said; "are you sad because you can not have *all* these riches? Don't, then, for some day you will learn whoso hath more wealth than is needed to minister to his wants must suffer for it. Every farthing above a certain reasonable sum will surely bring some worry, care, anxiety, or trouble. Three diamonds are your share; be content with them. But, dear me, here I am again neglecting my work! Here it is March, and I'm not half through yet!"

"Pray what is your work, venerable patriarch?" I asked; "and why has the Lord given you such a huge proboscis?"

"Ah! I see that you don't know me," he replied. "I am the chemist of the earth's bowels, and it is my duty to prepare all the sweet and delicate odors that the flowers have. I am busy all winter making them, and early in the spring my nymphs and apprentices deliver them to the Queen of the Flowers, who in turn gives them to her subjects. My nose is a little large because I have to do so much smelling. Come and see my laboratory."

His nose a little large! I laughed until I almost cried at this, while following him.

He opened a door, and entering, my nostrils met the oddest medley of odors I had ever smelled. Everywhere workmen with huge noses were busy mixing, filtering, distilling, and the like.

"Here," said the old man, "is a batch of odor that has been spoiled. Mistakes are frequent, but I find use for even such as that. The Queen of Flowers gives it to disobedient plants or flowers. You mortals call it asafœtida. Come in here and see my organ;" and he led the way into a large rocky room, at one end of which was a huge organ of curious construction. Mounting to the seat, he arranged the stops and began to play.

Not a sound could be heard, but a succession of odors swept past me, some slowly, some rapidly. I understood the grand idea in a moment. Here was music to which that of sound was coarse and earthly. Here was a harmony, a symphony, of odors! Clear and sharp, intense and less intense, sweet, less sweet, and again still sweeter, heavy and light, fast and slow, deep and narcotic, the odors, all in perfect harmony, rose and fell, and swept by me, to be succeeded by others.

Irresistibly I began to weep, and fast and thick fell the tears, until I found myself a little stream of water, that, rising in the rocky caverns of the mountain, dashed down its side into the plain below. Fiercely the hot sun beat upon my scanty waters, and like a thin gray mist I found myself rising slowly into the skies, no longer a stream. With other clouds I was swept away by the strong and rapid wind far across the Atlantic, over the burning sand wastes of Africa, dipping toward the Arabian Sea, and suddenly falling in huge rain-drops into the very heart of India, blossoming with poppies. As the ground greedily sucked up the refreshing drops I again assumed my form.

Suddenly the earth was rent apart, and falling upon the edge of a deep cavern, I saw far below me a molten, hissing sea of fire, above which a dense vapor hung. Issuing from this mist, a thousand anguished faces rose toward me on scorched and broken wings, shrieking and moaning as they came.

"Who in Heaven's name are these poor things?"

"These," said a voice at my side, "are the spirits, still incarnate, of individuals who, during life, sought happiness in the various narcotics. Here, after death, far beneath, they live a life of torture most exquisite, for it is their fate, ever suffering for want of moisture, to be obliged to yield day by day their life-blood to form the juice of poppy and resin of hemp in order that their dream, joys, hopes, pleasures, pains, and anguish of past and present may again be tasted by mortals."

As he said this I turned to see who he was, but he had disappeared. Suddenly I heard a fierce clamor, felt the scrawny arms of these foul spirits wound about my neck, in my hair, on my limbs, pulling me over into the horrible chasm, into the heart of hell, crying, shrilly, "Come! thou art one of us. Come! come! come!" I struggled fiercely, shrieked out in my agony, and suddenly awoke, with the cold sweat thick upon me.

"Are you, then, so fond of it that nothing can awaken you? Here have I been shaking and pulling you for the past five minutes.

Come, rouse yourself; your dreams seem to be unpleasant."

Gradually my senses became clearer. The odors of the room, the melodies of early evening, the pipe that had fallen from my hand, the faces and forms of the hemp-smokers, were once more recognized.

My companion wished me to stay, assuring me that I would see many queer sights before morning, but I declined, and after taking, by his advice, a cup of Paraguay tea (coca leaf), and then a cup of sour lemonade, I passed down-stairs, exchanged my present for my former dress, returned my pipe, and left the house.

The dirty streets, the tinkling car-horse bell, the deafening "Here you are! twenty sweet oranges for a quarter!" and the drizzling rain were more grateful by far than the odors, sounds, and sights, sweet though they were, that I had just left. Truly it was the cradle of dreams rocking placidly in the very heart of a great city, translated from Bagdad to Gotham.

JULES GIRAUD,
"HOW I CAME
TO HASHISH" * (1913)

Giraud (b. 1878?) consumed cannabis most of his adult life, and even made rather a career of it in his thirties, lecturing on the subject throughout France. His account of first trying the drug in 1908 seems quite modern in its wry wit and unself-consciousness. In the opening paragraph he castigates the "ferocious censors" who cannot tolerate intoxication in any form. Though they were vocal enough, they were not seen to be winning their crusade in France when Giraud attacked them in 1913, but three years later, after half the French army had been killed in the Great War, the moralists had their day and the frivolity of hashish was put an end to. A French law of July 12, 1916, prohibited the sale, importation, and use of all forms of cannabis, along with several other drugs on a "Table of Poisonous Substances." That law has not been superceded. Prohibition was at first not entirely effective. Physicians could still prescribe it, and did so in great quantities. Smugglers like Monfreid (see p. 263) began to do a huge business through the wide-open port of Marseille. Eventually, however, the law prevailed.

* Jules Giraud, "How I Came to Hashish," Chapter Five of *Testament d'un haschischéen* (Testament of a Hashish Eater), Paris, 1913.

The era had ended when a writer could describe intoxication with drugs and go uncensured. The nineteenth century was an era of greater personal freedom: the average citizen could usually do or say pretty much what he wished, and had to contend only with adverse public opinion, which he was at perfect liberty to scorn or ignore. Giraud, though he did not know it, was the last of his kind. Thenceforth those who would tell of their drug experiences freely and unself-consciously had to contend with the specter of the law and its disapproval, and hence, at least formally, society's as well—there was a sense they could not dispel: that they were condoning or encouraging a vice, even though it was only in themselves. For nearly all of them—from Henri Michaux and Jean Cocteau in the 1920s and 1930s to William Burroughs and Allen Ginsberg in our own day—it was a weight they could not lift from their shoulders.

De Quincey, justifying his turning to opium, is careful to say that he was led to it, and in a way forced into it, by physical suffering, which he thought gave him an apparent excuse, an attenuating circumstance.

But I strongly doubt that by this concession he appeased in any way the ferocious censors who, at the very mention of the word *drug*—no matter what drug—storm frantically in, indiscriminately casting anathemas about them on everyone who uses drugs, on the imbecilic maniac as well as on the lucid and prudent researcher.

So it would be useless for me to attempt a similar maneuver, even if I had the taste for it. These inflexible guardians of principle never change. I could never weaken them, even by suggesting a spiritual suffering at least as acute as the pains of De Quincey's unhappy youth: to wit, dissatisfaction with the human condition. They would never excuse me for it, and would laugh up their sleeve at these "imaginary" pains, as if they were no more tragic than a toothache.

Besides, I have already written too much about it to look for excuses now. Though I am condemned, at least it is worth noting that if moral suffering occurred it was in a muffled, hidden fashion, not an acute crisis of metaphysical anguish. Pure and simple curiosity impelled me: I turned to hashish with no other immediate intention than to enrich my experience, with no worry about possible danger, in the same spirit that I have since flown in a plane, as tomorrow I would, if the chance occurred, dive in a submarine, as I would be ready to sign up for the first space rocket, destination Mars or the Moon, even if the return trip were not guaranteed.

NAIVE EXPERIMENTS WITH DRUGS

The curious thing is that I waited until I was thirty to become acquainted with hashish. My curiosity about drugs had been awakened for a long time, and I had even experimented with several of them, but not with hashish, which I was rather keeping in reserve.

The clear revelation of their interest appeared to me for the first time fifteen or sixteen years earlier, when reading in a popularized book, Louis Figuier's *Wonders of Science*, a panegyric on ether and "nitrous oxide, or laughing gas." I can still see the two illustrations, in the style of 1880: one represented the dream of an ether inhaler—a circle of ballerinas, frogs, and spiders, from the imagination of a positivist lesser Breughel—the other was of the chemist Sir Humphrey Davy, in redingote and sideburns, half reclining on a sofa, breathing with a beatific smile from a flask containing the nitrous oxide that he had just discovered. I was at the time smitten with chemistry, and my father encouraged the game, in which he saw the precocious indication of a vocation. It was therefore easy for me to make up several liters of the celebrated laughing gas, which I avidly inhaled without the least result. My nitrous oxide was apparently worthless. Of course I also tried ether, at which I succeeded rather better, and which I later became familiar with.

About the same time my taste for experimenting led me into a bizarre adventure. Suicides from household gas intrigued me. I wondered what the victims could have felt, just before the mortal dose, when they were gathered up, stupefied. Or perhaps not as far as that—only a little bit, just to see what it's like: I would know how to stop any bad effects at the first disquieting symptoms. But these came too late. Feeling only the slightest dizziness and a faint ringing in my ears, I went on bravely breathing from the rubber tubing, and in the end I just barely had the strength to throw it aside, turn off the spigot, and take several steps back: I sank into a soft nausea, and fainted.

When they picked me up and I came to, still very woozy, I took care not to reveal the true origin of my illness—I blamed it on the heat in the attic, thus avoiding another reprimand for my "craze for stupid experiences." I had determined on household gas, but though it was an acceptable form of euthanasia, this hydrogen carbonate was worth nothing as an artificial paradise.

Then it was reading the passages of De Quincey, in Baudelaire's translation, that made me want to taste opium. Nothing was simpler in 1896 than buying that product. I went to the pharmacy, where they gave me, without the least formality, two hundred grams of extrafine Smyrna opium at thirty francs a kilo. But I used it with a touching clumsiness that will doubtless make initiates laugh. I was ignorant of the correct ritual, and only knew that opium was smoked in a pipe, so I took the largest briar I could find, stuffed the bowl with alternate layers of tobacco and bits of opium grated from my block of Smyrna. The result was not especially brilliant. Another attempt using a narghile, and still mixing the opium and tobacco, was still worse. The mixture steadfastly refused to burn, and every minute I had to use a fresh coal. It sizzled and sparked, smoked and carbonized, and the opium ashes extinguished everything. It was stinking and repulsive. After two or three more tries, either alone or with comrades at least as inexpert as I, I renounced opium forever, and put the block in the back of a drawer.

FIRST TRY AT HASHISH

I have read Baudelaire, and Dumas's *Monte Cristo,* and the wonders of *dawamesc* fascinated me. But my desire to try it remained entirely platonic, driven back into the realm of the unrealizable by the belief that *dawamesc* was an exotic product, difficult to get. Whenever the thought occurred to me, I thought vaguely that I would try it one day or another, that if I went to the Orient, there would be a chance then.

I didn't have to wait that long. One night in January 1908 I was having dinner with my friend Guy Bernier, along with René Delvaux, both young doctors. The conversation turned to Baudelaire and hashish. It was Guy who suggested the experiment.

"Just the same, we really must try it one of these days."

The two friends responded to my questions that even though the nonexistent *dawamesc* was the most agreeable form of hashish to take, nevertheless in the pharmacy there were two products currently available: the oil extract of Cannabis indica, and the hydroalcoholic extract, which was ten times stronger and more concentrated. They gave me to read the page in the Formulary that had the indications and dosage. If they were managed with prudence, the danger of toxicity from both these substances appeared to be extremely remote. The curiosity to verify Baudelaire's descriptions was almost as strong in my two friends as in myself. I had no difficulty in persuading them that it was then or never, and with no further delay, even before we sat down to eat, Guy went to the pharmacist on the corner, an acquaintance, to buy just the right quantity of oil extract, the one we had chosen.

We nearly bungled our initiation. In the first place we began too late, then we took too weak a dose, or at least I did, finally my comrades' reactions disturbed me and unfortunately deflected my own impressions.

As Baudelaire recommended, to avoid interrupting digestion by taking it too soon after the meal, Guy had us wait until ten o'clock in the evening. To avoid disturbing the cook at that late hour the coffee was put aside and we reheated it over an alcohol lamp. When the cups were full, everyone dissolved his portion of hashish. The oil extract was a sort of dark green glue with a penetrating smell of marshgrass and a sharp taste, like excessively concentrated souchong tea. Mixed with coffee, however, it was certainly drinkable, and a second cup of coffee dissipated the taste momentarily.

We had to be patient at first during an hour of waiting when nothing happened. Since dinner we had already reread bits of Baudelaire, all the while drinking kümmel and smoking cigars and pipes. Once we exhausted our interest in Baudelaire, Guy took down from his library the medical dictionary, volume F-K, and began to read us the article on hashish, to complete our information. As reading aloud made him dry, he drank without noticing it several more glasses of kümmel, because René's habit was never to allow a glass to remain empty around him. To this ill-timed overabundance of alcohol, as well as to the alarmist warnings of the medical authority of the possible dangers of poisoning, I mainly attribute the responsibility for Guy's feelings later and for the mishaps that spoiled our first attempt.

Despite my efforts to pay attention, I was distracted. This puzzling result disturbed me. The drug's apparent ineffectiveness baffled my experience, based on ether, which acts instantaneously. Leaning back in one of the armchairs near the fire, I looked closely at my two companions. René, in the opposite armchair, had stopped refilling the liqueur glasses, and with an absorbed air was smoking a long Dutch pipe. Guy, half lying on the couch on the other side of the table, was still reading aloud. I had considerable difficulty following him, and the time seemed to drag. In the intervals of silence I had to hold my breath in order to hear that the clock on the mantel was still running. I observed myself minutely. The annoying taste of marshgrass had returned to my palate. My throat was dry, my glass and cup empty, but I had no desire to get up and get the coffeepot to pour myself the few remaining drops. My legs became heavy, the heat from the coal fire made me feel slightly sleepy, not at all disagreeably. Nothing more. That was rather little, forty-five minutes after taking it.

But I jumped when Guy, having finished reading the article, closed the book with a bang that seemed to me as loud as a gunshot.

"Are you sure," I asked point-blank, "that you've given us enough hashish? I really don't feel anything. You gave us rather small rations."

"Only out of prudence. You haven't been listening to what I was reading, how the effects of hashish are very capricious, how even the smallest doses can, no one knows why or how, produce fearsome effects."

"*Fear*-some!" repeated René in a strange voice, sitting up straight in his chair. And without further explanation, as if this simple word had opened hidden treasures of comedy, he began to laugh, a little, dry, jerky laugh. He put down his long pipe on the table in order to laugh more easily, to laugh louder and longer, throwing back his head in the chair.

"There it is," Guy gravely commented. "It's the preliminary seizure of hilarity. He's lucky. I feel a bit ill at ease, myself. What about you?"

"I think it's beginning as well."

An insidious pinching suddenly grabbed the back of my neck: it was as if the lighting in the room had suddenly doubled in intensity. The electric ceiling light seemed to pour in huge quantities over the bindings on the bookshelves. And at the same time the walls were lengthening, and the room was visibly growing larger. My dizziness increased. It seemed that a subtle wave was coming up from the carpet, instantly engulfing me in water up to my neck, a wave of madness from which only my head was free, and I was going to be drowned in it. I had the weird sensation of inhabiting a strange body, of having never perceived how my body was a stranger to me.

Each physical effort became fatiguing. The simple gesture of turning my head toward Guy was painful. Therefore, not seeing any necessity to do so, since he was no longer speaking, I began to look at René, who was opposite me. A contraction of the muscles around my cheekbones made me feel a strange desire to laugh, also without any reason. But the reason appeared to me suddenly as I looked at René. Ah, him, I had never really looked at him! With his long pipe and glasses, he was extraordinary and hilarious. I had to laugh out loud, and exclaimed quickly, absurdly, "A monkey! My friend, you have exactly the head of a monkey!"

Far from taking offense, as would certainly have been natural for him in normal life, René began to laugh in turn, his mouth twisted into a grotesque grimace.

"A monkey! Yes, of course, a monkey! And you're another! You are, you're one too!"

In effect, I was one too.

Everything: my own words, René's face, the bookbindings, the japanese display case, the entire room down to the hands on the clock, everything assumed an irresistibly comic appearance. I straightened up in my chair so as to take a panoramic look at things, and began to improvise a burlesque lecture. Hilarious things flowed into my mind in such abundance that I had no time to develop them. I could only notice them as they passed in and out with the briefest references. But René was up to it, as he proclaimed in a hoarse shout, sitting up in his chair and gesturing with his pipe. He understood me without my saying anything, and even guessed with extraordinary perspicacity what I was about to say, replying to my sallies before I had uttered them in a sparkling, elliptical fashion. For those ten minutes we held the most extravagant laugh-fest anyone could imagine.

Suddenly Guy, whose existence we had completely forgotten, recalled himself to us in a cavernous, gloomy voice.

"You are insane! You've been hurting my ears for an hour. Have mercy, and speak less loud. I don't feel at all well, I assure you. This excessive light makes me ill. Won't you please turn off the ceiling light? I need a bit of time to recollect myself. I'm afraid the hashish isn't succeeding with me."

In a flow of friendly solicitude, René leaped from his chair. But he uttered a desperate cry.

"Damnation! I've broken my pipe!"

The incident grew into a catastrophe. In an instant his familiar metaphor assumed for me all the literalness of its evil meaning. I thought, and I'm sure he did too, that he was witnessing his own death. But Guy, with a lamenting, "The light! Turn off the light!" cut across our delusion. René finished the gesture he began, and turned the switch. The ceiling light went out, and the single lamp on the desk, under its rose silk shade, introduced instantly an atmosphere of repose, and dissociated, so to speak, the trio of hashish eaters. Everyone buried himself in his own dream, and uncountable ages rolled by. I was floating with the hashish, beginning to savor a rich procession of pictures and ideas.

How can I tell the ineffable? The room seemed isolated in space, a hundred thousand leagues from earth; we had crossed over onto another planet; my body enclosed a soul extremely nimble and subtle; brief flashes of consciousness were the sole memory of my earlier life. This was a prodigious and disquieting marvel, to have overcome the tedious limits of my individuality, to have thrown off the old envelope of everyday appearances, to feel things with new senses—who knows, perhaps in their essential aspects.

Indeed, to pierce reality's membrane is the fullest experience of hashish. My ideas, quick, abrupt, almost cinematographic, passed and developed before me, flowing as easily as the movement of a watch whose mainspring is broken. And over everything a blessed sense of rapture.

I was torn from this ecstasy by Guy's pained voice. According to the process of inordinate amplification normal to hashish, his insignificant distress had just transformed itself through his imagination into grave symptoms, which became graver and graver, and which were further embellished by his young knowledge of medicine. Caring nothing for my repose, he called me over to him and said that he was very worried about his condition, which did appear abnormal. So I didn't hesitate to arouse René, who followed me to the patient's bedside, after authoritatively switching the light back on. Unhappily sprawled on the divan, poor Guy described to us the pains in his chest, the palpitations, the cyanosis in his hands. He did indeed have a bit of dullness in the eyes, a greenish complexion, and blue hands. Soon he felt himself to be dying, and said so to Delvaux and me. But the sublime sereneness of the drug did not desert us in this catastrophe: leaning over him, on both sides of the divan, concerned but powerless to relieve him, we were entirely resigned, and followed the progress of his death throes.

"He's done for!" René murmured in a doctoral tone.

I nodded my head sadly, divided between the desire to lighten by my presence my unfortunate friend's last moments of life, and the longing to go back to my chair and enjoy in peace those blessed visions that had only just started. "If he has to die," the drug said inside me, "let him do it quickly. Whether he does it early or late won't matter to him at all, and then at least you will be undisturbed."

Yet Bernier did not pass away. On the contrary, the crisis lessened, and hope and life returned to him. But I congratulated myself too soon on this happy ending. Fearing a new crisis, and dragging along Delvaux, who said he didn't feel so well himself, Guy took advantage of the momentary break in his condition to go knock on the door of Dr. W——, his neighbor. It was then close to midnight, and the housemaid had retired long ago, as well as the cook, so I had to go downstairs with them to wait for them to come back.

It was an atrocious, interminable drudgery, going down those two flights of stairs, which had at least ten thousand steps, and it took us ages, measured by my centenary puffs on my pipe. They left and I remained behind alone. With my back against the wall of the cold foyer, I had more than enough time to see myself changed into a caryatid and to witness the temple crumble around me, when the two adventurers returned, bringing Dr. W—— with them, who looked greatly astonished and even a little worried.

They had their consultation standing at the foot of the staircase, with Guy declaiming, "My dear colleague, we have done a stupid experiment: we have taken hashish!" He described at great length his alarming symptoms, which had disappeared a long time before.

The honest colleague understood not a word, and seemed ignorant of the very existence and name of the drug. Rolling his eyes, he examined us each in turn, with our strange, haggard faces. With my Dutch pipe in my hand like a scepter, I strongly declared that as for me I was having no trouble at all—none!—for I was bothered by the idea of the antidote that Guy was clamoring for. I wanted none of their antidote, and wanted only to savor in peace the effects of the wonderful green drug, upstairs in the library's happy warmth.

After scribbling out a prescription form, all the while keeping his eye on the three fools surrounding him, the doctor slipped away, and my two comrades raced to the corner pharmacist who had furnished the cannabis extract. He was quite amused at their fright. "There's no danger with hashish at that dosage. If you'd taken ten times more, I wouldn't be so sure, but not now!" Nevertheless he had them swallow the prescribed potassium bromide, and they fortunately forgot to bring back a dose for me, as had been their intention.

Far from being an antidote to hashish, most authorities think that bromides accentuate its effects. But in the case of my two cowards the bromide did its work because it calmed their fears, and when finally—at what effort!—we regained the library, our gathering ended pitiably. It was two in the morning. The stages of the drama had taken up much time, and the drug's energy was used up. Weary of all this disorder, I had only been able to perceive a few of the splendid images that a *kif* experienced in peace and quiet can provide. We all three disengaged ourselves from the hashish, and fell back into the atmosphere of ordinary life. Tiredness arrived, and we had to think of sleeping. While Delvaux slept on the divan in the library, I went back without too much trouble to my family's house, for I was visiting my hometown, and finished the night in my own bed, in a half-sleep filled with sumptuous dreams.

All in all, this first attempt was a failure. My two accomplices, whom I met the following afternoon at Bernier's, agreed, and we decided to try again under better conditions. The first time never counted, and had only half opened for us the perspectives of the hashish paradise. If it had turned into a grotesque purgatory for Guy, that was only due, he recognized, to lack of a system, lack of proper timing, too many little glasses of kümmel, perhaps an insufficient dose. One can never know, with this capricious drug, the opinion of everyone who has tried it.

THE TENFOLD DOSE

My two friends laughed at their foolish adventure, and took my making fun of them in good part, vowing next time to avoid any baneful suggestions, and to experience the joys of hashish unalloyed.

Guy ran back again to his pharmacist. But by a sequence of misunderstandings that revealed themselves only subsequently, the man had run out of oil extract and could sell us only the hydroalcoholic, the one ten times stronger. Did he neglect to warn Guy? Or rather did Guy, distracted as always, fail to hear him? That's the mystery. The fact is that he returned with a little jar and a scale, which he handed to me, saying that I was to distribute the doses. Ignorant of the substitution of the product (which looked outwardly just the same) I set to work weighing the doses according to the formula the last time—four grams per person, instead of the forty centigrams that should have been the allowable maximum.

Because they had an unacknowledged fear of repeating their agonies of the previous evening, these two decided not to consume the whole of their portions, which I placed on pieces of paper, like little piles of green honey. I alone forged bravely ahead, dissolving into the ritual black coffee the entirety of my tenfold dose.

It worked overwhelmingly. Usually the first sensation of hashish develops at the end of an hour, but scarcely ten minutes had passed before I received that blow on the back of the neck that seems to snatch the mind away from its habitual moorings and launches it on its flight toward the hashish dimension. This rapidity stunned me, and I boasted of it to my two companions, who had felt nothing thus far.

But all of a sudden a new characteristic in this eruption of the drug warned me that it was no longer a repetition of the delights of the previous evening. My head, split by a broadsword, floated like a golden lily on an ocean of ecstasy; but something enormous and monstrous, a terrifying yet indefinite menace exploded within me, growing sharper with each passing second, clearly breaking down my features before the worried eyes of my friends.

The next instant I stiffened, struggling against the invasion. "What? My turn to die? Not me! That would be too stupid!" But a great blast of terror swept away my resistance and a frightful, measureless anguish possessed me. A glacial cold invaded my contracted legs and arms, and a blanket of ice crushed my chest. I drew a painful, oppressive breath, my ribs compressed into a corset like iron, and my breathing became more and more infrequent, even threatening to stop altogether. I escaped asphyxiation only by constant vigilance, and this was a great terror to my mind, which was then about to plunge into an unknown gulf. With great cries of pain I attempted to breathe, putting all my failing energy into this one means of salvation: "Breathe in! Again! Again, miserable soul! Don't stop! Don't forget to draw your breath, to prevent your heart from stopping, your already nearly frozen heart, on which Death herself is sitting, the bitch, with all the abominable weight of her icy behind!"

For hours, years, centuries, I struggled desperately, and from the

depths of this crushing agony I called for help to my two companions, for their medical assistance, as if they weren't just as
powerless as I had been the previous night.

"Do something for me, Guy! There must be a remedy! And you,
René? You know that the hashish . . . too strong a dose!"

For I knew then by intuition my horrific error.

But it was no good, for they were both now taken by the hashish.
René thumbed through the medical dictionary methodically and
placidly. Guy fussed about me, and seemed very annoyed, but
could find nothing to do other than to repeat to me endlessly that
I ought to vomit, so as to get rid of the poison.

"Come on, old man. Throw up! Stick your fingers down your
throat—way down! Come on, then, throw up!"

What misery! It was absolutely impossible for me to vomit. My
throat was as constricted, hard, and dry, it seemed to me, as the
stem of a clay pipe. My brain had shrunk in my head, dried out,
reduced to the size of a chick-pea. Fifteen minutes seemed to pass
between each respiration. The path of the terrifying cold had
finally reached my heart, which was no longer beating. From all
available evidence, I was going to die. In order to do so more com-
fortably, I asked my two nurses to carry me to the divan and lay
me out.

My implacable agony continued, but the appalling black
void that had surrounded me up until then began to lighten a bit
in a thundering downpour of insane, visionary images, such as
happen to those about to drown. At the same time a splendid
serenity before the fact of approaching death came over me bit by
bit, making me forget my pain. My lucid consciousness grew larger,
took over my entire body, and awakened it down to the very last
organic cells. I communed with the material that formed them, and
relived its panoramic history. I was outside my body, spreading out
in wonderful flashes of light, and I plunged my tentacles into the
infinite, extending through all the past history of the Earth my
mother, through all her geologic ages. I was the wondrous land-

scapes of the giant dinosaurs of the Mesozoic era, I was the Silurian ocean, I was the Carboniferous period. I was Earth herself in the ecstatic revolutions of the planets. I was divine, constantly enlarging, diffused in the ocean of the heavens, of which at the same time I was master, the lord of all the worlds. And among the glory of the stars, in an exploding apotheosis of suns and galaxies, I was the universal being, roaring through infinite space the triumphal hymn of my divinity.

All this I saw from within. But from without it appears I was babbling, with furious gestures and hoarse, inarticulate cries. My acolytes, good hashish-fed medical men, were watching my crisis and wondering what to use for a straitjacket. In the end their presence and whispering pulled me down from my exaltation: suddenly they were persecuting me. I saw them there, evil spirits with spectacles, grinning gnomes, plotting to perform some dangerous alchemical experiment on me. I repulsed them by incantations, exorcised the danger, and again forgot their existence in order to climb once again the manic heights of my dream.

When morning came I was still sunk in great toxic depths, yet I managed at length to get myself up and dressed, and accomplished the trek across town to my family's house. My instinct for self-preservation guided me, of course, but I saw the city streets only through heavy hallucinations, and trembled at the idea of the physical dangers I had to avoid. I succeeded in getting to my room without awakening my mother's attention any more than if I had had an ordinary night on the town. Once in bed, the hashish madness regained possession of me, my legs turned to marble, and I was like the young king in the *Thousand and One Nights*.* The icy marble climbed my body, first up to my waist, then still climbing, left me powerless to move, absolutely petrified, on my bed.

Why have they left my eyes open after my death, on this sinister rainy day in this bedroom with drawn shades? For I knew I was dead, for certain this time. And I finally knew Death's secret: by

* The 726th night; see also Gautier, p. 100.

some means that I judged was habitual in dead people, what remained of my consciousness had become forever immobilized at the instant death seized me. But what a horrible, sinister idea—to embalm my soul within the illusion of this sepulchral chamber, behind whose windows there was nothing, I knew, nothing but the eternal void, absolute blackness, nonbeing.

This macabre hallucination stretched on through eternities of desolation, and finally evolved, through snatches of opaque sleep interrupted by voluptuous *kifs,* into centuries of convalescence inundated with overwhelming sweetness. It was completely impossible for me to speak a word, and when my mother, my indulgent nurse, came in to bring me a cup of tea, I had to close my eyes so as to avoid interrogation by this phantom from the other world of living beings.

This affliction lasted all day. Only at twilight when the lamps were lit did I have the first faint recollection of my real state: the vague phrases came to me as if by magic—"Hashish . . . took too much hashish!"

Two days after the tenfold dose I took the train back home. But the hashish still had possession of me! I was in a dimension of space and time unknown to human beings, floating in an unheard-of atmosphere, through which the delights of paradise and frightful weariness would cross, one after another.

It was only on the third day, back in my apartment, that I returned approximately to normal after this momentous intoxication. I remained for several weeks without daring to taste the drug, the rest of which I had taken away with me in its little jar. For Delvaux intended to try no more of it, and Bernier swore by heaven that after the terrifying spectacle of my being poisoned, he would renounce it forever.

HENRY DE MONFREID, THE HASHISH CROSSING * (1933)

Monfried (1879–1974) wrote at great length of his experiences as a hashish smuggler, though he never tried it himself, for in the old custom those who dealt in a drug rarely used it. Monfreid plied his trade with his small sailboat, eventually covering the major markets of India, Egypt, Greece, Sudan, and France. He described the smuggling trade in a trilogy: La croisière du hachich *(Hashish Crossing, 1934),* La poursuite du "Kaipan" *(The Pursuit of the "Kaipan," 1934), and* L'homme sorti de la mer *(The Man from the Sea, 1951), which were followed by* La cargaison enchantée: charas *(The Enchanted Cargo: Charas, 1962). In these books he mainly describes his experiences as a disgruntled antibourgeois, escaping from the confinement of French society to live the life of an adventurer, renegade, ethnographer, and poet. He even converted to Islam, taking the name Abd el-Hai, yet though he lived for nearly twenty years as a seagoing nomad he remained essentially French in manner and style, almost never, for example, wearing foreign clothes and always keeping his journal up to date.*

About 1915, running low on funds, Monfreid decided to smug-

* Henry de Monfreid, *La croisière du hachich* (Paris: Ferenczi, 1934), pp. 47–48, 49–51, 171–175, 207–209.

gle hashish, which became a scarce commodity in the West—the demand for it from pharmaceutical companies and individual users was fairly constant—as soon as the British outlawed its cultivation and trade in Egypt, their protectorate. Monfreid was then living near Suez, and had to travel to Greece to purchase the hashish. For centuries, cannabis of a high quality had been grown there, most of it destined for export to the Ottoman Empire. Completely new to the hashish trade, Monfreid sailed from Cairo to Athens, then traveled by train to a village high in the western Peloponnesus, where he met his contact, a rich farmer called Petros.

THE INSIDE of his house suggested leisure, even wealth. I was quite surprised to find that the fortresslike ancient walls contained some good modern furniture.

Petros went off immediately to look for a sample of his hashish. What was I going to say, how was I to give an opinion of this thing I had never seen? I didn't even know how one showed he knew about its quality. I was afraid of showing what a fool I was, and revealing my ignorance at the same time, for after that I would be judged, and all their unsalable rejects would be palmed off on me. The only way out of such an embarrassment is, so far as possible, to keep silent. Petros came back with a piece of brownish material in his hand, and immediately gave me the clue to how to test the value of his merchandise. He began by sniffing it, then held it up for me to sniff. Then he took a piece of it and rolled it between his fingers into a small cone, which he lit. It burned with a small, rather smoky flame, which he quickly extinguished to release a heavy, odorous, white smoke. When it was my turn I took a piece and, like a perfect connoisseur, did exactly what he had done. However, having noticed how quickly he put out the flame, I let it burn instead. Then in silence, coldly and rather disdainfully, I held it out to him. He quickly interpreted my silence according to his fears, and exclaimed:

"Oh, don't worry, I have better than this. I only thought this grade might perhaps interest you, because it's much cheaper."

I replied with great dignity, "I have not come from so far away to buy rubbish. Please show me at once the very best you have."

He vanished again, and returned in a moment with a piece of the same material, but this time less brittle and of a greenish color. He went through the same operation, but this time the flame was long and very smoky, and he complacently let it burn out. That, I thought, is probably the sign of the highest quality. Now I know how to buy hashish. I said I was satisfied, and we settled on the quantity I would buy, four hundred *okes* (six hundred kilograms), at the price of twenty francs per *oke*.

"Now," he said, "we'll go get the goods from the warehouse where we keep them."

A serving girl brought us little wax torches, and two hefty workmen armed with enormous clubs came with us. Petros opened a vaulted door, behind which a stone staircase led down to the cellar. A musty, damp smell came from this underground passage, and we soon came to a crypt hewn from the living limestone. In this vaulted room, circular in form, there were piles of sacks: the hashish crop from the current harvest. The two workmen took down a number of sacks corresponding to my order, put them on the floor in the middle of the room, then attacked them with their clubs, so as to break up the contents and reduce them to dust.

We must have seemed an odd group. First there was Papamanoli, the priest, in his great black cassock, and beside him Petros, holding in his hand a piece of white paper, onto which he placed a sample out of each sack. We each held up one of the little wax torches to give light to the men who were furiously beating the bulging sacks. Our fantastic shadows danced along the vaults of the passage, and the bats, disturbed by the light, softly grazed against us in their flight, flickering the flames of our candles. I shall never forget this scene, though only I saw it in this romantic way. Petros poured the samples from each sack into a little bag, which he gave me as an indication of the average quality of my goods.

The sacks were then carried into the barn, so that the night's icy cold might prevent the powdered hashish from coagulating again.

The next morning I was awakened by the noise of activity filling the house like the murmur of a beehive. In the barn where the sacks were stored, a crowd of workers was milling around through a thick dust.

In the middle of the barn was a large table consisting of a very fine metal sieve on four legs. Onto it the powdered hashish was being thrown by the spadeful. A great sheet was wrapped around the outside of the table legs to prevent the fine powder that fell through the sieve from causing even greater clouds of dust. Women, their heads wrapped in kerchiefs, were spreading and agitating the powder, then pushing it through the sieve. Then the men shoveled it into an enormous galvanized iron basin so that it would be well mixed.

Madame Petros was sitting at her sewing machine, feverishly running up little white linen sacks. These were taken by another woman, who stamped an elephant mark on them with a rubber stamp. She then passed them to a third woman who filled them, weighed them exactly, and finally closed them up. The sacks were then stacked neatly in a great screw-press. When they had the right number between the flat steel plates, a workman with the muscles of Hercules tightened the vise and the stacks flattened out slowly until they became like little cakes, fifteen by thirty centimeters, but only four centimeters thick. They were hard as wax; this is the commercial form in which hashish is exported, and the elephant was Petros's own trademark. Now and then Petros himself lent a hand to the big man working the press. I could not see the latter's face because he had covered his head with a towel and only his eyes could be seen through it, but these seemed quite familiar, and suddenly I realized that he was the priest, Papamanoli. Laughing, he took off his mask, freeing his great beard and long hair, which he had rolled into a knot on top of his head. He wore the im-provised cowl to protect this luxuriant growth. He was in the

family, so nothing was more natural than to see him lending a
hand at a busy time.

Bit by bit the dust from the hashish began to excite the men
and women working on it, and they began to sing as loud as they
could, joking and laughing like madmen over nothing at all. I felt
myself drawn into this gay whirlwind even without realizing it,
and even Petros's ugly little niece from Tripolis grew rather flirta-
tious. Fortunately, the work was soon completed, or I don't know
how it would all have ended. Outside, a plumber finished soldering
the zinc linings of the packing cases into which the hashish cakes
would go.

While this feverish work was drawing to a close, the serving girls
were setting a table in the shade of a walnut tree before the barn.
They had put on their Sunday dresses as if the day were a holiday,
and soon everyone, masters and servants, sat down to lunch together
as in ancient times. It was a Pantagruellian repast: there was a
whole roasted sheep, several chickens, and many trout, a meal such
as one only encounters in countries where the land is bountiful. It
made me think of the prodigious repasts in the Middle Ages that
the chroniclers tell about. But there was nothing indecent about it
in the slightest: in the isolation of their mountains, these simple
people had remained too close to nature ever to forget modesty and
decency.

For those who are curious I will tell how the hashish arrived at
the state in which I first saw it, powdered and stored in sacks in
the cellar. The fields where the hemp grows are carefully weeded,
and all the male plants eliminated. The remaining female plants
thus cannot bear seeds, and this allows the leaves to become fully
charged with a resinous material. The richness of this secretion is
further increased by breaking off the top of each plant when it has
reached full development. When the first leaves, the lowest ones,
begin to turn yellow, the plants are carefully cut down about four
inches above the ground, to avoid soiling the harvest with sand or
dirt. Then they dry the crop in the shade and store it in the barn.

Some growers keep only the leaves, for the stems have absolutely no value. On the very coldest winter days, when there is a hard frost and the waxy secretion on the leaves has become brittle as resin, they break up the dried plants by rubbing them between two sheets of canvas. This gives them a dust made up of broken leaves and the resin which is the active part of hashish. It is this resin that gives the powder the property of forming a hard cake when pressed, and of softening again when heated.

All the farms in this district prepared hashish on their property —it was their chief crop. Each estate had its brand, its first and second growths, all classified and rated; there were even good and bad years, exactly as for wine.

TRAVELERS' TALES

Here is a collection of notes and obiter dicta by travelers and historians about their experiences with cannabis, some of them written from firsthand experience, others from hearsay. It shows that there was a growing awareness of the drug among some Europeans well before the generation of early nineteenth-century Arabic scholars or that of the true believers of the 1840s.

It is believed that Herodotus, the first European to mention cannabis, was not very widely traveled, but the others were nothing less than free-lance adventurers, seeking on their voyages to the East a fame and excitement that Europe could not offer. They learned new languages, adopted native dress and customs, and evidently burned to relate their experiences in books that their fellow Europeans might read. The people back home readily considered them heroes, venerated them as authorities on the Orient, a subject that was ever fascinating.

The last entry is a sociologist's comprehensive description of an African spitting game, which anyone can play who has a talent for following directions and a copious supply of saliva.

HERODOTUS, *Histories,* iv. 73–75
(Fifth Century B.C.)

This dates from the fifth century B.C., *and is the oldest mention of hemp intoxication we possess. The Scythians lived in central Asia and the Crimea, north of the Black Sea, the Thracians in northeast Mesopotamia.*

ALL THE OTHER Scythians [except the kings], when they die, are laid on wagons and carried about among their friends by their next of kin; all receive and entertain the retinue hospitably, setting before the dead man about as much of the food as the rest are served. All but the kings are carried about in this way for forty days and then buried. After the burial the Scythians cleanse themselves as I will show. First, they anoint and wash their heads; then, for their bodies, they set up three poles leaning together in a point and cover these with woollen mats; then, in the place so enclosed, to the best of their power, they make a pit in the center beneath the mat-covered poles and throw red-hot stones into it.

They have hemp [*kánnabis*] growing in their country, very like flax [*líno*] except that the hemp is by far the thicker and taller. It grows both by itself and also by their sowing it, and from it the Thracians even make garments that are very like linen; nor could anyone, unless he were a past master in hemp, tell whether they are hempen or linen; whoever has never seen hemp will think the garment is linen.

The Scythians then take the seeds of this hemp and, creeping under the mats, they throw them on the red-hot stones; and, being so thrown, they smolder and send forth so much steam that no Greek vapor-bath could surpass it. The Scythians howl in their joy at their vapor-bath. This serves them instead of bathing, for they never wash their bodies with water. But their women pound on a rough stone cypress, cedar, and frankincense wood, mixing water also with it, and with the thick stuff so pounded they anoint all their bodies and faces, whereby not only does a fragrant scent linger about them, but when on the second day they take off the ointment their skin has become clean and shining.

GARCIA DA ORTA, *Coloquios dos simples e drogas he cousas*
mediçinais da India e assi d'algunas frutas achadas nella
onde se tratam algunas cousas tocantes a mediçina pratica e outras
cousas boas pera saber compostos pello Dr. Garcia Dorta,
Goa, pp. 217–218 (1563)

Da Orta, whose name means "of the garden," was a world-famous Portuguese botanist. In 1534, probably then in his twenties, he went to Goa as first physician to the Count of Redondo, then named viceroy of the Indies, and never afterward returned to Europe. He collected all the plants he could find in India, and planted a garden in Bombay with the rarest trees and plants of the subcontinent, among which he spent his life, reputedly dying at an advanced age. His one work, the "History of Drugs and Certain Simple Medicaments from India," was translated into nearly every European language, and Garcia was quoted by botanists and ethnologists for centuries to come. He gets very close to the truth about the Indian use of cannabis in the section "On bhang" closer indeed than many who followed and copied him but did not understand him.

ON BHANG

Because some people have been of the opinion that the bhang of India differs in no way from opium—wł.ich they are wont to call osium corruptly—it seems appropriate for me to say something about bhang.

Bhang is a plant which resembles hemp very much, except that the seed is a little smaller, and not so white. Also its woody parts are not covered by any bark, which also makes it quite the contrary of hemp. And finally the Indians eat the leaves and the seeds, so as the more to incline themselves to the venereal act; of course great authors attribute contrary faculties to hemp seeds, since hemp dries up semen.

Its juice is expressed from the crushed leaves, and sometimes the seeds too, to which is sometimes added faufel [?] that is still green (which injures in no way the sense of the brain), or some nutmeg, or mace, or sometimes cloves, and sometimes also some camphor from Borneo; others add amber and musk, and some add opium, as do the richest and most opulent among the Moors. They get no usefulness from this, unless it is in the fact that they become ravished by ecstasy, and delivered from all worries and cares, and laugh at the least little thing.

After all, it is said that it was they who first found the use of it, when their generals and men of war, exhausted by constant watches, having drunk a little bhang with wine or opium, became as if drunk, and slept as if delivered from all cares.

The great Sultan Badur was accustomed to say to Martin Alfonso da Sousa, counselor to the king, whom he much loved, and to whom he revealed his greatest secrets, that whenever he would dream of going to Portugal, Brazil, Asia Minor, Arabia, or Persia, he would simply take a little bhang mixed with a little sugar and the simples mentioned above: they call this *maju.*

JAN HUYGHEN VAN LINSCHOTEN, *The Voyage to the East Indies: From the Old English Translation of 1598,* vol. ii. ed. P.A. Tiele (Hakluyt Society, first series, vol. 71), London, 1885, pp. 115–117 (1598)

Linschoten (1563–1611) was at the age of twenty named secretary to the Archbishop of Goa, where he stayed, gathering his impressions in voluminous notes, until 1589. His work is sometimes very derivative, but the following chapter is mainly his own. His Reysgheschrift (travelogue) received translation into most European languages. Linschoten here does a cross-cultural analysis of cannabis, an extraordinary feat for his time. This excerpt is from the 1598 English translation.

THE 79. CHAPTER. OF BANGUE

Bangue is also a common meate in India, serving to the same effect that Amfion [opium] doth. It is a seed like Hempe-seed, but somewhat smaller and not so white. Also the thing whereon it groweth is like Hempe, but it hath no substance whereof to make any thing. The Indians eate this seede or the leaves thereof being stamped, saying, that it maketh a good appetite, but useth most to provoke lust; as it is commonly used and sold in the shops, it is mingled with some poulder of the leaves and the seed together: They likewise put greene Arecca unto it, therewith to make a man drunke, or in a manner out of his wits: Sometimes also they mixe it with Nutmegs and Mace, which doth also make a man drunke: Others (that is to saye, the rich and wealthy persons) mix it with Cloves, Camphora, Ambar, Muske, and Opium, which (as the Moores likewise affirme) maketh a man pleasant, and forgetting himself, performing all kinds of labour and toyle without once thinking of any paine: but onely laughing, playing, and sleeping quietly. The common women use it when they meane to have a mans companie, to be merrie, and to set all care aside. It was first invented by Captains and souldiers, when they had layne long in the field, continually waking and with great travell, they desiring againe to comfort themselves, thereby to settle their braines doe use Bangue, in such manner as is aforesaid. It causeth such as eate it, to reele and looke as if they were drunke, and halfe foolish, doing nothing but laugh and bee merrie, as long as it worketh in their bodies. It is verie much used by the Indians, and likewise by the Portingales [Portuguese], but most by the slaves thereby to forget their labour: to conclude it is a small comfort to melancholy.

Bangue is likewise much used in Turkie and Ægypt, and is made in three sorts, having also three severall names. The first by the Ægyptians is called Assis, which is the poulder of Hemp, or of Hemp leaves, with water made in paste or dough, whereof they eate five peeces, as bigge as a Chesnut; such as eate it, for an hower after, are as if they were drunke, without sence, and as it were beside themselves, thinking they see many strange sights, wherein they are much pleased. This is used by the common people, because it is of a small price, and it is no wonder, that such virtue proceedeth from the Hempe, for that according to Galens opinion, Hempe excessively filleth the head. The second they name Bosa, which is stronger than Assis: It is made of the meale of Lolium, by us called Dronkardes weede or Hearbe, and of the Hempseede with water as aforesaid: others presse out the iuice, and eat that. The thirde is called Bernavi, which is the right Bangue, which they have readie dressed out of India whereof they take about an ounce, & at the first are merie, talking much & singing pleasant songs, laughing without measure, and using many foolish toyes: which continueth almost an hower. After that they are in a manner furious, given to chiding and fighting, which continueth likewise a little space, that done they are possessed with heavinesse, and feare, that many times they crie out. In the end when they have played al these parts they fall in a sleepe, and being awakened they are as they were at the first. This is much used by foolish Iesters and Iuglers at feasts and banquets, to delight the guests. The Ægyptians use also another sorte called Bers, that is to say, health for an hower. It is made of white pepper, white Bilzen seede [hyoscyamus], of each five ounces, and of Opium, two ounces and a halfe, Spica Nardi, Euphorbium, Bertram, of each one Mitchell, Saffran, fifteene Scruples, all beaten in a Marble morter, and mixed with Honnie whereof they make a confection.

LAURENT D'ARVIEUX, *Voyage dans la Palestine, vers le Grand Emir, Chef des Princes Arabes du Desert, connus sous le nom de Bedoüins,* Paris, 1717, pp. 15–20 (1711)

The Chevalier d'Arvieux (1635–1702) was taken on his first voyage to the Middle East at eighteen, but his most extensive travel was in 1665–1666, when he was thirty. His facility for languages became legendary: on his various voyages he acquired a thorough knowledge of Hebrew, Syriac, Arabic, Turkish, and Persian. He was indeed so proficient in Turkish that when he was in the country, dressed à la turque, the inhabitants invariably mistook him for one of their own. In this part of his narrative, he is eager to meet the emir of Palestine, and has dressed for the occasion in Arab garb. He rides out into a desert camp, where he is introduced to the emir and his court, who are all surprised at seeing him so dressed and so fluent in their language. A meal of fruits is presented, followed by coffee, tobacco, and hashish. D'Arvieux was one of the first Europeans to eat the drug, though he didn't quite realize what it was at the time, or afterward. The notes, surprisingly ill-informed, were added later by d'Arvieux.

WHILE WE were smoking they served around coffee in little cups and sherbet in a large porcelain basin that easily held four quarts, and which was passed from hand to hand, each man serving his neighbor after he had taken some. Then they brought up to the emir a little stoneware pot, full of a sweet made with the plant which the Arabs call Berge.* It is another name for opium, and has about the same quality and effect, although it is less violent. He took a piece about the size of a nut, swallowed it with a cup of coffee, and then smoked a pipe of tobacco.

He urged me to take a little dose of it, and offered it to me in a frank manner on the point of his knife, and I couldn't refuse him, because it was a singular favor he offered me. The drug did not seem disagreeable in taste, but it made me drowsy, and I was dreaming for the rest of the day. It was also in order to dream that the emir took it, and, excusing myself from the second helping the emir wanted to give me, I asked him what good it did him.

---

* Or rather Benge. Benge is actually henbane, which has the quality of making one drunk and sleepy. The Arabs also give the name Benge to a conserve of hemp leaves prepared as a treacle, and that produces the same effects as henbane. They use one as frequently as the other.

He told me that when the Berge began to work on him, he would fly away to India, and a sweet reverie would show him all that was most agreeable in the world, and the vapors that this substance would carry to his brain would enliven his spirits, fortify his memory, and give him the rationality to undertake a long conversation. I noticed however that this herb had so weakened his nerves that he was continually trembling in all his members, and he could hold nothing in his hands firmly. It is said that people who have used this Berge for a long time, just as with those who use opium, are usually so profoundly sleepy, that if they were to hear someone fire a rifle near them, or if someone were to shout rather loudly into their ears, they would faint away from fear, or at least would awaken with a great start, and would be just as disturbed as if they had returned from the nether world. The misfortune of this habit is that they do not know how to do without Berge: they die of grief when they have none of it, they like to eat nothing except fruits instead of meat, and very little of anything else; they cannot support wine, and nothing at all which might excite joy. These people then, who are called Afiouni,* pass the day smoking tobacco; they dream away, and are put into a bad humor by those who interrupt them. It is a rather pleasant scene to see these opium and Berge eaters, called Teriakis † in their

---

* From the word *opium,* the black juice of the poppy, they have made by corruption the word *Afioun,* and *Afiouni,* takers of Afioun; the Turks call them Benghi.

† Those who take Benge or Afioun are condemned by the strict Moslems, because these things produce the same effects as wine, and since *theriaque* [Fr.: treacle] is sometimes used in these two drugs, they call those who use Afioun and Benge, *Theriaki* [treacle-eaters]. The word means also a debauched person. The story is told about a preacher who, declaiming one day against this abuse, became so carried away that the paper where he kept his Benge—which he often used himself —fell from his breast into the middle of his audience. Without stopping or losing countenance, he cried, "There it is, the enemy! The very devil of which I speak! Watch out that it does not jump on one of you and possess you!" And so forth. He got out of his difficulty by this ruse, but a poet who was in the audience sent him the next day an epigram in Turkish verses in which, after warning him that one must preach by example, he said to him, "Before examining the accounts of others, work to pay your own debts."

language, singing, laughing alone, and telling stories at the beginning of the drug's operation; while on the contrary, when the vapors have dissipated, they are pale, yellow, drowsy, somber, and sad; then their pleasure is only in dreaming, muttering, and saying intemperate things to those who bother them.

I held a conversation for some little time, which cost me a good deal of trouble, and after the emir had stopped asking me questions several Arab princes of his family, who had run to the camp on hearing the rumor of the arrival of a Frenchman, began in their turn to inform themselves of what was happening in Europe, as if they were asking for news of another world.

I began to be a little bored, and the Berge the emir had given me was already incommoding me quite a good deal when, happily, something of consequence intervened. All the company took their leave, and I also retired with Omar Aga into the same tent we had on our arrival, waiting, according to custom, for the emir to give orders for my board and lodging. Just then I was seized with such a great desire for sleep, caused by the Berge, that I fell asleep fully dressed, and lay there until five o'clock in the evening.

JEAN CHARDIN, *Voyages du Chevalier Chardin en Perse, et autres lieux de l'orient*, 4 vol., Amsterdam, 1735, vol. ii, pp. 15, 94 (1686)

The Chevalier Chardin (1643?–1713) was the son of a rich jeweler in Paris, and was sent to Persia by his father to buy gems. His two principal Oriental voyages were 1665–1670 and 1671–1681. His "Travels in Persia" was first published in 1686, and reprinted many times during the next century; a ten-volume edition was done as late as 1811. Filled with an original variety of precise facts, wittily observed, Chardin's book in its great popularity satisfied the French taste for orientalia throughout the eighteenth century.

SOME PEOPLE [among the Persians], who love to become drunk with tobacco, mix it with some hemp seeds, which makes the smoke rise to the brain, and makes one's head swim in a very short time. . . .

There is an infusion of poppyseed with the seeds of hemp and nux vomica. This infusion, which they call *Bueng* and *Poust,* is very strong. According to the dose one takes, it throws one into a comical or gay madness, and in a little while it stupefies completely. It is also forbidden by name in the religion. The Indians generally use it on state criminals whose lives are not to be ended, so as to take away their spirit, and on children of royal blood whom they wish to render incapable of reigning. They say that this is less inhumane than killing them, as is done in Turkey, or blinding them, as the Persians do. The Uzbeks found a way of taking these seeds in smoke, mixed with tobacco, and they brought this habit into Persia. It is not so harmful taken that way.

The Indian *Bueng* is simpler than this one I am speaking about, though this does not keep its effects from being equally baleful. It is composed of hemp alone, seeds, bark, and leaves ground and mixed together with no poppyseed. Often they only use the leaves, and making it is extremely easy, because they have only to grind the leaf in a wooden mortar with a little water, and when the leaf is pulverized and the water thickened, they drink the mixture. Only the Mohammedans use it, along with some Indian sects; the Banjans [brahmins] have forbidden its use, because of its evil effects upon the spirit. But in all the sects it is only the worthless people who drink it, particularly tramps and beggars. These never miss taking it at least once a day, unless they are traveling, in which case they take it three or four times, the virtue of this potion making them more vigorous and better disposed to walking. There are public-houses in Persia for this beverage, just as for coffee. One never goes there in the morning, but at three or four in the afternoon you will see them full of people searching in this intoxication for a respite from their cares and misery. The habit is fatal after a time, as with opium, but death would come quicker in cold countries, the drug's malign quality deadening the spirits there more quickly. Continual usage makes one pale, and wonderfully enfeebles the body and spirit; when once the drug is taken, the person who before never stopped laughing, joking, and moving about, falls from this height and resembles a dying man. An hour or two afterward he comes to, little by little. The habit of this drug is just as dangerous as opium; people who are used to it cannot stop taking it, being so dependent on it that they would die if they were deprived of it.

The seed of the hemp has more virtues than the leaves, and the bark has more than either. In 1678, when I was at Surat, two English ladies were one day looking out their window and saw a fakir or beggar pounding some of these intoxicating leaves. It gave them the desire to taste some of it, either because they were attracted by the color of the drug, which is a beautiful green, or because they were seized by one of those extravagant appetites that often occur in women. One of their servants brought some to each of them in a little glass, and to lessen the force of the drug he mixed it with some sugar and crushed cinnamon. They felt at the end of three or four hours the mad and pleasant intoxication which the beverage infallibly produces. They laughed and laughed, and wanted to dance, and told outrageous stories until the drug had stopped working.

There is another intoxicating decoction, also forbidden by the Mohammedan religion, even more so than the others, because its effect is even more debilitating than the decoctions of the poppy. The Persians call it *Tchorié*. It is made from a flower that resembles hemp.

GERHARD ROHLFS, *Adventures in Morocco,*
London, pp. 62, 69, 83, 87 (1874)

Rohlfs, a physician from Bremen, spent several years in the 1860s in Morocco, a country then almost totally unknown to Europeans. In order to travel freely through the country he de-

cided, against the strong advice of the Europeans in Tangiers, to convert to Islam, don Arab clothes, and go in search of the sultan, in whose army he finally enlisted as a surgeon. His observations of the people of Morocco are thus closely felt and unusually compassionate. He often sees cannabis smoked but does not appear especially interested in it. "Tobacco and haschish are in general use; but are not, as a whole, taken in excess" (p. 46). Later, he describes the Moroccan version of the Islamic afterlife.

A WALL DIVIDES paradise from hell, and it is a kind of neutral ground, serving as a residence for those who have done much good and much evil, or else who have done little good and little evil. Paradise abounds with purling streams of milk and honey, with black-eyed houris formed of musk, with wine which does not inebriate, and with slaves, of which true believers will have 80,000 a piece. The Moors have a special doctrine of their own that they will also be regaled with a kind of haschish which will never do them any harm; and that instead of black-eyed houris, they will be blessed with the companionship of blue-eyed golden-haired English girls, whom the Moors esteem the most beautiful of women. . . .

[During the month of Ramadan] there are some saints called Elatkaf, who, even in the night-time, take only a little bread and water; but for people in general the nights of the month . . . are festal in their character—opium, haschish, tobacco, and even spiritous drinks are indulged in to the full. . . .

The Moors like a tangible result [from medical treatment], and if a patient suffers plenty of pain from such remedies, he is quite contented, whether he is cured or not. They themselves make a preparation of cantharides with honey and haschish into a paste, to serve as an aphrodisiac, and it is needless to say that such sweetmeats (called *madjun*) are exceedingly injurious. . . .

The Moors employ as ordinary vermifuges a decoction of thyme and rosemary, with other odoriferous plants. . . . The *taenia solium* [an intestinal worm] is expelled as follows, according to the

statements of my Moroccan colleagues: the patient takes a table-
spoonful of pounded haschish, which sends the worm to sleep, and
it is then ejected with a purgative composed of aloes, sulphur, and
senna leaves.

HENRI A. JUNOD, *The Life of a South African Tribe,*
2 vol., London, vol. i, pp. 342–345 (1927)

*In the scanty research that has been done on the place of canna-
bis in southern Africa, this report stands out. Junod describes a
spitting game played by the Thonga tribe.*

ANOTHER PASTIME, very much appreciated by some . . . is
hemp smoking and the accompanying *saliva contest.* Hemp
(*mbange*) has been cultivated for a considerable time amongst the
Thongas, especially on the coast, not to make ropes, but for
smoking. The date of its introduction and its origin are unknown.
The pipe used for smoking is made of a reed (*lihlanga*) with a
small pierced wooden or stone ball (*mbiza*) fixed at its upper extremity. In the ball the hemp is placed and lit. The lower extremity
of the reed is introduced into a horn half filled with water. The
reed soaks in this water. With one hand, the smoker closes the
horn, leaving only a narrow opening through which he sucks
vigorously so as to form a vacuum. The smoke is thus drawn
through the reed and the water into the mouth of the smoker. Its
passage through the water cools it. Without this precaution the
smoke would be too strong, stop the saliva, and make the man
drunk at once. It is called *shingwandja,* when pure, and is not
liked, whilst they say that when it has gone through water, it has
an agreeable taste. It makes the smokers cough terribly, but they
thoroughly enjoy this exercise. Moreover it excites an abundant
flow of saliva which is the chief requisite for their favourite game.
They take a hollow grass, called *shenga,* and begin the fight by
blowing their saliva through it on to the ground. The simplest

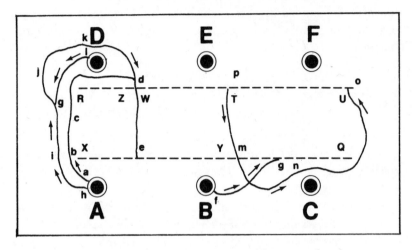

Illustration of the saliva contest of hemp-smokers.

form of the game consists in squirting as long streams of saliva as possible. He who squirts the furthest wins. But it is sometimes much more complicated. In the accompanying diagram the reader can follow the wonderful combinations of this game, called *ku tjhuma* or *hlazelana*. There are two sides, each with its pipe. Three men, A. B. C. oppose three others, D. E. F. First of all, each side protects itself by making a saliva fence, line X. Q. for the first side, R. U. for the second. Unhappily for D. E. F. the saliva dries up on the point Z. W. and so their fence is broken. A. takes his advantage. He begins to squirt out his saliva on the line *a, b, c, d* . . . passes through the opening Z. W., and, having come back victoriously to *e*, he has destroyed all the fortifications R. Z. Suppose D. wants to protect himself. He tries to close the access to his position by drawing the line *f, g*. But, arrived at *g*, he comes to the end of his saliva (*a helela*), and A. who started at *h*, having arrived at *i*, turns round the point *g*, where his enemy has stopped miserably, and, going on, *j, k,* reaches the opening *d* and triumphantly ends his campaign in *e!*

But E. of the opposite camp has noticed a gate in the barrier X. Q. The saliva has dried there. He quickly carries his blow-pipe across the battle field, squirting all the time, and passes through the opening Y. He draws the line *l, m, n, o* and so destroys the part Q. Y. of the fortification X. Q. Should B. be quick enough, he might prevent him accomplishing his plan by drawing the line *p, q* . . . And so on! Young men, even men of ripe age, take an immense delight in these saliva battles. But the saliva must be blackish. . . . It must be *ntjutju* saliva, viz., saliva produced by hemp, and not the ordinary white saliva, called *matjafula.* Should one of the players try to supplement the blackish by the white, he would be disqualified. . . . His enemy would seize him by the forehead, and force him to lift his head and stop his attack. Should he go on, however, the other would say: "What? You come to me with *matjafula!*" This may lead to quarrels, even to blows. . . . The hemp-pipe falls down and it all ends in cordial laughter.

This hemp-smoking custom becomes a passion with many young men. To cure them their parents break the pipe, take a little of the soot which is found inside, and mix it with their food without their being aware of it. When this has been done three times, it is said to fill them with disgust for hemp. . . . *Similia similibus curantur* . . . We . . . often meet with this medical principle in the Thonga superstitions.

INDEX

Abernethy, John, 185n
Africa, southern, 8, 281-283
Alamut, castle of, 16, 20n
alcohol, 8
Alcott, Louisa May, 217-232
Aleppo, 17
Alexander the Great, 175n
America. *See* United States
Antioch, 17
Arabia, 29
Arabian Nights, 29-39, 48, 100, 126, 157, 237, 261
Arvieux, Laurent d', 274-277
Assassins, 15-28, 40, 76, 89-90
Athens, 264

Baghdad, 29, 157
Bahrein, 28
Balzac, Honoré de, 81-82
Batenites, 22
Baudelaire, Charles, 41, 42-85, 88n, 105, 124, 250, 251
Beirut, 41
bhang, 9, 143, 271-272, 273-274
Boissard, Fernand, 42
Bombay, 271
Burroughs, William, 248
Burton, Sir Richard, 9n

Cairo, 41, 264
La Canebierre, 122
cannabis
  American consumption, 141-142, 156-157, 172-174, 217-218, 233-234
  European consumption, 10-11, 41
  fantasies, 8
  illegality, 7, 8, 247-248
  in southern Africa, 281-283
  as textile crop, 8
cantharides, 9
Caspian Sea, 16
Catholic Church, 85
Central America, 10
charas, 9
Chardin, Jean, 277-279
Chinatown, 233
Church of the Holy Sepulcher, 105n
Club des Hachichins, 40-112, 113, 125
coca, 239

Cocteau, Jean, 248
Coleridge, Samuel Taylor, 8
Confessions of an English Opium Eater (De Quincey), 10, 50, 72, 173-174
Congress, U.S., 7
Connecticut, 156
The Count of Monte Cristo (Dumas), 125-140, 251
Crusades, 15, 105n

Damascus, 17, 41, 141, 156
Dante Alighieri, 15
dawamesc, 9, 251
De Quincey, Thomas, 9-10, 50, 72, 173-174, 248, 250
Dumas, Alexandre, 125-140, 251

Egypt, 8, 16, 28, 29, 40, 105-112, 113, 142-145, 263, 264
Egyptian Expedition, 40, 117n
Eldorado (Taylor), 141
Esther (Racine), 62
Ethiopia, 113
Europe
  cannabis consumption, 11
  cannabis cultivation, 8

Fatimite caliphate, 16
Faust (Goethe), 141
Feuchères, Jean, 44
Flaubert, Gustave, 85
Les fleurs du mal (Baudelaire), 44
Fourier, Charles, 73
France, 10, 247, 263
Frederick Barbarossa, Holy Roman emperor, 16

Galland, Antoine, 29
ganja, 9, 239
Garcia da Orta, 271-272
Gautier, Théophile, 41, 42-48, 82n, 85-104, 125, 173
Genghis Khan, 20n
Germany, 142
Ginsberg, Allen, 248
Giraud, Jules, 247-262
Goa, 271, 272
Gray, Thomas, 175n
Great Britain, 172

Greece, 263-268

Hakim, caliph of Egypt, 105n
Hammer-Purgstall, Joseph von, 24
Hanska, Mme., 82n
Haroun al-Rashid, 29, 157
Harper's Magazine, 10, 233
Hasan-i Sabbah, 15-16
"The Haschish" (Whittier), 13
"The Hashheesh Eater" (Anon.), 156-171, 209
The Hasheesh Eater (Ludlow), 172-216
hashish
  and the Assassins, 17, 18, 20-25
  discovery of, 26-28
  in Egypt, 105-112
  etymology, 25
  in Greece, 264-268
  and the Hashish-eaters Club, 40-112, 125
  in India, 7, 9, 29, 263, 271-274, 278-279
  in Morocco, 279-281
  vs. opium, 71-72
  in Palestine, 275-276
  preparing, 8
  smuggling, 263-268
  in U.S., 141-142, 156-157, 172-174, 217-218, 233-234
  using, 8
Hashish-eaters Club, 40-112, 113, 125
"A Hashish-house in New York" (Anon.), 233-246
Hashish (Lallemand), 113-124
"The Hashish Poem" (Baudelaire), 52-85
hashishi, 25
Hassan Mohammed ibn-Chirazi, 26-28
Hell's Kitchen, 233
hendi, 9
Herodotus, 269, 270-271
hôtel, 42n
"How I Came to Hashish" (Giraud), 247-262
Les Huguenots (Meyerbeer), 128
Hülegü, 20n, 26

India, 7, 9, 29, 263, 271-274, 278-279
Inferno (Dante), 15
Iraq, 28
Ismaili sect, 15-16, 18n, 20n, 21-22, 26, 76

Junod, Henri A., 281-283

Khorasan, 26, 28
kif, 9, 97n, 257
Koran, 29, 105n
Kubla Khan (Coleridge), 8

Lallemand, François, 9, 113-124
Lambert, Louis, 82
laudanum, 8
Lauzun, duc de, 86
Lebanon, 40
Lewis, Bernard, 25n
Linschoten, Jan Huyghen van, 272-274
Little Women (Alcott), 217
Littmann, Enno, 30
London, 9n
Louis Philippe, king of France, 125
Lübeck, Arnold of, 16-18
Ludlow, Fitz Hugh, 141, 156, 172-216, 218
Ludlow, Henry G., 173, 211n

majoun, 9, 237
Manet, Edouard, 51
Maqrizi, 26
Mardrus, J. C. V., 29-30
Marihuana Tax Act of 1937, 7
Marseille, 113, 122, 247
Masyaf, castle of, 22n
maté, 239
Maturin, Charles Robert, 81n
Mes Mémoires (Dumas), 125
Mexico, 10
Michaux, Henri, 248
Monfreid, Henry de, 247, 263-268
Montferrat, Conrad of, king of Jerusalem, 16
Montpellier, University of, 113
Moreau, Jacques-Joseph, 88n
Morocco, 279-281
mulhid, 18n, 22
Mustansir, caliph of Baghdad, 28

Napoleon I, 40, 117n
Nerval, Gérard de, 41, 104-112, 125
New York City, 141, 233-246

An Old-Fashioned Girl (Alcott), 217
Old Man of the Mountain, 15-28, 89-90
opium, 8, 41, 50, 71-72, 173, 233, 250
Ormuz, 28
Ottoman Empire, 8, 264

Palestine, 40, 275

Les paradis artificiels (Baudelaire), 44, 52-85
Paris, 113, 173, 277
Pascal, Blaise, 53n
Peloponnesus, 264
"Perilous Play" (Alcott), 217-232
Persia, 15, 16, 18, 20n, 26, 29, 277
Persian Gulf, 28
Poe, Edgar Allen, 70
Polo, Marco, 18-21, 23
Poughkeepsie, N.Y., 173, 189n
La Presse, 85n, 88n
Protestantism, 157
Pythagoras, 172

Quintus Curtius, 175

Racine, Jean, 62
Redondo, count of, 271
Richard, king of England, 16
Rohlfs, Gerhard, 279-281
Rousseau, Jean-Jacques, 79
Rukn al-Din, 20n
rumi, 9

Sabian sect, 105n
Saint-Louis, Île, 41, 86
Saladin, 22
Scythians, 270-271
Seljuk dynasty, 16
sheik, 16
"Sinbad the Sailor" (Dumas), 125-140
"A Slight Experience of Hasheesh" (Taylor), 141-155

Sonnerat, Albert, 117n
Sorbonne, 49
South America, 8
Sudan, 263
Suez, 264
Swedenborg, Emanuel, 73
Sylvestre de Sacy, Antoine, 20-24, 25, 26, 40
Syria, 16, 25, 28, 40, 104

Taylor, Bayard, 141-155, 173, 218
Thonga tribe, 281
Thousand and One Nights, 29-39, 48, 100, 126, 157, 237, 261
troubadours, 15
Tudela, Benjamin of, 22
Turkey, 104
Tyre, 16

Union College, N.Y., 207
United States
    cannabis use, 7, 172-173, 218, 233-234
    freedom of manners, 10, 218

Views Afoot (Taylor), 141
Voltaire, 80n
Voyage en Orient (Nerval), 104

Wendover, Roger of, 15
Whittier, John Greenleaf, 13
Wiet, G., 26n
Willey, P. R. E., 26n
World War I, 247